D1164022

HAWTHORNE'S WORKS

WITH INTRODUCTIONS BY
KATHERINE LEE BATES
Professor of English Literature in Wellesley College

Fanshawe
Grandfather's Chair
Biographical Stories

THOMAS Y. CROWELL & CO.
PUBLISHERS : : : NEW YORK

FANSHAWE

A TALE

CONTENTS.

BIOGRAPHICAL SKETCH.

NATHANIEL HAWTHORNE came of genuine Puritan stock. The original immigrant was William Hathorne, who arrived at Boston on the " Arbella," in 1630, at the age of twenty-three, and for half a century took a vigorous part in laying the foundations of New England. After a few years in Dorchester, he settled permanently in Salem, where, magistrate, major, legislator, he sent vagabonds to the stocks and Quakers to the lash, fought the Indians, explored the wilderness, preached, traded, and won a place in Massachusetts colonial history as first Speaker of the House of Representatives.

His son, Colonel John Hathorne, merchant, attained the dignity of Judge of the Supreme Court, and left a sinister fame as a persecutor of witches. The legend goes that one of his victims invoked so potent a curse on him and all his race that the fortunes of the family forthwith began to wane. In his preface to *The Scarlet Letter*, Hawthorne speaks modestly of his Salem forefathers as seldom or never, " after the first two generations, performing any memorable deed, or so much as putting forward a claim to public notice. Gradually, they have sunk almost out of sight ; as old houses, here and there about the streets, get covered half-way to the eaves by the accumulation of new soil. From father to son, for above a hundred years, they followed the sea ; a gray-headed shipmaster, in each generation, retiring from the quarterdeck to the homestead, while a boy of fourteen took the hereditary place before the mast, confronting the salt spray and the gale, which had blustered against his sire and grandsire. The boy, also, in due time, passed from the forecastle to the cabin, spent a tempestuous manhood, and returned from his world-wanderings, to grow old, and die, and mingle his dust with the natal earth."

But Nathaniel Hathorne, son of the Revolutionary privateer known in ballad as "Bold Daniel" and himself a captain in the merchant marine, did not return. At the age of thirty-three he died in a foreign port, of yellow fever. His only son, Nathaniel Hawthorne, born July 4, 1804, was destined to raise the family name to universal honor, yet by achievements which, he used to fancy, his ghostly ancestors, especially those first two "stern and black-browed Puritans," would have disowned. "'What is he?' murmurs one gray shadow of my forefathers to the other. 'A writer of story-books! What kind of a business in life, — what mode of glorifying God, or being serviceable to mankind in his day and generation, — may that be? Why, the degenerate fellow might as well have been a fiddler!' Such are the compliments bandied between my great-grandsires and myself, across the gulf of time! And yet, let them scorn me as they will, stray traits of their nature have intertwined themselves with mine."

Hawthorne's father is remembered as a grave and reticent man; but the mother, also of the ascetic Puritan strain, carried reserve to the point of morbidness. On the word of her husband's death she became a lifelong recluse, and her children grew up like plants of some shadowed cloister-garden, their natural sensitiveness intensified by the atmosphere of her sequestered grief. But there were indulgent uncles and aunts; and at Raymond, in Maine, the ancestral home of Mrs. Hawthorne's family, the boy had the freedom of the wilds. With an old fowling-piece over his shoulder, he would plunge into the trackless forest, or "skate until midnight, all alone, upon Sebago Lake, with the deep shadows of the icy hills on either hand." A lameness, which passed with childhood, had early made him a reader. *Pilgrim's Progress* was one of his favorites, and the first book he bought with his own money was the *Faery Queene*. The *Newgate Calendar* figures on his list, with Shakespeare, Milton, and Rousseau. He was fitted for college at Salem, by a private tutor. At seventeen he was ready for Bowdoin and started out from Boston in the old-fashioned stage-coach, — a slender, bright-eyed lad, with clustering dark hair, — to seek that somewhat primitive well of knowledge. He had Longfellow for a classmate and Franklin Pierce for a friend, but seems to have given his confidence most freely to Horatio Bridge, who predicted great things for him. " I know not whence your faith came," wrote Hawthorne to Bridge, in the preface to *The Snow Image*, "but, while we were lads together at a country college, — gathering blueberries in study hours, under those tall academic pines; or watching the great logs, as they tumbled along the current of the Androscoggin; or shooting pigeons and gray squirrels in the woods; or bat-fowling in the summer twilight; or catching trouts in the shadowy little stream which, I suppose, is still wandering riverward through the forest, — though you and I will never cast a line in it again, — two idle lads, in short (as we need not fear to acknowledge now), doing a hundred things that the Faculty never heard of, or else it had been the worse for us, — still it was your prognostic of your friend's destiny that he was to be a writer of fiction." The future master of romance meanwhile ranked low in mathematics and metaphysics, and the required chapel declamations were as appalling to him as an after-dinner speech in later years. Latin was more to his mind, but he neglected all his academic tasks, even themes, and sowed a few Puritan wild oats at a secret and perilous card-table. He went through Commencement without embarrassment of college honors, and was not heard from for twelve years after. In 1837 a very slight stir in the literary world signalled the appearance of *Twice-Told Tales*.

During this interval Hawthorne had resided in Salem. In an upper-story room of the unvisited house where his mother and sisters led lives as silent as his own, he had brooded, written and burned, and written again, and bided his hour of fame. When he had been but a short time out of Bowdoin, he wrote a college novel, *Fanshawe*, which he published at his own expense, and almost immediately withdrew from circulation. Another 'prentice volume, *Seven Tales of my Native Land,* met with such disheartening treatment from the publishers that the proud young author cast the whole budget into the fire. His occasional contributions to *The Salem Gazette, The Token, The New England Magazine,* were anonymous; and he lived in his haunted chamber, from twenty-one to thirty-three, "the most obscure man of letters in America." His Bowdoin mates were well advanced on the trodden ways of the world, variously successful in politics, business, and the professions; Longfellow had won a Harvard chair; but Hawthorne had nothing to show for his hidden life save the first series of *Twice-Told Tales.*

This volume, though cordially greeted by Longfellow in the *North American Review,* made but slight impression on the public. It was five years before Hawthorne followed it up by the second series, and four years more before he published *Mosses from an Old Manse.* Meanwhile he had issued, in 1841, three small books of colonial stories for children, *Grandfather's Chair, Famous Old People,* and *Liberty Tree, with Last Words of Grandfather's Chair.* The year 1842 witnessed the publication of *Biographical Stories for Children.* It was the year of the second series of *Twice-Told Tales,* and, most important of all, the year of Hawthorne's marriage.

His betrothal to Sophia Peabody, an invalid daughter of a neighboring family, had come about through her sister's interest in his writings, spurring him to the unwonted achievement of a call. During the protracted engagement the bride had recovered health, and Hawthorne's long habit of solitude had been broken. It was high time, for he had learned his art and needed now the stimulus of life. That lonely existence in a locked chamber, with the tray of food placed outside the door, and the day's long dreaming and writing relieved only by an evening walk upon the beach, had done its work. He who in boyhood had avowed that he did "not want to be a doctor and live by men's diseases, nor a minister to live by their sins, nor a lawyer and live by their quarrels," had become, as he hoped, an author, to live by men's love of the beautiful.

As the prospect of marriage grew definite, Hawthorne had to face the practical question of gaining a livelihood. All his writing had brought him only a few hundred dollars, but Van Buren's administration prided itself on its care for literary Democrats, and a post in the Boston Custom House, under Bancroft the historian, was offered to Hawthorne the romancer. For the two years 1839–1840 the new weigher and gauger endured that "very grievous thraldom," and when, at the next Presidential election, the Whigs turned him out of office, he had saved from his salary of twelve hundred a year one thousand dollars, which he promptly sunk in the Brook Farm experiment. Casting in his lot with Ripley's enthusiasts, Hawthorne entered upon the April ploughing and planting with a humorous zest, hoping soon to marry and bring his wife to share that "Age of Reason in a patty-pan," as Curtis called it, but by another spring the "witty potato patches" and "sparkling cornfields" had lost their charm. He was thirty-eight years old, with little sign of worldly wealth, when he brought the happiest of brides to Concord, where they added another lustre to the memories of the *Old Manse.* "Nobody but we ever knew what it is to be married," wrote the new Adam to the new Eve, and out of the heart of his joy he looked back upon that dreary chamber in Salem with more than content. "I am disposed to thank God for the gloom and chill of my early life, in the hope that my share of adversity came then, when I bore it alone." But except with his wife he still kept his dark mantle of reserve folded close about him. Curtis, who had a blithe young share in all the phases of Transcendentalism, gives a roguish account of a representative Concord gathering in Emerson's study, where the philosophers talked Orphic secrets and ate russet apples, while "Hawthorne, a statue of night and silence, sat a little removed, under a portrait of Dante, gazing imperturbably upon the group."

Plain fare and rickety furniture count for little in

Eden, but debts weigh upon an upright soul, and when another Democratic administration came in, Hawthorne went resignedly back to Salem to barter "the delicate harvest of fancy and sensibility" for "a pittance of the public gold." Three years he served in the Custom House, his imagination all the while "a tarnished mirror," and when the political pendulum swung the Whigs again into office, they did better than they meant in turning Hawthorne out. The discharged surveyor of customs wrote *The Scarlet Letter*, which, published in 1850, called forth an instantaneous acclaim that was not to die away. At forty-six, after twenty-five years of striving, Hawthorne had won fame. In this brief romance all his past — the stern heredity and youthful dream, the lonely devotion to his art, and the realization, through love, of the vital forces of life — broke into flower, and a wonderful, blood-red flower it was. That most friendly of publishers, James T. Fields, clamored for a second manuscript, and obtained *The House of the Seven Gables*. This sweeter and less powerful romance, written in the red cottage at Lenox with the buoyancy born of unaccustomed praise, eased the author's mind of the old witch-curse pronounced upon his persecuting ancestor, Judge Hathorne. The year of *The House of the Seven Gables*, 1851, saw, too, the writing of *A Wonder Book* and the publication of *The Snow Image*. In the least mystical, and hence the least characteristic of his long stories, *The Blithedale Romance*, written the following year at West Newton, Hawthorne drew upon his memories of Brook Farm.

The election to the presidency of Hawthorne's college comrade, Franklin Pierce, for whom he had been persuaded to write a campaign biography, brought upon the sensitive romancer, once again, the blight of public office. In the "stifled chamber" of the American consulate at Liverpool he "spent wearily a considerable portion of more than four good years." He supported his family and paid his debts, but no adequate literary result came from this English residence. *Our Old Home* (1863), made up from his journals, was, as he said, "not a good or a weighty book." After the publication of *Tanglewood Tales*, in 1853, Hawthorne was silent until 1860, when Italy spoke through him in *The Marble Faun*. The story, as he at first conceived it, was to have "all sorts of fun and pathos in it," but when he came to "close grips" with his romance, it took on, amid supreme beauty of detail, the true Hawthornesque semblance of tragic mystery. In *The Marble Faun* his pure and tranquil grace of style is at its best.

Just before the Civil War Hawthorne came home, — a woeful time for any patriot, but most for one of divided sympathies. In that strong sketch, *Septimius Felton*, which, like *The Dolliver Romance* and *Doctor Grimshawe's Secret*, he was never to fill out, he dwells upon the wretched sense of being "ajar with the human race" which besets "a man of brooding thought" in any violent crisis. He took up his abode at The Wayside, in Concord, and while insidious disease was stealing upon his system, strove to fashion this new "Romance of Immortality." The unfinished manuscript was laid upon his coffin.

Hawthorne died on May 19th, 1864. His body lies in Sleepy Hollow, Concord. Of his three children, Una, the eldest, a sensitive and saintly woman, died in 1877; Julian Hawthorne is well known in the world of letters; Mrs. Rose Hawthorne Lathrop, now Mother Mary Alphonsa, has given herself to works of mercy. The literary tradition bids fair to be continued in the third generation by Julian Hawthorne's daughter, Hildegarde Hawthorne.

KATHARINE LEE BATES.

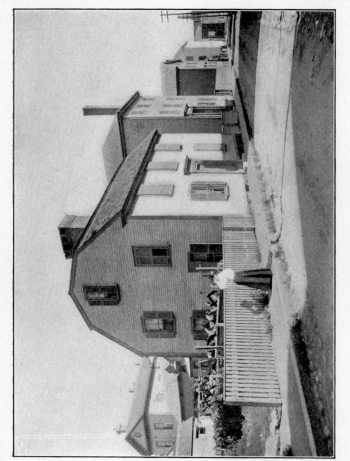

HAWTHORNE'S BIRTHPLACE — SALEM.

INTRODUCTION.

THE reason for Hawthorne's prompt condemnation of this, his first printed book, is not known. There may have been some sting of a forgotten review or even some domestic criticism. His elder sister, Elizabeth, whose literary ability Hawthorne held in high respect, seems to have recognized the lack of distinction in *Fanshawe*. In the absence of evidence, however, it is natural to suppose that the crudity of his work became more apparent to the young author in print than it had been in manuscript. At all events, *Fanshawe* was scarcely published when Hawthorne did his best to blot it out of existence and out of memory. Julian Hawthorne's biography of his parents prints a letter from his Aunt Elizabeth touching on this subject. Speaking of Hawthorne, she writes : —

"It was while in college that he formed the design of becoming an author by profession. In a letter to me he says that he had 'made progress on my novel.' I have already told you that he wrote some tales to be called *Seven Tales of my Native Land*, with the motto from Wordsworth, 'We are Seven.' I read them and liked them. I think they were better than *Fanshawe*. Mr. Goodrich (Peter Parley) told him afterward that he thought *Fanshawe* would have brought him some profit if it had had an enterprising publisher. These *Seven Tales* he attempted to publish ; but one publisher, after keeping them a long time, returned them with the acknowledgment that he had not read them. It was the summer of 1825 that he showed them to me. One was a tale of witchcraft, — *Alice Doane*, I believe it was called ; and another was *Susan Gray*. There was much more of his peculiar genius in them than in *Fanshawe*. I recollect that he said, when he was still in hopes to

publish them, that he would write a story which would
make a smaller book, and get it published immediately,
if possible, before the arrangements for bringing out the
Tales were completed. So he wrote *Fanshawe* and
published it at his own expense, paying one hundred
dollars for that purpose. There were a few copies sold,
and he gave me one; but afterward he took possession
of it and no doubt burned it. We were enjoined to
keep the authorship a profound secret, and of course
we did, with one or two exceptions; for we were in
those days almost absolutely obedient to him. I do
not quite approve of either obedience or concealment.
Your father kept his very existence a secret, as far as
possible."

Horatio Bridge, college friend though he was, did not
have Hawthorne's confidence as to this college novel.
The account given in Bridge's *Personal Recollections
of Nathaniel Hawthorne* fails to mention through what
leak the dark secret trickled out to him.

" It is well known that, soon after graduating, he prepared for the press a little volume of tales, entitled
Seven Tales of my Native Land. The publisher who
engaged to bring out the book was so dilatory that at
last Hawthorne, becoming impatient and dissatisfied
with the excuses given, peremptorily demanded the
return of the manuscript. The publisher, aroused to a
sense of his duty and ashamed of his broken promises,
apologized and offered to proceed with the work at
once; but Hawthorne was inexorable; and though, as
he wrote me at the time, he was conscious of having
been too harsh in his censures, he would not recede, and
he burned the manuscript, in a mood half savage, half
despairing. As I expressed to him, — perhaps too
strongly, — my regret for this proceeding, he did not,
when *Fanshawe* was published, confide to me the fact.
Hearing, though, of the publication, I procured a copy,
and subsequently mentioned it to Hawthorne. He had
meantime become dissatisfied with the book, and he
called in and destroyed all the copies he could reach.
At his request I burned my copy, and we never alluded

to *Fanshawe* afterward. It was at this time, I think, that he became utterly disheartened, and, though conscious of possessing more than ordinary literary talent, he almost abandoned all expectation of success as an author."

There remains the personal testimony of James T. Fields (*Hawthorne*, pp. 14–15): —

"In 1828 Hawthorne published a short anonymous romance called *Fanshawe*. I once asked him about this disowned publication, and he spoke of it with great disgust, and afterward he thus referred to the subject in a letter written to me in 1851: 'You make an inquiry about some supposed former publication of mine. I cannot be sworn to make correct answers as to all the literary or other follies of my nonage; and I earnestly recommend you not to brush away the dust that may have gathered over them. Whatever might do me credit you may be pretty sure I should be ready enough to bring forward. Anything else it is our mutual interest to conceal; and so far from assisting your researches in that direction, I especially enjoin it on you, my dear friend, not to read any unacknowledged page that you may suppose to be mine.'"

But who had let the cat out of the bag? The publishers? One, at least, should be held guiltless, for in the Boston Public Library copy, presented by Mr. Nahum Capen, is pasted a letter from him declaring that the authorship of the book had been made known without his agency. The following note is added by Mr. J. Winsor, then superintendent: "Oct. 10, '71, Mr. Capen stated to me orally that the edition was 1000 copies, and that a portion of it was burned in his store on Washington St. It was kindly received, as he says, but made no stir. He does not know of another copy in existence."

A pencil note beneath, by Mr. L. Swift, states: "Mr. C. E. Norton, of Cambridge, owns a copy."

A cutting from the *Boston Advertiser* (no date), fastened by Mr. Capen into the Boston Library copy, asserts, "A note from a correspondent in Salem assures us that there are at least two copies in existence of Hawthorne's juvenile romance," but does not locate them.

Miss Rebecca Manning, Hawthorne's cousin, holds one of the Salem copies. She states, in regard to a second : " Many years ago, Mr. David Roberts of Salem, an old friend of Hawthorne, gave his copy to Una Hawthorne." Mrs. Fields treasures her husband's copy. Mr. G. M. Williamson, a Hawthorne collector and bibliographer, owns a copy, five more New York copies are reported, and three have been sold at New York auctions since 1894, the last bringing a price of $410.

This rare book is a duodecimo of 141 pages, bound in buff boards and backed with russet paper. The title-page reads : —

FANSHAWE,

A TALE.

" Wilt thou go with me ? " — *Southey.*

BOSTON:

Marsh & Capen, 362 Washington Street.
Press of Putnam and Hunt.
1828.

Now that Hawthorne has so unmistakably withdrawn the invitation to "go with" him, one feels reluctant to discuss *Fanshawe;* yet it may be legitimate to ask how closely this college novel reflects the college that Hawthorne knew.

The charter of Bowdoin dates from 1794. In September, 1802, a president and a professor of ancient languages were inaugurated in the pine grove. The next day eight students, all but two of them under sixteen, were admitted, and college work began in Massachusetts Hall. The president taught mathematics, and this study, with Latin and Greek, constituted the curriculum. President McKeen lived to preside at only one Commencement, when diplomas were handed to seven graduates. It was a greater occasion than a muster, and people flocked to Brunswick by stage and coaster. Guests came even from Boston in their private chaises. There was a September gale at the time; President McKeen presided under a restive umbrella in the unroofed chapel, and General Knox's fine equipage was upset in returning through the stormy night from the Commencement ball, rolling its gay ladies and cavaliers down a miry bank.

The second president, also a Dartmouth graduate, was an example of the early ascetic type of the New England minister. Zealously evangelical, President Appleton established Sunday evening "Bible study" and Thursday afternoon "theological lectures." Determined to master all the subjects taught in his college, he allowed himself, for years, but four hours of the twenty-four for sleep. The Bowdoin of his day grew to be a college of five teachers and fifty students. Thirteen classes, ranging in numbers from three (1807) to nineteen (1818) were graduated during his presidency. Commencement was still a grand holiday for all the country round. Booths for the sale of pie, gingerbread, cider, and root beer dotted the campus; the graduates wore silk gowns over their figured waistcoats and knee-breeches, and the Faculty added to this costume the Oxford cap.

The premature death of President Appleton occurred in 1819, the year before Maine was made an independent state. The third president was a Harvard man of some literary reputation, who had married the wealthy daughter of a Dartmouth president. Representing, therefore, both culture and social position, President Allen and his lady entered Brunswick in their own "coach and pair." His first work was the establishment of the Medical School. The Commencement of 1821 was the most magnificent ever known. The governor of the new state attended with his staff and an escort of cavalry. Maine men waxed enthusiastic over their own seat of learning, and the entering class was the largest in the history of the institution. This was Hawthorne's class, which numbered thirty-eight at graduation.

Bowdoin was still, however, a plain country college.

Tuition was twenty-four dollars a year; room-rent, ten;
the highest charge for table-board was two dollars a
week. Hawthorne's bill for the term ending May 21,
1824, amounted to $19.62, of which $2.36 is made up
of fines, usually by way of discipline. One item is $0.20
for neglect of theme. President Allen, though his formal
manners made him unpopular with the students, had
gathered an able faculty. Natural science, philosophy,
and rhetoric were already added to the curriculum. It
was not until after Hawthorne's graduation that the
modern language professorship was established, since
known, from its first incumbent, as the Longfellow professorship. In 1824 great interest was aroused by the
novelty introduced by a young mathematical tutor, —
the use of the blackboard in teaching algebra. It was the
sophomore class that was thus enabled to lay aside the
historic slate; and the junior class, incredible though it
seems, petitioned to repeat the course as extra work
under these enchanting new conditions.

But this Down-East Bowdoin, with its study-bells, its
literal recitations, its fines of fifty cents for card-playing
and twenty-five cents for a Sabbath stroll, turned out,
year by year, men of mark. In the class of 1824 were
Franklin Pierce and Calvin Ellis Stowe. The roll of
1825 numbers sixteen lawyers, several of whom attained
political eminence, seven clergymen, two of whom, John
S. C. Abbott and Dr. George B. Cheever, were also
authors, six physicians, two merchants, two publishers
and booksellers, one banker, one teacher, Longfellow,
Hawthorne, and one other, an ardent student, holding
second rank in the class, who died on the eve of graduation.

This youth, Gorham Deane, who, like President Appleton, cut his sleeping hours down to four in his passion
for study, and stooped over his books until consumption
ravaged the compressed chest, may have suggested the
figure of Fanshawe. Lathrop is doubtless right in sur-
mising that in the last paragraphs of the second chapter
the lonely young genius of Salem was revealing himself.
But Hawthorne's college career had little in common

with Fanshawe's. Hawthorne's graduating rank was eighteen, a trifle above the middle of the class; he had, it is true, the name of being poetical, — though he declined, in 1840, to contribute to a volume called *The Bowdoin Poets*, — and he belonged to the Athenæum Society; but he loved to idle in the pine forest, where a stream, now nearly dried up, became known as Hawthorne Brook; his sensibilities did not forbid his shooting the wood-pigeons that haunted the blueberry pastures and the stubbles, nor the wild-fowl of river and coast; he even liked to bear a quiet part in the student convivialities at Ward's tavern. Yet the name Fanshawe is remotely suggestive of Hawthorne, and the author's sympathy is evidently more with this pallid hero than with the handsome, vigorous Edward Walcott from the fashionable seaport.

We have no right to ask for contemporary local color in Hawthorne's college novel. By a stretch of chronology, he puts Harley some eighty years back from the Bowdoin of 1825. For realistic pictures of Bowdoin life a few years later, one can turn to Dr. Hamlin's (class of '34) *My Life and Times*, or to Elijah Kellogg's (class of '40) *Whispering Pines* series. But even of an antique Bowdoin, Harley College, except for the surrounding landscape, is hardly suggestive. Dr. Melmoth does not seem to be drawn from any one of the three presidents, but is, rather, a conventional type of the gentle, unworldly, wool-gathering old scholar.

Lathrop finds in the story "a faint reflection" of Scott, but certainly the influence of Godwin, whose gloomy, passionate heroes had been familiar to Hawthorne from boyhood, is no less marked. Hawthorne does not confuse hero with villain, but he gives his villain traits familiar to all who are versed in the Brockden Brown school of romance. Ellen is such a softly shining image of girlhood as might well haunt the reveries of young collegians. The story has spirited and impressive passages, and every now and then, as in the rocks "that thrust their huge gray heads from the ground," or that gleeful flow of talk "such as one might expect from a bottle of champagne endowed by a fairy with the gift of speech," we feel the exquisite Hawthorne touch. As a story, however, *Fanshawe* falls between two stools. The frank actualities of college life are hardly reproduced, while the illusion of an ideal world fails to possess the reader.

KATHARINE LEE BATES.

FANSHAWE.

CHAPTER I.

Our court shall be a little academy

SHAKSPEARE.

In an ancient, though not very populous settlement, in
a retired corner of one of the New-England States,
arise the walls of a seminary of learning, which, for the
convenience of a name, shall be entitled 'Harley College.' This institution, though the number of its years
is inconsiderable, compared with the hoar antiquity of
its European sisters, is not without some claims to reverence on the score of age ; for an almost countless multitude of rivals, by many of which its reputation has been
eclipsed, have sprung up since its foundation. At no
time, indeed, during an existence of nearly a century,
has it acquired a very extensive fame, and circumstances, which need not be particularized, have of late
years involved it in a deeper obscurity. There are now
few candidates for the degrees that the college is authorized to bestow. On two of its annual 'Commencement
Days,' there has been a total deficiency of Baccalaure-
ates ; and the lawyers and divines, on whom Doctorates
in their respective professions are gratuitously inflicted,
are not accustomed to consider the distinction as an
honor. Yet the sons of this seminary have always
maintained their full share of reputation, in whatever
paths of life they trod. Few of them, perhaps, have
been deep and finished scholars ; but the College has
supplied — what the emergencies of the country demanded — a set of men more useful in its present state,
and whose deficiency in theoretical knowledge has not
been found to imply a want of practical ability.

I

The local situation of the College, so far secluded from the sight and sound of the busy world, is peculiarly favorable to the moral, if not to the literary habits of its students; and this advantage probably caused the founders to overlook the inconveniences that were inseparably connected with it. The humble edifices rear themselves almost at the farthest extremity of a narrow vale, which, winding through a long extent of hill-country, is well-nigh as inaccessible, except at one point, as the Happy Valley of Abyssinia. A stream, that farther on becomes a considerable river, takes its rise at a short distance above the College, and affords, along its wood-fringed banks, many shady retreats, where even study is pleasant, and idleness delicious. The neighborhood of the institution is not quite a solitude, though the few habitations scarcely constitute a village. These consist principally of farm-houses, — of rather an ancient date, for the settlement is much older than the college, — and of a little inn, which, even in that secluded spot, does not fail of a moderate support. Other dwellings are scattered up and down the valley; but the difficulties of the soil will long avert the evils of a too dense population. The character of the inhabitants does not seem — as there was perhaps room to anticipate — to be in any degree influenced by the atmosphere of Harley College. They are a set of rough and hardy yeomen, much inferior, as respects refinement, to the corresponding classes in most other parts of our country. This is the more remarkable, as there is scarcely a family in the vicinity that has not provided, for at least one of its sons, the advantages of a ‘liberal education.’

Having thus described the present state of Harley College, we must proceed to speak of it as it existed about eighty years since, when its foundation was recent and its prospects flattering. At the head of the institution, at this period, was a learned and orthodox Divine, whose fame was in all the churches. He was the author of several works which evinced much erudition and depth of research; and the public perhaps thought the more highly of his abilities from a singularity in the purposes to which he applied them, that added much to the curiosity of his labors, though little to their usefulness. But however fanciful might be his private pursuits, Doctor Melmoth, it was universally allowed, was diligent and successful in the arts of instruction. The young men of his charge prospered beneath his eye, and regarded him with an affection, that was strengthened by the little foibles which occasionally excited their ridicule. The president was assisted in the discharge of his duties by two inferior officers, chosen from the Alumni of the college, who, while they imparted to others the knowledge they had already imbibed, pursued the study of Divinity under the direction of their principal. Under such auspices the institution grew and flourished. Having at that time but two rivals in the country (neither of them within a considerable distance) it became the general resort of the youth of the province in which it was situated. For several years in succession, its students amounted to nearly fifty, — a number which, relatively to the circumstances of the country, was very considerable.

From the exterior of the Collegians, an accurate observer might pretty safely judge how long they had been inmates of those classic walls. The brown cheeks and the rustic dress of some would inform him that they had but recently left the plough, to labor in a not less toilsome field; the grave look and the intermingling of garments of a more classic cut, would distinguish those who had begun to acquire the polish of their new residence; — and the air of superiority, the paler cheek, the less robust form, the spectacles of green, and the dress in general of threadbare black, would designate the highest class, who were understood to have acquired nearly all the science their Alma Mater could bestow, and to be on the point of assuming their stations in the world. There were, it is true, exceptions to this general description. A few young men had found their way hither from the distant seaports; and these were the models of fashion to their rustic companions, over whom they asserted a superiority in exterior accomplishments, which

the fresh though unpolished intellect of the sons of the
forest denied them in their literary competitions. A
third class, differing widely from both the former, consisted of a few young descendants of the aborigines, to
whom an impracticable philanthropy was endeavoring
to impart the benefits of civilization.

If this institution did not offer all the advantages of
elder and prouder seminaries, its deficiencies were com-
pensated to its students by the inculcation of regular
habits, and of a deep and awful sense of religion, which
seldom deserted them in their course through life. The
mild and gentle rule of Doctor Melmoth, like that of a
father over his children, was more destructive to vice
than a sterner sway; and though youth is never without
its follies, they have seldom been more harmless than
they were here. The students, indeed, ignorant of their
own bliss, sometimes wished to hasten the time of their
entrance on the business of life; but they found, in after
years, that many of their happiest remembrances, —
many of the scenes which they would with least reluctance live over again, — referred to the seat of their
early studies. The exceptions to this remark were
chiefly those whose vices had drawn down, even from
that paternal government, a weighty retribution.

Doctor Melmoth, at the time when he is to be introduced to the reader, had borne the matrimonial yoke
(and in his case it was no light burthen) nearly twenty
years. The blessing of children, however, had been
denied him, — a circumstance which he was acustomed
to consider as one of the sorest trials that chequered his
pathway; for he was a man of a kind and affectionate
heart, that was continually seeking objects to rest itself
upon. He was inclined to believe, also, that a common
offspring would have exerted a meliorating influence on
the temper of Mrs. Melmoth, the character of whose
domestic government often compelled him to call to mind
such portions of the wisdom of antiquity, as relate to
the proper endurance of the shrewishness of woman.
But domestic comforts, as well as comforts of every
other kind, have their draw-backs; and so long as the

balance is on the side of happiness, a wise man will not murmur. Such was the opinion of Doctor Melmoth; and with a little aid from philosophy and more from religion, he journeyed on contentedly through life. When the storm was loud by the parlor hearth, he had always a sure and quiet retreat in his study, and there, in his deep though not always useful labors, he soon forgot whatever of disagreeable nature pertained to his situation. This small and dark apartment was the only portion of the house, to which, since one firmly repelled invasion, Mrs. Melmoth's omnipotence did not extend. Here (to reverse the words of Queen Elizabeth) there was ' but one Master and no Mistress '; and that man has little right to complain who possesses so much as one corner in the world, where he may be happy or miserable, as best suits him. In his study, then, the Doctor was accustomed to spend most of the hours that were unoccupied by the duties of his station. The flight of time was here as swift as the wind, and noiseless as the snow-flake; and it was a sure proof of real happiness, that night often came upon the student, before he knew it was mid-day.

Doctor Melmoth was wearing towards age, having lived nearly sixty years, when he was called upon to assume a character, to which he had as yet been a stranger. He had possessed, in his youth, a very dear friend, with whom his education had associated him, and who, in his early manhood, had been his chief intimate. Circumstances, however, had separated them for nearly thirty years, half of which had been spent by his friend, who was engaged in mercantile pursuits, in a foreign country. The Doctor had nevertheless retained a warm interest in the welfare of his old associate, though the different nature of their thoughts and occupations had prevented them from corresponding. After a silence of so long continuance, therefore, he was surprised by the receipt of a letter from his friend, containing a request of a most unexpected nature.

Mr. Langton had married rather late in life, and his wedded bliss had been but of short continuance. Certain misfortunes in trade, when he was a Benedict of three years standing, had deprived him of a large portion of his property, and compelled him, in order to save the remainder, to leave his own country for what he hoped would be but a brief residence in another. But, though he was successful in the immediate objects of his voyage, circumstances occurred to lengthen his stay far beyond the period which he had assigned to it. It was difficult so to arrange his extensive concerns, that they could be safely trusted to the management of others; and when this was effected, there was another not less powerful obstacle to his return. His affairs, under his own inspection, were so prosperous, and his gains so considerable, that, in the words of the old ballad, 'He set his heart to gather gold'; and to this absorbing passion he sacrificed his domestic happiness. The death of his wife, about four years after his departure, undoubtedly contributed to give him a sort of dread of returning, which it required a strong effort to overcome. The welfare of his only child he knew would be little affected by this event; for she was under the protection of his sister, of whose tenderness he was well assured. But, after a few more years, this sister, also, was taken away by death; and then the father felt that duty imperatively called upon him to return. He realized, on a sudden, how much of life he had thrown away in the acquisition of what is only valuable as it contributes to the happiness of life, and how short a time was left him for life's true enjoyments. Still, however, his mercantile habits were too deeply seated to allow him to hazard his present prosperity by any hasty measures; nor was Mr. Langton, though capable of strong affections, naturally liable to manifest them violently. It was probable, therefore, that many months might yet elapse, before he would again tread the shores of his native country.

But the distant relative, in whose family, since the death of her aunt, Ellen Langton had remained, had been long at variance with her father, and had unwillingly assumed the office of her protector. Mr. Langton's request, therefore, to Doctor Melmoth, was, that his ancient friend (one of the few friends that time had left him) would be as a father to his daughter, till he could himself relieve him of the charge.

The Doctor, after perusing the epistle of his friend, lost no time in laying it before Mrs. Melmoth, though this was, in truth, one of the very few occasions on which he had determined that his will should be absolute law. The lady was quick to perceive the firmness of his purpose; and would not (even had she been particularly averse to the proposed measure) hazard her usual authority by a fruitless opposition. But, by long disuse, she had lost the power of consenting graciously to any wish of her husband's.

'I see your heart is set upon this matter,' she observed; 'and, in truth, I fear we cannot decently refuse Mr. Langton's request. I see little good of such a friend, Doctor, who never lets one know he is alive, till he has a favor to ask.'

'Nay, but I have received much good at his hand,' replied Doctor Melmoth; 'and if he asked more of me, it should be done with a willing heart. I remember in my youth, when my worldly goods were few and illmanaged (I was a bachelor, then, dearest Sarah, with none to look after my household) how many times I have been beholden to him. And see, — in his letter he speaks of presents, of the produce of the country, which he has sent both to you and me.'

'If the girl were country-bred,' continued the lady, 'we might give her house-room, and no harm done. Nay, she might even be a help to me; for Esther, our maid-servant, leaves us at the month's end. But I warrant she knows as little of household matters as you do yourself, Doctor.'

'My friend's sister was well grounded in the 're familiari,'' answered her husband; 'and doubtless she hath imparted somewhat of her skill to this damsel. Besides, the child is of tender years, and will profit much by your instruction and mine.'

'The child is eighteen years of age, Doctor,' observed

Mrs. Melmoth, 'and she has cause to be thankful that she will have better instruction than yours.'

This was a proposition that Doctor Melmoth did not choose to dispute; though he perhaps thought, that his long and successful experience in the education of the other sex might make him an able coadjutor to his wife, in the care of Ellen Langton. He determined to journey in person to the seaport, where his young charge resided, leaving the concerns of Harley College to the direction of the two tutors. Mrs. Melmoth, who, indeed anticipated with pleasure the arrival of a new subject to her authority, threw no difficulties in the way of his intention. To do her justice, her preparations for his journey, and the minute instructions with which she favored him, were such as only a woman's true affection coald have suggested. The traveller met with no incidents important to this tale; and, after an absence of about a fortnight, he and Ellen Langton alighted from their steeds (for on horseback had the journey been performed) in safety at his own door.

If pen could give an adequate idea of Ellen Langton's loveliness, it would achieve what pencil (the pencils at least, of the Colonial artists who attempted it) never could; for, though the dark eyes might be painted, the pure and pleasant thoughts that peeped through them could only be seen and felt. But descriptions of beauty are never satisfactory. It must, therefore, be left to the imagination of the reader to conceive of something not more than mortal, — nor, indeed, quite the perfection of mortality, — but charming men the more, because they felt, that, lovely as she was, she was of like nature to themselves.

From the time that Ellen entered Doctor Melmoth's habitation, the sunny days seemed brighter, and the cloudy ones less gloomy, than he had ever before known them. He naturally delighted in children; and Ellen, though her years approached to womanhood, had yet much of the gaiety and simple happiness, because the innocence, of a child. She consequently became the very blessing of his life, — the rich recreation that he promised himself for hours of literary toil. On one occasion, indeed, he even made her his companion in the sacred retreat of his study, with the purpose of entering upon a course of instruction in the learned languages. This measure, however, he found inexpedient to repeat; for Ellen, having discovered an old romance among his heavy folios, contrived, by the charm of her sweet voice, to engage his attention therein, till all more important concerns were forgotten.

With Mrs. Melmoth, Ellen was not, of course, so great a favorite as with her husband; for women cannot, so readily as men, bestow upon the offspring of others those affections that nature intended for their own; and the Doctor's extraordinary partiality was anything rather than a pledge of his wife's. But Ellen differed so far from the idea she had previously formed of her, as a daughter of one of the principal merchants, who were then, as now, like nobles in the land, that the stock of dislike which Mrs. Melmoth had provided, was found to be totally inapplicable. The young stranger strove so hard, too, (and undoubtedly it was a pleasant labor) to win her love, that she was successful, to a degree of which the lady herself was not, perhaps, aware. It was soon seen that her education had not been neglected in those points which Mrs. Melmoth deemed most important. The nicer departments of cookery, after sufficient proof of her skill, were committed to her care; and the Doctor's table was now covered with delicacies, simple indeed, but as tempting on account of their intrinsic excellence as of the small white hands that made them. By such arts as these — which in her were no arts, but the dictates of an affectionate disposition — by making herself useful where it was possible, and agreeable on all occasions, Ellen gained the love of every one within the sphere of her influence.

But the maiden's conquests were not confined to the members of Dr. Melmoth's family. She had numerous admirers among those, whose situation compelled them to stand afar off and gaze upon her loveliness; as if she were a star, whose brightness they saw, but whose warmth they could not feel. These were the young men of Harley College, whose chief opportunities of beholding Ellen were upon the Sabbaths, when she worshipped with them in the little chapel, which served the purposes of a church to all the families of the vicinity. There was, about this period, (and the fact was undoubtedly attributable to Ellen's influence) a general and very evident decline in the scholarship of the college, — especially in regard to the severer studies. The intellectual powers of the young men seemed to be directed chiefly to the construction of Latin and Greek verse, many copies of which, with a characteristic and classic gallantry, were strewn in the path where Ellen Langton was accustomed to walk. They, however, produced no perceptible effect; nor were the aspirations of another ambitious youth, who celebrated her perfections in Hebrew, attended with their merited success.

But there was one young man, to whom circumstances, independent of his personal advantages, afforded a superior opportunity of gaining Ellen's favor. He was nearly related to Dr. Melmoth, on which account he received his education at Harley College, rather than at one of the English Universities, to the expenses of which his fortune would have been adequate. This connexion entitled him to a frequent and familiar access to the domestic hearth of the dignitary, — an advantage of which, since Ellen Langton became a member of the family, he very constantly availed himself.

Edward Walcott was certainly much superior, in most of the particulars of which a lady takes cognizance, to those of his fellow-students who had come under Ellen's notice. He was tall; and the natural grace of his manners had been improved (an advantage which few of his associates could boast) by early intercourse with polished society. His features, also, were handsome, and promised to be manly and dignified, when they should cease to be youthful. His character as a scholar was more than respectable, though many youthful follies, sometimes, perhaps, approaching near to vices, were laid to his charge. But his occasional derelictions from discipline were not such as to create any very serious apprehensions respecting his future welfare; nor were they greater than, perhaps, might be expected from a young man who possessed a considerable command of money, and who was, besides, the fine gentleman of the little community of which he was a member, — a character which generally leads its possessor into follies that he would otherwise have avoided.

With this youth, Ellen Langton became familiar, and even intimate; for he was her only companion, of an age suited to her own, and the difference of sex did not occur to her as an objection. He was her constant companion, on all necessary and allowable occasions, and drew upon himself, in consequence, the envy of the college.

CHAPTER II.

Why, all delights are vain, but that most vain,
Which, with pain purchased, doth inherit pain;
   As painfully to pore upon a book,
    To seek the light of truth, while truth the while
Doth falsely blind the eye-sight of his look.
SHAKSPEARE.

ON one of the afternoons which afforded to the students a relaxation from their usual labors, Ellen was attended by her cavalier in a little excursion over the rough bridle-roads that led from her new residence. She was an experienced equestrian, — a necessary accomplishment at that period, when vehicles of every kind were rare. It was now the latter end of spring; but the season had hitherto been backward, with only a few warm and pleasant days. The present afternoon, however, was a delicious mingling of Spring and Summer, forming in their union, an atmosphere so mild and pure, that to breathe was almost a positive happiness. There was a little alternation of cloud across the brow of Heaven, but only so much as to render the sunshine more delightful.

The path of the young travellers lay sometimes among tall and thick standing trees, and sometimes over naked and desolate hills, whence man had taken the natural vegetation, and then left the soil to its barrenness. Indeed, there is little inducement to a cultivator to labor among the huge stones, which there peep forth from the earth, seeming to form a continued ledge for several miles. A singular contrast to this unfavored tract of country is seen in the narrow but luxuriant, though sometimes swampy, strip of interval, on both sides of the stream, that, as has been noticed, flows down the valley. The light and buoyant spirits of Edward Walcott and Ellen rose higher as they rode on, and their way was enlivened, wherever its roughness did not forbid, by their conversation and pleasant laughter. But at length Ellen drew her bridle, as they emerged from a thick portion of the forest, just at the foot of a steep hill.

'We must have ridden far,' she observed, — 'farther than I thought. It will be near sunset before we can reach home."

'There are still several hours of daylight,' replied Edward Walcott; 'and we will not turn back without ascending this hill. The prospect from the summit is beautiful, and will be particularly so now, in this rich sunlight. Come Ellen, — one light touch of the whip : — your pony is as fresh as when we started.'

On reaching the summit of the hill, and looking back in the direction in which they had come, they could see the little stream, peeping forth many times to the daylight, and then shrinking back into the shade. Farther on, it became broad and deep, though rendered incapable of navigation, in this part of its course, by the occasional interruption of rapids.

'There are hidden wonders of rock and precipice and cave, in that dark forest,' said Edward, pointing to the space between them and the river. 'If it were earlier in the day, I should love to lead you there. Shall we try the adventure now, Ellen ?'

'O no!' she replied; 'let us delay no longer. I fear I must even now abide a rebuke from Mrs. Melmoth, which I have surely deserved. But who is this, who rides on so slowly before us?'

She pointed to a horseman, whom they had not before observed. He was descending the hill; but, as his steed seemed to have chosen his own pace, he made a very inconsiderable progress.

'O, do you not know him? — But it is scarcely possible you should,' exclaimed her companion. 'We must do him the good office, Ellen, of stopping his progress, or he will find himself at the village, a dozen miles farther on, before he resumes his consciousness.'

'Has he then lost his senses?' inquired Miss Langton.

'Not so, Ellen, — if much learning has not made him mad,' replied Edward Walcott. 'He is a deep scholar, and a noble fellow; but I fear we shall follow him to his grave ere long. Dr. Melmoth has sent him to ride in pursuit of his health. He will never overtake it, however, at this pace.'

As he spoke, they had approached close to the subject of their conversation, and Ellen had a moment's space for observation, before he started from the abstraction, in which he was plunged. The result of her scrutiny was favorable, yet very painful.

The stranger could scarcely have attained his twentieth year, and was possessed of a face and form, such as Nature bestows on none but her favorites. There was a nobleness on his high forehead, which time would have deepened into majesty; and all his features were formed with a strength and boldness, of which the paleness, produced by study and confinement, could not deprive them. The expression of his countenance was not a melancholy one; — on the contrary, it was proud and high — perhaps triumphant — like one who was a ruler in a world of his own, and independent of the beings that surrounded him. But a blight, of which his thin, pale cheek and the brightness of his eye, were alike proofs, seemed to have come over him ere his maturity.

The scholar's attention was now aroused by the hoof-tramps at his side, and starting, he fixed his eye on Ellen, whose young and lovely countenance was full of the interest he had excited. A deep blush immediately suffused his cheek, proving how well the glow of health would have become it. There was nothing awkward, however, in his manner; and soon recovering his self-possession, he bowed to her and would have rode on.

'Your ride is unusually long, to-day, Fanshawe,' observed Edward Walcott. 'When may we look for your return?'

The young man again blushed, but answered, with a smile that had a beautiful effect upon his countenance, 'I was not, at the moment, aware in which direction my horse's head was turned. I have to thank you for arresting me in a journey, which was likely to prove much longer than I intended.'

The party had now turned their horses and were about to resume their ride in a homeward direction; but Edward perceived that Fanshawe, having lost the excitement of intense thought, now looked weary and dispirited.

'Here is a cottage close at hand,' he observed. 'We have ridden far, and stand in need of refreshment. Ellen, shall we alight?'

She saw the benevolent motive of his proposal, and did not hesitate to comply with it. But, as they paused at the cottage door, she could not but observe, that its exterior promised few of the comforts which they required. Time and neglect seemed to have conspired its ruin, and but for a thin curl of smoke from its clay chimney, they could not have believed it to be inhabited. A considerable tract of land, in the vicinity of the cottage, had evidently been, at some former period, under cultivation, but was now overrun by bushes and dwarf pines, among which many huge gray rocks, ineradicable by human art, endeavored to conceal themselves. About half an acre of ground was occupied by the young blades of Indian corn, at which a half-starved cow gazed wistfully, over the mouldering log fence. These

were the only agricultural tokens. Edward Walcott
nevertheless drew the latch of the cottage door, after
knocking loudly, but in vain.

The apartment, which was thus opened to their view,
was quite as wretched as its exterior had given them
reason to anticipate. Poverty was there, with all its
necessary, and unnecessary concomitants. The intruders
would have retired, had not the hope of affording relief
detained them.

The occupants of the small and squallid apartment
were two women, both of them elderly, and, from the
resemblance of their features, appearing to be sisters.
The expression of their countenances, however, was
very different. One, evidently the younger, was seated
on the farther side of the large hearth, opposite to the
door, at which the party stood. She had the sallow
look of long and wasting illness, and there was an
unsteadiness of expression about her eyes, that immediately struck the observer. Yet her face was mild
and gentle, therein contrasting widely with that of her
companion.

The other woman was bending over a small fire of
decayed branches, the flame of which was very dispro-
portionate to the smoke, scarcely producing heat sufficient for the preparation of a scanty portion of food.
Her profile, only, was visible to the strangers, though,
from a slight motion of her eye, they perceived that she
was aware of their presence. Her features were pinched
and spare, and wore a look of sullen discontent, for
which the evident wretchedness of her situation afforded
a sufficient reason. This female, notwithstanding her
years and the habitual fretfulness, that is more wearing
than time, was apparently healthy and robust, with a
dry, leathery complexion. A short space elapsed before
she thought proper to turn her face towards her visitors,
and she then regarded them with a lowering eye, without speaking, or rising from her chair.

'We entered,' Edward Walcott began to say, 'in the
hope;—' but he paused, on perceiving that the sick
woman had risen from her seat, and with slow and

tottering footsteps was drawing near to him. She took his hand in both her own, and, though he shuddered at the touch of age and disease, he did not attempt to withdraw it. She then perused all his features with an expression, at first of eager and hopeful anxiety, which faded by degrees into disappointment. Then, turning from him, she gazed into Fanshawe's countenance with the like eagerness, but with the same result. Lastly, tottering back to her chair, she hid her face, and wept bitterly. The strangers, though they knew not the cause of her grief, were deeply affected; and Ellen approached the mourner with words of comfort, which, more from their tone than their meaning, produced a transient effect.

'Do you bring news of him?' she inquired, raising her head. 'Will he return to me? Shall I see him before I die?' Ellen knew not what to answer, and ere she could attempt it, the other female prevented her.

'Sister Butler is wandering in her mind,' she said, 'and speaks of one she will never behold again. The sight of strangers disturbs her, and you see we have nothing here to offer you.'

The manner of the woman was ungracious, but her words were true. They saw that their presence could do nothing towards the alleviation of the misery they witnessed, and they felt that mere curiosity would not authorize a longer intrusion. So soon, therefore, as they had relieved, according to their power, the poverty that seemed to be the least evil of this cottage, they emerged into the open air.

The breath of heaven felt sweet to them, and removed a part of the weight from their young hearts, which were saddened by the sight of so much wretchedness. Perceiving a pure and bright little fountain, at a short distance from the cottage, they approached it, and using the bark of a birch tree as a cup, partook of its cool waters. They then pursued their homeward ride with such diligence, that, just as the sun was setting, they came in sight of the humble wooden edifice, which was dignified with the name of Harley College. A golden ray rested upon the spire of the little chapel, the bell of which sent its tinkling murmur down the valley, to summon the wanderers to evening prayers.

Fanshawe returned to his chamber, that night, and lit his lamp as he had been wont to do. The books were around him, which had hitherto been to him like those fabled volumes of Magic, from which the reader could not turn away his eye, till death were the consequence of his studies. But there were unaccustomed thoughts in his bosom, now; and to these, leaning his head on one of the unopened volumes, he resigned himself.

He called up in review the years, that, even at his early age, he had spent in solitary study, — in conversation with the dead, — while he had scorned to mingle with the living world, or to be actuated by any of its motives. He asked himself, to what purpose was all this destructive labor, and where was the happiness of superior knowledge. He had climbed but a few steps of a ladder that reached to infinity, — he had thrown away his life in discovering, that, after a thousand such lives, he should still know comparatively nothing. He even looked forward with dread — though once the thought had been dear to him — to the eternity of improvement that lay before him. It seemed now a weary way, without a resting place and without a termination; and, at that moment, he would have preferred the dreamless sleep of the brutes that perish, to man's proudest attribute, of immortality.

Fanshawe had hitherto deemed himself unconnected with the world, unconcerned in its feelings, and uninfluenced by it in any of his pursuits. In this respect he probably deceived himself. If his inmost heart could have been laid open, there would have been discovered that dream of undying fame, which, dream as it is, is more powerful than a thousand realities. But, at any rate, he had seemed, to others and to himself, a solitary being, upon whom the hopes and fears of ordinary men were ineffectual.

But now he felt the first thrilling of one of the many ties, that, so long as we breathe the common air, (and who shall say how much longer?) unite us to our kind. The sound of a soft, sweet voice, — the glance of a gentle eye, — had wrought a change upon him, and, in his ardent mind a few hours had done the work of many. Almost in spite of himself, the new sensation was inexpressibly delightful. The recollection of his ruined health, — of his habits, so much at variance with those of the world, — all the difficulties that reason suggested, — were inadequate to check the exulting tide of hope and joy.

CHAPTER III.

And let the aspiring youth beware of love, —
Of the smooth glance, beware; for 't is too late,
When on his heart the torrent softness pours.
Then wisdom prostrate lies, and fading fame
Dissolves in air away.

THOMSON.

A few months passed over the heads of Ellen Langton and her admirers, unproductive of events, that separately, were of sufficient importance to be related. The summer was now drawing to a close, and Dr. Melmoth had received information that his friend's arrangements were nearly completed, and that, by the next home-bound ship he hoped to return to his native country. The arrival of that ship was daily expected.

During the time that had elapsed since his first meeting with Ellen, there had been a change, yet not a very remarkable one, in Fanshawe's habits. He was still the same solitary being, so far as regarded his own sex, and he still confined himself as sedulously to his chamber, except for one hour — the sunset hour — of every day. At that period, unless prevented by the inclemency of the weather, he was accustomed to tread a path that wound along the banks of the stream. He had discovered that this was the most frequent scene of Ellen's walks, and this it was that drew him thither.

Their intercourse was at first extremely slight. A bow on the one side, a smile on the other, and a passing word from both, — and then the student hurried back to his solitude. But, in course of time, opportunities occurred for more extended conversation; so that, at the period with which this chapter is concerned, Fanshawe was, almost as constantly as Edward Walcott himself, the companion of Ellen's walks.

His passion had strengthened more than proportionably to the time that had elapsed since it was conceived; but the first glow and excitement which attended it, had now vanished. He had reasoned calmly with himself and rendered evident to his own mind the almost utter hopelessness of success. He had also made his resolution strong, that he would not even endeavor to win Ellen's love, the result of which, for a thousand reasons, could not be happiness. Firm in this determination, and confident of his power to adhere to it, — feeling, also, that time and absence could not cure his own passion, and having no desire for such a cure, — he saw no reason for breaking off the intercourse that was established between Ellen and himself. It was remarkable, that, notwithstanding the desperate nature of his love, that, or something connected with it, seemed to have a beneficial effect upon his health. There was now a slight tinge of color in his cheek, and a less consuming brightness in his eye. Could it be that hope, unknown to himself, was yet alive in his breast? — that a sense of the possibility of earthly happiness was redeeming him from the grave?

Had the character of Ellen Langton's mind been different, there might, perhaps, have been danger to her from an intercourse of this nature with such a being as Fanshawe; for he was distinguished by many of those asperities around which a woman's affection will often cling. But she was formed to walk in the calm and quiet paths of life, and to pluck the flowers of happiness from the way-side where they grow. Singularity of character, therefore, was not calculated to win her love. She undoubtedly felt an interest in the solitary student, and perceiving, with no great exercise of vanity, that her society drew him from the destructive intensity of his studies, she perhaps felt it a duty to exert her influence. But it did not occur to her, that her influence had been sufficiently strong to change the whole current of his thoughts and feelings.

Ellen and her two lovers (for both, though perhaps, not equally deserved that epithet) had met, as usual, at the close of a sweet summer day, and were standing by the side of the stream, just where it swept into a deep pool. The current, undermining the bank, had formed a recess which, according to Edward Walcott, afforded at that moment a hiding-place to a trout of noble size.

'Now would I give the world,' he exclaimed, with great interest, 'for a hook and line, — a fish-spear, or any piscatorial instrument of death! Look, Ellen, you can see the waving of his tail from beneath the bank!'

'If you had the means of taking him, I should save him from your cruelty, thus,' said Ellen, dropping a pebble into the water just over the fish. 'There! he has darted down the stream. How many pleasant caves and recesses there must be, under these banks, where he may be happy! May there not be happiness in the life of a fish?' she added, turning with a smile to Fanshawe.

'There may,' he replied, 'so long as he lives quietly in the caves and recesses of which you speak. Yes, there may be happiness, though such as few would envy; — but then, the hook and line — '

'Which, there is reason to apprehend, will shortly destroy the happiness of our friend the trout,' interrupted Edward, pointing down the stream. 'There is an angler on his way towards us, who will intercept him.'

'He seems to care little for the sport, to judge by the pace at which he walks,' said Ellen.

'But he sees, now, that we are observing him, and is willing to prove that he knows something of the art,' replied Edward Walcott. 'I should think him well acquainted with the stream; for, hastily as he walks, he has tried every pool and ripple, where a fish usually hides. But that point will be decided when he reaches yonder old bare oak-tree.'

'And how is the old tree to decide the question?' inquired Fanshawe. 'It is a species of evidence of which I have never before heard.'

'The stream has worn a hollow under its roots,' answered Edward, — 'a most delicate retreat for a trout. Now, a stranger would not discover the spot; or, if he did, the probable result of a cast would be the loss of hook and line, — an accident that has occurred to me more than once. If, therefore, this angler takes a fish from thence, it follows that he knows the stream.'

They observed the fisher, accordingly, as he kept his way up the bank. He did not pause when he reached the old leafless oak, that formed with its roots an obstruction very common in American streams; but, throwing his line with involuntary skill, as he passed, he not only escaped the various entanglements, but drew forth a fine large fish.

'There, Ellen, he has captivated your protégée, the trout, — or, at least, one very like him in size,' observed Edward. 'It is singular,' he added, gazing earnestly at the man.

'Why is it singular?' inquired Ellen Langton. 'This person perhaps resides in the neighborhood, and may have fished often in the stream.'

'Do but look at him, Ellen, and judge whether his life can have been spent in this lonely valley,' he replied. 'The glow of many a hotter sun than ours has darkened his brow; and his step and air have something foreign in them, like what we see in sailors, who have lived more in other countries than in their own. Is it not so, Ellen? — for your education in a sea port must have given you skill in these matters. But come, — let us approach nearer.'

They walked towards the angler, accordingly, who still remained under the oak, apparently engaged in ar-

ranging his fishing-tackle. As the party drew nigh, he
raised his head and threw one quick, scrutinizing glance
towards them, disclosing, on his part, a set of bold and
rather coarse features, weather-beaten, but indicating
the age of the owner to be not above thirty. In person
he surpassed the middle size, was well set, and evidently
strong and active.

'Do you meet with much success, Sir?' inquired
Edward Walcott, when within a convenient distance
for conversation.

'I have taken but one fish,' replied the angler, in an
accent which his hearers could scarcely determine to be
foreign, or the contrary. 'I am a stranger to the stream,
and have doubtless passed over many a likely place for
sport.'

'You have an angler's eye, Sir,' rejoined Edward.
'I observed that you made your casts as if you had
often trod these banks, and I could scarcely have guided
you better myself.'

'Yes, I have learnt the art, and I love to practise it,'
replied the man. 'But will not the young lady try her
skill?' he continued, casting a bold eye on Ellen. 'The
fish will love to be drawn out by such white hands as
those.'

Ellen shrank back, though almost imperceptibly, from
the free bearing of the man. It seemed meant for
courtesy; but its effect was excessively disagreeable.
Edward Walcott, who perceived and coincided in Ellen's
feelings, replied to the stranger's proposal.

'The young lady will not put the gallantry of the fish
to the proof, Sir,' he said, 'and she will therefore have
no occasion for your own.'

'I shall take leave to hear my answer from the young
lady's own mouth,' answered the stranger, haughtily.
'If you will step this way, Miss Langton,'— here he
interrupted himself, — 'if you will cast the line by
yonder sunken log, I think you will meet with success.'

Thus saying, the angler offered his rod and line to
Ellen. She at first drew back, — then hesitated, — but
finally held out her hand to receive them. In thus com-

plying with the stranger's request, she was actuated by a desire to keep the peace, which, as her notice of Edward Walcott's crimsoned cheek and flashing eye assured her, was considerably endangered. The angler led the way to the spot which he had pointed out, which, though not at such a distance from Ellen's companions but that words in a common tone could be distinguished, was out of the range of a lowered voice.

Edward Walcott and the student remained by the oak, the former biting his lip with vexation; the latter, whose abstraction always vanished where Ellen was concerned, regarding her and the stranger with fixed and silent attention. The young men could at first hear the words that the angler addressed to Ellen. They related to the mode of managing the rod; and she made one or two casts under his direction. At length, however, as if to offer his assistance, the man advanced close to her side, and seemed to speak; but in so low a tone, that the sense of what he uttered was lost, before it reached the oak. But its effect upon Ellen was immediate, and very obvious. Her eyes flashed, and an indignant blush rose high on her cheek, giving to her beauty a haughty brightness, of which the gentleness of her disposition in general deprived it. The next moment, however, she seemed to recollect herself, and, restoring the angling rod to its owner, she turned away, calmly, and approached her companions.

'The evening breeze grows chill, and mine is a dress for a summer day,' she observed. 'Let us walk homeward.'

'Miss Langton, is it the evening breeze, alone, that sends you homeward?' inquired Edward.

At this moment, the angler, who had resumed and seemed to be intent upon his occupation, drew a fish from the pool, which he had pointed out to Ellen.

'I told the young lady,' he exclaimed, 'that, if she would listen to me a moment longer, she would be repaid for her trouble; — and here is the proof of my words.'

'Come, let us hasten towards home,' cried Ellen, eagerly; and she took Edward Walcott's arm, with a freedom that, at another time, would have enchanted him. He at first seemed inclined to resist her wishes; but complied, after exchanging, unperceived by Ellen, a glance with the stranger, the meaning of which the latter appeared perfectly to understand. Fanshawe also attended her. Their walk towards Dr. Melmoth's dwelling was almost a silent one, and the few words that passed between them did not relate to the adventure which occupied the thoughts of each. On arriving at the house, Ellen's attendants took leave of her, and retired.

Edward Walcott, eluding Fanshawe's observation with little difficulty, hastened back to the old oak-tree. From the intelligence with which the stranger had received his meaning glance, the young man had supposed that he would here await his return. But the banks of the stream, upward and downward, so far as his eye could reach, were solitary. He could see only his own image in the water, where it swept into a silent depth; and could hear only its ripple, where stones and sunken trees impeded its course. The object of his search might, indeed, have found concealment among the tufts of alders, or in the forest that was near at hand; but thither it was in vain to pursue him. The angler had apparently set little store by the fruits of his assumed occupation; for the last fish that he had taken lay yet alive on the bank, gasping for the element to which Edward was sufficiently compassionate to restore him. After watching him as he glided down the stream, making feeble efforts to resist its current, the youth turned away, and sauntered slowly towards the college.

Ellen Langton, on her return from her walk, found Dr. Melmoth's little parlor unoccupied, that gentleman being deeply engaged in his study, and his lady busied in her domestic affairs. The evening, notwithstanding Ellen's remark concerning the chillness of the breeze, was almost sultry, and the windows of the apartment were thrown open. At one of these, which looked into the garden, she seated herself, listening, almost unconsciously, to the monotonous music of a thousand insects, varied occasionally by the voice of a whippoor-will, who, as the day departed, was just commencing his song. A dusky tint, as yet almost imperceptible, was beginning to settle on the surrounding objects, except where they were opposed to the purple and golden clouds, which the vanished sun had made the brief inheritors of a portion of his brightness. In these gorgeous vapors, Ellen's fancy, in the interval of other thoughts, pictured a fairyland, and longed for wings to visit it.

But as the clouds lost their brilliancy, and assumed first a dull purple, and then a sullen grey tint, Ellen's thoughts recurred to the adventure of the angler, which her imagination was inclined to invest with an undue singularity. It was, however, sufficiently unaccount-able, that an entire stranger should venture to demand of her a private audience; and she assigned, in turn, a thousand motives for such a request, none of which were in any degree satisfactory. Her most prevailing thought, though she could not justify it to her reason, inclined her to believe that the angler was a messenger from her father. But wherefore he should deem it necessary to communicate any intelligence, that he might possess, only by means of a private interview, and without the knowledge of her friends, was a mys-tery she could not solve. In this view of the matter, however, she half regretted that her instinctive delicacy had impelled her so suddenly to break off their con-ference, admitting, in the secrecy of her own mind, that, if an opportunity were again to occur, it might not again be shunned. As if that unuttered thought had power to conjure up its object, she now became aware of a form standing in the garden, at a short distance from the window where she sat. The dusk had deepened, during Ellen's abstraction, to such a degree, that the man's features were not perfectly dis-tinguishable; but the maiden was not long in doubt of his identity, for he approached, and spoke in the same

low tone in which he had addressed her when they
stood by the stream.

'Do you still refuse my request, when its object is
but your own good, and that of one who should be
most dear to you?' he asked.

Ellen's first impulse had been, to cry out for assistance — her second was to fly; — but rejecting both
these measures, she determined to remain, endeavoring
to persuade herself that she was safe. The quivering
of her voice, however, when she attempted to reply,
betrayed her apprehensions.

'I cannot listen to such a request from a stranger,'
she said. 'If you bring news from — from my father,
why is it not told to Dr. Melmoth?'

'Because what I have to say is for your ear alone,'
was the reply; 'and if you would avoid misfortune now,
and sorrow hereafter, you will not refuse to hear me.'

'And does it concern my father?' asked Ellen,
eagerly.

'It does — most deeply,' answered the stranger.

She meditated a moment, and then replied, 'I will not
refuse, I will hear — but speak quickly.'

'We are in danger of interruption in this place, — and
that would be fatal to my errand,' said the stranger. 'I
will await you in the garden.'

With these words, and giving her no opportunity for
reply, he drew back; and his form faded from her eyes.
This precipitate retreat from argument was the most
probable method, that he could have adopted, of gaining his end. He had awakened the strongest interest in
Ellen's mind, and he calculated justly, in supposing that
she would consent to an interview upon his own terms.

Dr. Melmoth had followed his own fancies in the mode
of laying out his garden; and, in consequence, the plan
that had undoubtedly existed in his mind, was utterly
incomprehensible to every one but himself. It was an
intermixture of kitchen and flower garden, — a labyrinth
of winding paths, bordered by hedges, and impeded by
shrubbery. Many of the original trees of the forest were
still flourishing among the exotics, which the doctor had

transplanted thither. It was not without a sensation of fear, stronger than she had ever before experienced, that Ellen Langton found herself in this artificial wilderness, and in the presence of the mysterious stranger. The dusky light deepened the lines of his dark, strong features, and Ellen fancied that his countenance wore a wilder and a fiercer look than when she had met him by the stream. He perceived her agitation, and addressed her in the softest tones of which his voice was capable.

'Compose yourself,' he said; 'you have nothing to fear from me. But we are in open view from the house, where we now stand; and discovery would not be without danger, to both of us.'

'No eye can see us here,' said Ellen, trembling at the truth of her own observation, when they stood beneath a gnarled, low-branched pine, which Dr. Melmoth's ideas of beauty had caused him to retain in his garden. 'Speak quickly; for I dare follow you no farther.'

The spot was indeed sufficiently solitary, and the stranger delayed no longer to explain his errand.

'Your father,' he began,—'do you not love him? Would you do aught for his welfare?'

'Everything that a father could ask I would do,' exclaimed Ellen, eagerly. 'Where is my father; and when shall I meet him?'

'It must depend upon yourself, whether you shall meet him in a few days or never.'

'Never!' repeated Ellen. 'Is he ill?—Is he in danger?'

'He is in danger,' replied the man; 'but not from illness. Your father is a ruined man. Of all his friends, but one remains to him. That friend has travelled far, to prove if his daughter has a daughter's affection.'

'And what is to be the proof?' asked Ellen, with more calmness than the stranger had anticipated; for she possessed a large fund of plain sense, which revolted against the mystery of these proceedings. Such a course, too, seemed discordant with her father's character, whose strong mind and almost cold heart were little likely to demand, or even to pardon, the romance of affection.

'This letter will explain,' was the reply to Ellen's question. 'You will see that it is in your father's hand; and that may gain your confidence, though I am doubted.'

She received the letter; and many of her suspicions of the stranger's truth were vanquished by the apparent openness of his manner. He was preparing to speak further, but paused, — for a footstep was now heard, approaching from the lower part of the garden. From their situation, at some distance from the path, and in the shade of the tree, they had a fair chance of eluding discovery from any unsuspecting passenger; and, when Ellen saw that the intruder was Fanshawe, she hoped that his usual abstraction would assist their concealment.

But, as the student advanced along the path, his air was not that of one, whose deep, inward thoughts withdrew his attention from all outward objects. He rather resembled the hunter, on the watch for his game; and while he was yet at a distance from Ellen, a wandering gust of wind waved her white garments and betrayed her.

'It is as I feared,' said Fanshawe to himself. He then drew nigh, and addressed Ellen with a calm authority that became him well, notwithstanding that his years scarcely exceeded her own. 'Miss Langton,' he inquired, 'what do you here, at such an hour, and with such a companion?'

Ellen was sufficiently displeased at what she deemed the unauthorized intrusion of Fanshawe in her affairs; but his imposing manner and her own confusion prevented her from replying.

'Permit me to lead you to the house,' he continued, in the words of a request, but in the tone of a command. 'The dew hangs dank and heavy on these branches, and a longer stay would be more dangerous than you are aware.'

Ellen would fain have resisted; but though the tears hung as heavy on her eyelashes, between shame and anger, as the dew upon the leaves, she felt compelled to accept the arm that he offered her. But the stranger, who, since Fanshawe's approach, had remained a little apart, now advanced.

'You speak as one in authority, young man,' he said. 'Have you the means of compelling obedience? Does your power extend to men? — Or do you rule only over simple girls? Miss Langton is under my protection, and till you can bend me to your will, she shall remain so.'

Fanshawe turned, calmly, and fixed his eye on the stranger. 'Retire, Sir,' was all he said.

Ellen almost shuddered, as if there were a mysterious and unearthly power in Fanshawe's voice; for she saw that the stranger endeavored in vain, borne down by the influence of a superior mind, to maintain the boldness of look and bearing that seemed natural to him. He at first made a step forward, — then muttered a few half-audible words; — but, quailing at length beneath the young man's bright and steady eye, he turned and slowly withdrew.

Fanshawe remained silent, a moment, after his opponent had departed; and when he next spoke, it was in a tone of depression. Ellen observed, also, that his countenance had lost its look of pride and authority; and he seemed faint and exhausted. The occasion that called forth his energies had passed; and they had left him.

'Forgive me, Miss Langton,' he said, almost humbly, 'if my eagerness to serve you has led me too far. There is evil in this stranger, more than your pure mind can conceive. I know not what has been his errand; but let me entreat you to put confidence in those to whose care your father has intrusted you. Or if I, — or — or Edward Walcott; — But I have no right to advise you; and your own calm thoughts will guide you best.'

He said no more; and, as Ellen did not reply, they reached the house, and parted in silence.

CHAPTER IV.

The seeds by nature planted
Take a deep root i' th' soil, and though for a time
The trenchant share and tearing harrow may
Sweep all appearance of them from the surface,
Yet with the first warm rains of Spring they 'll shoot,
And with their rankness smother the good grain.
Heaven grant, it may n't be so with him.

RICHES.

The scene of this tale must now be changed to the
little Inn, which at that period, as at the present, was
situated in the vicinity of Harley College. The site
of the modern establishment is the same with that of
the ancient, but everything of the latter, that had been
built by hands, has gone to decay and been removed,
and only the earth, beneath and around it, remains the
same. The modern building, a house of two stories,
after a lapse of twenty years, is yet unfinished. On
this account, it has retained the appellation of the 'new
Inn,' though, like many who have frequented it, it has
grown old ere its maturity. Its dingy whiteness, and
its apparent superfluity of windows (many of them being
closed with rough boards) give it somewhat of a dreary
look, especially in a wet day.

The ancient Inn was a house, of which the eaves
approached within about seven feet of the ground,
while the roof, sloping gradually upward, formed an
angle at several times that height. It was a comfortable and pleasant abode to the weary traveller, both
in summer and winter; for the frost never ventured
within the sphere of its huge hearths; and it was pro-
tected from the heat of the sultry season by three large
elms that swept the roof with their long branches, and
seemed to create a breeze where there was not one.
The device upon the sign, suspended from one of these
trees, was a Hand, holding a long necked Bottle, and
was much more appropriate than the present unmeaning
representation, of a Black Eagle. But it is necessary
to speak rather more at length of the Landlord, than of
the house over which he presided.

Hugh Crombie was one, for whom most of the wise men, who considered the course of his early years, had predicted the gallows as an end, before he should arrive at middle age. That these prophets of ill had been deceived was evident from the fact, that the doomed man had now past the fortieth year, and was in more prosperous circumstances than most of those who had wagged their tongues against him. Yet the failure of their forebodings was more remarkable than their fulfilment would have been.

He had been distinguished almost from his earliest infancy by those precocious accomplishments, which, because they consist in an imitation of the vices and follies of maturity, render a boy the favorite plaything of men. He seemed to have received from nature the convivial talents, which, whether natural or acquired, are a most dangerous possession; and before his twelfth year he was the welcome associate of all the idle and dissipated of his neighborhood, and especially of those who haunted the tavern of which he had now become the landlord. Under this course of education Hugh Crombie grew to youth and manhood; and the lovers of good words could only say in his favor, that he was a greater enemy to himself than to any one else, and that, if he should reform, few would have a better chance of prosperity than he.

The former clause of this modicum of praise (if praise it may be termed) was indisputable; but it may be doubted, whether, under any circumstances where his success depended on his own exertions, Hugh would have made his way well through the world. He was one of those unfortunate persons, who, instead of being perfect in any single art or occupation, are superficial in many, and who are supposed to possess a larger share of talent than other men, because it consists of numerous scraps, instead of a single mass. He was partially acquainted with most of the manual arts that gave bread to others; but not one of them, nor all of them, would give bread to him. By some fatality, the only two of his multifarious accomplishments, in which his excellence was generally conceded, were both calculated to keep him poor rather than to make him rich. He was a musician and a poet.

There are yet remaining in that portion of the country, many ballads and songs — set to their own peculiar tunes — the authorship of which is attributed to him. In general, his productions were upon subjects of local and temporary interest, and would consequently require a bulk of explanatory notes, to render them interesting or intelligible to the world at large. A considerable proportion of the remainder are Anacreontics, — though, in their construction, Hugh Crombie imitated neither the Teian nor any other bard. These latter have generally a coarseness and sensuality, intolerable to minds even of no very fastidious delicacy. But there are two or three simple little songs, into which a feeling and a natural pathos have found their way, that still retain their influence over the heart. These, after two or three centuries, may perhaps be precious to the collectors of our early poetry. At any rate, Hugh Crombie's effusions, tavern-haunter and vagrant though he was, have gained a continuance of fame (confined, indeed, to a narrow section of the country) which many who called themselves poets then, and would have scorned such a brother, have failed to equal.

During the long winter evenings, when the farmers were idle round their hearths, Hugh was a courted guest; for none could while away the hours more skilfully than he. The winter therefore was his season of prosperity; in which respect he differed from the butterflies and useless insects, to which he otherwise bore a resemblance. During the cold months, a very desirable alteration for the better appeared in his outward man. His cheeks were plump and sanguine; his eyes bright and cheerful, and the tip of his nose glowed with a Bardolphian fire, — a flame, indeed, which Hugh was so far a vestal as to supply with its necessary fuel, at all seasons of the year. But, as the Spring advanced, he assumed a lean and sallow look, wilting and fading in the sunshine, that brought life and joy to every animal and vegetable except himself. His winter patrons eyed him with an austere regard, and some even practised upon him the modern and fashionable courtesy of the 'cut direct.'

Yet, after all, there was good, or something that Nature intended to be so, in the poor outcast, — some lovely flowers, the sweeter even for the weeds that choked them. An instance of this was his affection for an aged father, whose whole support was the broken reed — his son. Notwithstanding his own necessities, Hugh contrived to provide food and raiment for the old man, — how, it would be difficult to say, and perhaps as well not to inquire. He also exhibited traits of sensitiveness to neglect and insult, and of gratitude for favors; both of which feelings a course of life like his is usually quick to eradicate.

At length the restraint, for such his father had ever been, upon Hugh Crombie's conduct was removed by his death; and then the wise men and the old began to shake their heads; and they who took pleasure in the follies, vices, and misfortunes of their fellow-creatures, looked for a speedy gratification. They were disappointed, however; for Hugh had apparently determined, that, whatever might be his catastrophe, he would meet it among strangers, rather than at home. Shortly after his father's death, he disappeared altogether from the vicinity; and his name became, in the course of years, an unusual sound, where once the lack of other topics of interest had given it a considerable degree of notoriety. Sometimes, however, when the winter blast was loud round the lonely farm-house, its inmates remembered him who had so often chased away the gloom of such an hour, and, though with little expectation of its fulfilment, expressed a wish to behold him again.

Yet that wish, formed perhaps because it appeared so desperate, was finally destined to be gratified. One summer evening, about two years previous to the period of this tale, a man of sober and staid deportment, mounted upon a white horse, arrived at the Hand and Bottle, to which some civil or military meeting had

chanced that day, to draw most of the inhabitants of
the vicinity. The stranger was well, though plainly
dressed, and anywhere but in a retired country town
would have attracted no particular attention; but here,
where a traveller was not of every day occurrence, he
was soon surrounded by a little crowd, who, when his
eye was averted, seized the opportunity diligently to
peruse his person. He was rather a thick-set man, but
with no superfluous flesh; his hair was of iron-grey;
he had a few wrinkles; his face was so deeply sun
burnt, that, excepting a half-smothered glow on the tip
of his nose, a dusky yellow was the only apparent hue.
As the people gazed, it was observed that the elderly
men, and the men of substance, gat themselves silently
to their steeds, and hied homeward with an unusual
degree of haste; till at length the inn was deserted
except by a few wretched objects to whom it was a
constant resort. These, instead of retreating, drew
closer to the traveller, peeping anxiously into his face,
and asking, ever and anon, a question, in order to discover the tone of his voice. At length, with one consent, and as if the recognition had at once burst upon
them, they hailed their old boon-companion, Hugh
Crombie, and, leading him into the inn, did him the
honor to partake of a cup of welcome at his expense.

But, though Hugh readily acknowledged the not very
reputable acquaintances who alone acknowledged him,
they speedily discovered that he was an altered man.
He partook with great moderation of the liquor, for
which he was to pay; he declined all their flattering
entreaties for one of his old songs; and finally, being
urged to engage in a game at all-fours, he calmly
observed, almost in the words of an old clergyman, on
a like occasion, that his principles forbade a profane
appeal to the decision by lot.

On the next sabbath Hugh Crombie made his appearance at public worship, in the chapel of Harley
College, and here his outward demeanor was unexcep-
tionally serious and devout, — a praise, which, on that
particular occasion, could be bestowed on few besides.

From these favorable symptons, the old established prej-
udices against him began to waver; and as he seemed
not to need, and to have no intention to ask, the assistance of any one, he was soon generally acknowledged
by the rich, as well as by the poor. His account of his
past life and of his intentions for the future was brief,
but not unsatisfactory. He said, that, since his departure, he had been a sea-faring man, and that, having
acquired sufficient property to render him easy in the
decline of his days, he had returned to live and die in
the town of his nativity.

There was one person, and the one whom Hugh was
most interested to please, who seemed perfectly satisfied
of the verity of his reformation. This was the landlady
of the inn, whom, at his departure, he had left a gay,
and, even at thirty-five, a rather pretty wife, and whom,
on his return, he found a widow of fifty, fat, yellow,
wrinkled, and a zealous member of the church. She,
like others, had at first cast a cold eye on the wanderer;
but it shortly became evident, to close observers, that a
change was at work in the pious matron's sentiments,
respecting her old acquaintance. She was now careful
to give him his morning dram from her own peculiar
bottle, — to fill his pipe from her private box of Virginia,
— and to mix for him the sleeping-cup, in which her late
husband had delighted. Of all these courtesies Hugh
Crombie did partake, with a wise and cautious moderation, that, while it proved them to be welcome, expressed
his fear of trespassing on her kindness. For the sake
of brevity, it shall suffice to say, that, about six weeks
after Hugh's return, a writing appeared on one of the
elm-trees in front of the tavern, (where, as the place of
greatest resort, such notices were usually displayed)
setting forth, that marriage was intended between Hugh
Crombie and the Widow Sarah Hutchins. And the
ceremony, which made Hugh a landholder, a house-
holder, and a substantial man, in due time took place.

As a landlord, his general conduct was very praiseworthy. He was moderate in his charges, and attentive
to his guests; he allowed no gross and evident disorders

in his house, and practised none himself; he was kind and charitable to such as needed food and lodging, and had not wherewithal to pay, — for with these his experience had doubtless given him a fellow-feeling. He was also sufficiently attentive to his wife; though it must be acknowledged that the religious zeal, which had had a considerable influence in gaining her affections, grew, by no moderate degrees, less fervent. It was whispered, too, that the new landlord could, when time, place, and company were to his mind, upraise a song as merrily, and drink a glass as jollily, as in the days of yore. These were the weightiest charges that could now be brought against him; and wise men thought, that, whatever might have been the evil of his past life, he had returned with a desire (which years of vice, if they do not sometimes produce, do not always destroy) of being honest if opportunity should offer; — and Hugh had certainly a fair one.

On the afternoon previous to the events related in the last chapter, the personage whose introduction to the reader has occupied so large a space, was seated under one of the elms, in front of his dwelling. The bench which now sustained him, and on which were carved the names of many former occupants, was Hugh Crombie's favorite lounging place, unless when his attentions were required by his guests. No demand had that day been made upon the hospitality of the Hand and Bottle, and the landlord was just then murmuring at the unfrequency of employment. The slenderness of his profits, indeed, were no part of his concern; for the Widow Hutchins' chief income was drawn from her farm, nor was Hugh ever miserly inclined. But his education and habits had made him delight in the atmosphere of the Sun, and in the society of those who frequented it; and of this species of enjoyment his present situation certainly did not afford an overplus.

Yet had Hugh Crombie an enviable appearance of indolence and ease, as he sat under the old tree, polluting the sweet air with his pipe, and taking occasional draughts from a brown jug, that stood near at hand.

The basis of the potation contained in this vessel, was harsh old cider, from the Widow's own orchard; but its coldness and acidity were rendered innocuous by a due proportion of yet older brandy. The result of this mixture was extremely felicitous, pleasant to the taste, and producing a tingling sensation on the coats of the stomach, uncommonly delectable to so old a toper as Hugh.

The landlord cast his eye, ever and anon, along the road that led down the valley in the direction of the village; and at last, when the sun was wearing westward, he discovered the approach of a horseman. He immediately replenished his pipe, took a long draught from the brown jug, summoned the ragged youth who officiated in most of the subordinate departments of the Inn, and who was now to act as ostler; and then prepared himself for confabulation with his guest.

'He comes from the sea-coast,' said Hugh to himself, as the traveller emerged into open view on the level road. 'He is two days in advance of the post, with its news of a fortnight old. Pray heaven he prove communicative!' Then, as the stranger drew nigher, 'one would judge that his dark face had seen as hot a sun as mine. He has felt the burning breeze of the Indies, East and West, I warrant him. Ah, I see we shall send away the evening merrily! Not a penny shall come out of his purse, — that is, if his tongue runs glibly. Just the man I was praying for — Now may the Devil take me if he is!' interrupted Hugh in accents of alarm, and starting from his seat. He composed his countenance, however, with the power that long habit and necessity had given him over his emotions, and again settled himself quietly on the bench.

The traveller, coming on at a moderate pace, alighted, and gave his horse to the ragged ostler. He then advanced towards the door near which Hugh was seated, whose agitation was manifested by no perceptible sign, except by the shorter and more frequented puffs with which he plied his pipe. Their eyes did not meet till just as the stranger was about to enter, when he started apparently with a surprise and alarm similar to those of

Hugh Crombie. He recovered himself, however, sufficiently to return the nod of recognition with which he
was favored, and immediately entered the house, the
landlord following.

'This way, if you please, Sir,' said Hugh. 'You will
find this apartment cool and retired.'

He ushered his guest into a small room, the windows
of which were darkened by the creeping plants that clustered round them. Entering and closing the door, the
two gazed at each other, a little space, without speaking.
The traveller first broke silence.

'Then this is your living self, Hugh Crombie?' he
said. The landlord extended his hand as a practical
reply to the question. The stranger took it, though with
no especial appearance of cordiality.

'Ay, this seems to be flesh and blood,' he said in the
tone of one who would willingly have found it otherwise.
'And how happens this, friend Hugh? I little thought
to meet you again in this life. When I last heard from
you, your prayers were said, and you were bound for a
better world.'

'There would have been small danger of your meeting
me there,' observed the landlord, dryly.

'It is an unquestionable truth, Hugh,' replied the
traveller. 'For which reason I regret that your voyage
was delayed.

'Nay, that is a hard word to bestow on your old comrade,' said Hugh Crombie. 'The world is wide enough
for both of us, and why should you wish me out of it?'

'Wide as it is,' rejoined the stranger, 'we have stum-
bled against each other, — to the pleasure of neither of
us, if I may judge from your countenance. Methinks
I am not a welcome guest at Hugh Crombie's Inn.'

"Your welcome must depend on the cause of your
coming, and the length of your stay,' replied the landlord.

'And what if I come to settle down among these quiet
hills where I was born?' inquired the other. 'What if
I, too, am weary of the life we have led, — or afraid,
perhaps, that it will come to too speedy an end? Shall

I have your good word, Hugh, to set me up in an honest way of life? Or will you make me a partner in your trade, since you know my qualifications? A pretty pair of publicans should we be, and the quart pot would have little rest between us.'

'It may be as well to replenish it now,' observed Hugh, stepping to the door of the room, and giving orders accordingly. 'A meeting between old friends should never be dry. But for the partnership, it is a matter in which you must excuse me. Heaven knows, I find it hard enough to be honest, with no tempter but the devil and my own thoughts; and if I have you also to contend with, there is little hope of me.'

'Nay, that is true. Your good resolutions were always like cobwebs, and your evil habits like five inch cables,' replied the traveller. 'I am to understand, then, that you refuse my offer?'

'Not only that, — but if you have chosen this valley as your place of rest, Dame Crombie and I must look through the world for another. But, hush, here comes the wine.'

The ostler, in the performance of another part of his duty, now appeared, bearing a measure of the liquor that Hugh had ordered. The wine of that period, owing to the comparative lowness of the duties, was of more moderate price than in the mother country, and of purer and better quality than at the present day.

'The stuff is well chosen, Hugh,' observed the guest, after a draught large enough to authorize an opinion. 'You have most of the requisites for your present station, and I should be sorry to draw you from it. I trust there will be no need.'

'Yet you have a purpose in your journey hither,' observed his comrade.

'Yes, — and you would fain be informed of it,' replied the traveller. He arose, and walked once or twice across the room; then seeming to have taken his resolution, he paused and fixed his eye stedfastly on Hugh Crombie. 'I could wish, my old acquaintance,' he said, 'that your lot had been cast anywhere rather than here. Yet

if you choose it, you may do me a good office, and one
that shall meet with a good reward. Can I trust you?'

'My secrecy, you can,' answered the host, 'but nothing farther. I know the nature of your plans, and
whither they would lead me, too well to engage in them.
To say the truth, since it concerns not me, I have little
desire to hear your secret.'

'And I as little to tell it, I do assure you,' rejoined
the guest. 'I have always loved to manage my affairs
myself, and to keep them to myself. It is a good rule,
but it must sometimes be broken. And now, Hugh,
how is it that you have become possessed of this comfortable dwelling and of these pleasant fields?'

'By my marriage with the Widow Sarah Hutchins,'
replied Hugh Crombie, staring at a question, which
seemed to have little reference to the present topic of
conversation.

'It is a most excellent method of becoming a man
of substance,' continued the traveller; — 'attended with
little trouble, and honest withal.'

'Why, as to the trouble,' said the landlord, 'it follows
such a bargain, instead of going before it. And for
honesty — I do not recollect that I have gained a penny
more honestly these twenty years.'

'I can swear to that,' observed his comrade. 'Well,
mine host, I entirely approve of your doings; and,
moreover, have resolved to prosper after the same
fashion myself.'

'If that be the commodity you seek,' replied Hugh
Crombie, 'you will find none here to your mind. We
have widows in plenty, it is true, but most of them have
children and few have houses and lands. But now to
be serious — and there has been something serious in
your eye, all this while — what is your purpose in coming hither? You are not safe here. Your name has
had a wider spread than mine, and if discovered it will
go hard with you.'

'But who would know me, now?' asked the guest.

'Few, — few indeed,' replied the landlord, gazing at
the dark features of his companion, where hardship,

peril and dissipation had each left their traces. 'No, you are not like the slender boy of fifteen, who stood on the hill by moonlight, to take a last look at his father's cottage. There were tears in your eyes, then; and, as often as I remember them, I repent that I did not turn you back, instead of leading you on.'

'Tears, were there? Well, there have been few enough since,' said his comrade, pressing his eyelids firmly together, as if even then tempted to give way to the weakness that he scorned. 'And, for turning me back, Hugh, it was beyond your power. I had taken my resolution, and you did but shew me the way to execute it.'

'You have not inquired after those you left behind,' observed Hugh Crombie.

'No, — no; — nor will I have aught of them,' exclaimed the traveller, starting from his seat, and pacing rapidly across the room. 'My father, I know, is dead, and I have forgiven him. My mother — What could I hear of her but misery? — I will hear nothing.'

'You must have passed the cottage, as you rode hitherward,' said Hugh. 'How could you forbear to enter?'

'I did not see it,' he replied. 'I closed my eyes and turned away my head.'

'O, if I had had a mother — a loving mother, — if there had been one being in the world, that loved me, or cared for me, I should not have become an utter cast away,' exclaimed Hugh Crombie.

The landlord's pathos, — like all pathos that flows from the wine cup, — was sufficiently ridiculous; and his companion, who had already overcome his own brief feelings of sorrow and remorse, now laughed aloud.

'Come, come, mine host of the Hand and Bottle,' he cried in his usual hard, sarcastic tone; 'be a man, as much as in you lies. You had always a foolish trick of repentance; but, as I remember, it was commonly of a morning, before you had swallowed your first dram. And now, Hugh, fill the quart pot again, and we will to business.'

When the landlord had complied with the wishes of his guest, the latter resumed in a lower tone than that of his ordinary conversation.

'There is a young lady, lately become a resident hereabouts. Perhaps you can guess her name ; for you have a quick apprehension in these matters.'

'A young lady?' repeated Hugh Crombie. 'And what is your concern with her? Do you mean Ellen Langton, daughter of the old Merchant Langton, whom you have some cause to remember?'

'I do remember him ; but he is where he will speedily be forgotten,' answered the traveller. 'And this girl — I know your eye has been upon her, Hugh. Describe her to me.'

'Describe her!' exclaimed Hugh, with much animation. 'It is impossible, in prose; but you shall have her very picture, in a verse of one of my own songs.'

'Nay, mine host, I beseech you to spare me. This is no time for quavering,' said the guest. 'However, I am proud of your approbation, my old friend, — for this young lady do I intend to take to wife. What think you of the plan?'

Hugh Crombie gazed into his companion's face for the space of a moment, in silence. There was nothing in its expression that looked like a jest. It still retained the same hard, cold look, that, except when Hugh had alluded to his home and family, it had worn through their whole conversation.

'On my word, comrade!' he at length replied, 'my advice is, that you give over your application to the quart pot, and refresh your brain by a short nap. And yet, your eye is cool and steady. What is the meaning of this?'

'Listen, and you shall know,' said the guest. 'The old man, her father, is in his grave.' —

'Not a bloody grave, I trust,' interrupted the landlord, starting, and looking fearfully into his comrade's face.

'No, a watery one,' he replied, calmly. 'You see, Hugh, I am a better man than you took me for. The old man's blood is not on my head, though my wrongs are on his. Now listen. He had no heir but this only daughter; and to her, and to the man she marries, all his wealth will belong. She shall marry me. Think you her father will rest easy in the ocean, Hugh Crombie, when I am his son-in-law?'

'No, he will rise up to prevent it, if need be,' answered the landlord. 'But the dead need not interpose to frustrate so wild a scheme.'

'I understand you,' said his comrade. 'You are of opinion that the young lady's consent may not be so soon won as asked. Fear not for that, mine host. I have a winning way with me, when opportunity serves; and it shall serve with Ellen Langton. I will have no rivals in my wooing.'

'Your intention, if I take it rightly, is to get this poor girl into your power, and then to force her into a marriage,' said Hugh Crombie.

'It is; and I think I possess the means of doing it,' replied his comrade. 'But methinks, friend Hugh, my enterprise has not your good wishes.'

'No; and I pray you to give it over,' said Hugh Crombie, very earnestly. 'The girl is young, lovely, and as good as she is fair. I cannot aid in her ruin. Nay more — I must prevent it.'

'Prevent it!' exclaimed the traveller, with a darkening countenance. 'Think twice before you stir in this matter, I advise you. Ruin, do you say? Does a girl call it ruin, to be made an honest wedded wife? No, no, mine host; nor does a widow either, — else have you much to answer for.'

'I gave the Widow Hutchins fair play, at least; which is more than poor Ellen is likely to get,' observed the landlord. 'My old comrade, will you not give up this scheme?'

'My old comrade, I will not give up this scheme,' returned the other, composedly. 'Why, Hugh, what has come over you since we last met? Have we not done twenty worse deeds of a morning, and laughed over them at night?'

'He is right there,' said Hugh Crombie, in a meditative tone. 'Of a certainty, my conscience has grown unreasonably tender, within the last two years. This one small sin, if I were to aid in it, would add but a trifle to the sum of mine. But then the poor girl.' —

His companion overheard him thus communing with himself, and, having had much former experience of his infirmity of purpose, doubted not that he should bend him to his will. In fact, his arguments were so effectual, that Hugh at length, though reluctantly, promised his co-operation. It was necessary that their motions should be speedy ; for, on the second day thereafter the arrival of the post would bring intelligence of the shipwreck, by which Mr. Langton had perished.

'And after the deed is done,' said the landlord, 'I beseech you never to cross my path again. There have been more wicked thoughts in my head, within the last hour, than for the whole two years that I have been an honest man.'

'What a saint art thou become, Hugh!' said his comrade. 'But fear not that we shall meet again. When I leave this valley, it will be to enter it no more.'

'And there is little danger that any other, who has known me, will chance upon me here,' observed Hugh Crombie. 'Our trade was unfavorable to length of days, and I suppose most of our old comrades have arrived at the end of theirs.'

'One whom you knew well, is nearer to you than you think,' answered the traveller ; 'for I did not travel hitherward entirely alone.'

CHAPTER V.

A naughty night to swim in.

SHAKSPEARE.

The evening of the day succeeding the adventure of the angler, was dark and tempestuous. The rain descended almost in a continued sheet, and occasional powerful gusts of wind drove it hard against the north-eastern windows of Hugh Crombie's inn. But at least one apartment of the interior presented a scene of comfort, and of apparent enjoyment; the more delightful from its contrast with the elemental fury that raged without. A fire, which the chillness of the evening, though a summer one, made necessary, was burning brightly on the hearth; and in front was placed a small round table, sustaining wine and glasses. One of the guests, for whom these preparations had been made, was Edward Walcott. The other was a shy, awkward young man, distinguished, by the union of classic and rural dress, as having but lately become a student of Harley College. He seemed little at his ease, — probably from a consciousness that he was on forbidden ground, and that the wine, of which he nevertheless swallowed a larger share than his companion, was an unlawful draught.

In the catalogue of crimes, provided against by the laws of Harley College, that of tavern-haunting was one of the principal. The secluded situation of the Seminary, indeed, gave its scholars but a very limited choice of vices; and this was therefore the usual channel by which the wildness of youth discharged itself. Edward Walcott, though naturally temperate, had been not an unfrequent offender in this respect; for which a superfluity both of time and money might plead some excuse. But since his acquaintance with Ellen Langton he had rarely entered Hugh Crombie's doors; and an interruption in that acquaintance was the cause of his present appearance there.

Edward's jealous pride had been considerably touched on Ellen's compliance with the request of the angler. He had, by degrees, imperceptible perhaps to himself, assumed the right of feeling displeased with her conduct; and she had as imperceptibly accustomed herself to consider what would be his wishes, and to act accordingly. He would, indeed, in no contingency, have ventured an open remonstrance; and such a proceeding would have been attended by a result, the reverse of what he desired. But there existed between them a silent compact (acknowledged perhaps by neither, but felt by both), according to which they had regulated the latter part of their intercourse. Their lips had yet spoken no word of love; but some of love's rights and privileges had been assumed on the one side, and at least not disallowed on the other.

Edward's penetration had been sufficiently quick to discover that there was a mystery about the angler — that there must have been a cause for the blush that rose so proudly on Ellen's cheek; and his quixotism had been not a little mortified, because she did not immediately appeal to his protection. He had however paid his usual visit, the next day, at Dr. Melmoth's, expecting that, by a smile of more than common brightness, she would make amends to his wounded feelings, — such having been her usual mode of reparation in the few instances of disagreement that had occurred between them. But he was disappointed. He found her cold, silent, and abstracted, inattentive when he spoke, and indisposed to speak herself. Her eye was sedulously averted from his; and the casual meeting of their glances, only proved, that there were feelings in her bosom which he did not share. He was unable to account for this change in her deportment; and, added to his previous conceptions of his wrongs, it produced an effect upon his rather hasty temper, that might have manifested itself violently, but for the presence of Mrs. Melmoth. He took his leave in very evident displeasure; but, just as he closed the door, he noticed an expression in Ellen's countenance, that, had they been alone, and had not he been quite so proud, would have drawn him down to her feet. Their eyes met, — when, suddenly, there was a gush of tears into those of Ellen, and a deep sadness, almost despair, spread itself over her features. He paused a moment, and then went his way; equally unable to account for her coldness, or for her grief. He was well aware, however, that his situation in respect to her, was unaccountably changed, — a conviction so disagreeable, that, but for a hope that is latent, even in the despair of youthful hearts, he would have been sorely tempted to shoot himself.

The gloom of his thoughts — a mood of mind the more intolerable to him, because so unusual — had driven him to Hugh Crombie's inn in search of artificial excitement. But even the wine had no attractions; and his first glass stood now almost untouched before him, while he gazed in heavy thought into the glowing embers of the fire. His companion perceived his melancholy, and essayed to dispel it by a choice of such topics of conversation, as he conceived would be most agreeable.

'There is a lady in the house,' he observed. 'I caught a glimpse of her in the passage as we came in. Did you see her, Edward?'

'A lady!' repeated Edward, carelessly. 'What know you of ladies? No, I did not see her; but I will venture to say that it was dame Crombie's self, and no other.'

'Well, perhaps it might,' said the other, doubtingly. 'Her head was turned from me, and she was gone like a shadow.'

'Dame Crombie is no shadow, and never vanishes like one,' resumed Edward. 'You have mistaken the slip-shod servant-girl for a lady.'

'Ay; but she had a white hand, a small white hand,' said the student, piqued at Edward's contemptuous opinion of his powers of observation, — 'as white as Ellen Langton's.' He paused, for the lover was offended by the profanity of the comparison, as was made evident by the blood that rushed to his brow.

'We will appeal to the landlord,' said Edward, recovering his equanimity, and turning to Hugh, who just then entered the room — 'Who is this angel, mine host, that has taken up her abode in the Hand and Bottle?'

Hugh cast a quick glance from one to another, before he answered, 'I keep no angels here, gentlemen. Dame Crombie would make the house anything but heaven, for them and me.'

'And yet Glover has seen a vision in the passage way,
— a lady with a small white hand.'

'Ah, I understand, — a slight mistake of the young
gentleman's,' said Hugh, with the air of one who could
perfectly account for the mystery. 'Our passageway
is dark, — or perhaps the light had dazzled his eyes.
It was the widow Fowler's daughter, that came to
borrow a pipe of tobacco for her mother. By the same
token, she put it into her own sweet mouth, and puffed
as she went along.'

'But the white hand,' said Glover, only half convinced.

'Nay, I know not,' answered Hugh. 'But her hand
was at least as white as her face; that I can swear.
Well, gentlemen, I trust you find everything in my
house to your satisfaction. When the fire needs renew-
ing, or the wine runs low, be pleased to tap on the
table. I shall appear with the speed of a sunbeam.'

After the departure of the landlord, the conversation
of the young men amounted to little more than mono-
syllables. Edward Walcott was wrapped in his own
contemplations; and his companion was in a half-
slumberous state, from which he started every quarter
of an hour, at the chiming of the clock that stood in a
corner. The fire died gradually away, the lamps began
to burn dim, and Glover, rousing himself from one of
his periodical slumbers, was about to propose a return
to their chambers. He was prevented, however, by the
approach of footsteps along the passageway; and Hugh
Crombie, opening the door, ushered a person into the
room, and retired.

The new comer was Fanshawe. The water, that
poured plentifully from his cloak, evinced that he had
but just arrived at the inn; but, whatever was his
object, he seemed not to have attained it, in meeting
with the young men. He paused near the door, as if
meditating whether to retire.

'My intrusion is altogether owing to a mistake, either
of the landlord's or mine,' he said; 'I came hither to
seek another person; but, as I could not mention his
name, my inquiries were rather vague.'

'I thank Heaven for the chance that sent you to us,' replied Edward, rousing himself; 'Glover is wretched company, and a duller evening have I never spent. We will renew our fire, and our wine, and you must sit down with us. And for the man you seek,' he continued in a whisper, 'he left the inn within a half-hour after we encountered him. I inquired of Hugh Crombie, last night.'

Fanshawe did not express his doubts of the correctness of the information on which Edward seemed to rely. Laying aside his cloak, he accepted his invitation to make one of the party, and sat down by the fireside.

The aspect of the evening now gradually changed. A strange wild glee spread from one to another of the party, which, much to the surprise of his companions, began with, and was communicated from, Fanshawe. He seemed to overflow with conceptions, inimitably ludicrous, but so singular, that, till his hearers had imbibed a portion of his own spirit, they could only wonder at, instead of enjoying them. His applications to the wine were very unfrequent; yet his conversation was such as one might expect from a bottle of champagne, endowed by a fairy with the gift of speech. The secret of this strange mirth lay in the troubled state of his spirits, which, like the vexed ocean at midnight, (if the simile be not too magnificent) tossed forth a mysterious brightness. The undefined apprehensions, that had drawn him to the inn, still distracted his mind; but mixed with them, there was a sort of joy not easily to be described. By degrees, and by the assistance of the wine, the inspiration spread, each one contributing such a quantity, and such quality of wit and whim, as was proportioned to his genius; but each one, and all, displaying a greater share of both, than they had ever been suspected of possessing.

At length, however, there was a pause, — the deep pause of flagging spirits, that always follows mirth and wine. No one would have believed, on beholding the pensive faces, and hearing the involuntary sighs, of the party, that from these, but a moment before, had arisen so loud and wild a laugh. During this interval, Edward Walcott, (who was the poet of his class) volunteered the following song, which, from its want of polish, and from its application to his present feelings, might charitably be taken for an extemporaneous production.

> The wine is bright, the wine is bright,
>   And gay the drinkers be;
> Of all that drain the bowl to-night,
>   Most jollily drain we.
> Oh, could one search the weary earth,
>   The earth from sea to sea, —
> He 'd turn and mingle in our mirth,
>   For we 're the merriest three.
>
> Yet there are cares, oh, heavy cares, —
>   We know that they are nigh;
> When forth each lonely drinker fares,
>   Mark then his altered eye.
> Care comes upon us when the jest
>   And frantic laughter, die;
> And care will watch the parting guest, —
>   O late, then, let us fly!

Hugh Crombie, whose early love of song and min-strelsy was still alive, had entered the room at the sound of Edward's voice, in sufficient time to accompany the second stanza on the violin. He now, with the air of one who was entitled to judge in these matters, expressed his opinion of the performance.

'Really, master Walcott, I was not prepared for this,' he said in a tone of condescending praise, that a great man uses to his inferior, when he chooses to overwhelm him with excess of joy. 'Very well, indeed, young gentleman. Some of the lines, it is true, seem to have been dragged in by the head and shoulders; but I could scarcely have done much better myself, at your age. With practice, and with such instruction as I might afford you, I should have little doubt of your becoming a distinguished poet. A great defect in your seminary, gentlemen, — the want of due cultivation in this heavenly art.'

'Perhaps, sir,' said Edward, with much gravity, 'you

might yourself be prevailed upon to accept the Professorship of Poetry?'

'Why, such an offer would require consideration,' replied the landlord. 'Professor Hugh Crombie, of Harley College; — it has a good sound, assuredly. But I am a public man, Master Walcott, and the public would be loath to spare me from my present office.'

'Will Professor Crombie favor us with a specimen of his productions?' inquired Edward.

'Ahem, I shall be happy to gratify you, young gentlemen,' answered Hugh. 'It is seldom, in this rude country, Master Walcott, that we meet with kindred genius; and the opportunity should never be thrown away.'

Thus saying, he took a heavy draught of the liquor by which he was usually inspired, and the praises of which were the prevailing subject of his song. Then, after much hemming, thrumming, and prelusion, and with many queer gestures and gesticulations, he began to effuse a lyric, in the following fashion.

> I 've been a jolly drinker this five and twenty year,
> And still a jolly drinker, my friends, you see me here;
> I sing the joys of drinking; — bear a chorus, every man,
> With pint pot and quart pot and clattering of can.

The sense of the professor's first stanza was not in exact proportion to the sound; but, being executed with great spirit, it attracted universal applause. This, Hugh appropriated with a condescending bow and smile; and making a signal for silence, he went on —

> King Solomon of old, boys, (a jolly king was he,) —

But here he was interrupted by a clapping of hands, that seemed a continuance of the applause bestowed on his former stanza. Hugh Crombie, who, as is the custom of many great performers, usually sang with his eyes shut, now opened them, intending gently to rebuke his auditors for their unseasonable expression of delight. He immediately perceived, however, that the fault was to be attributed to neither of the three young men; and following the direction of their eyes, he saw, near the door, in the dim back-ground of the apartment, a figure in a cloak. The hat was flapped forward, the cloak muffled round the lower part of the face, and only the eyes were visible.

The party gazed a moment in silence, and then rushed *en masse* upon the intruder, the landlord bringing up the rear, and sounding a charge upon his fiddle. But as they drew nigh, the black cloak began to assume a familiar look, — the hat, also, was an old acquaintance; — and, these being removed, from beneath them shone forth the reverend face and form of Doctor Melmoth.

The President, in his quality of clergyman, had, late in the preceding afternoon, been called to visit an aged female who was supposed to be at the point of death. Her habitation was at the distance of several miles from Harley College; so that it was nightfall before Doctor Melmoth stood at her bed-side. His stay had been lengthened beyond his anticipation, on account of the frame of mind in which he found the dying woman; and after essaying to impart the comforts of religion to her disturbed intellect, he had waited for the abatement of the storm, that had arisen while he was thus engaged. As the evening advanced, however, the rain poured down in undiminished cataracts; and the Doctor, trusting to the prudence, and sure-footedness of his steed, had, at length set forth on his return. The darkness of the night, and the roughness of the road, might have appalled him, even had his horsemanship and his courage been more considerable than they were; but by the special protection of Providence, as he reasonably supposed, (for he was a good man, and on a good errand,) he arrived safely as far as Hugh Crombie's inn. — Doctor Melmoth had no intention of making a stay there; but as the road passed within a very short distance, he saw lights in the windows, and heard the sound of song and revelry. It immediately occurred to him, that these midnight rioters were, probably, some of the young men of his charge, and he was impelled, by a sense of duty, to enter and disperse them. Directed by the voices, he found his way, with some difficulty, to the apartment, just as Hugh concluded his first stanza, and amidst the subsequent applause, his entrance had been unperceived.

There was a silence of a moment's continuance, after the discovery of Dr. Melmoth, during which he attempted to clothe his round, good-natured face, in a look of awful dignity. But, in spite of himself, there was a little twisting of the corners of his mouth, and a smothered gleam in his eye.

'This has apparently been a very merry meeting, young gentlemen,' he at length said; 'but I fear my presence has cast a damp upon it.'

'O yes! your Reverence's cloak is wet enough to cast a damp upon anything,' exclaimed Hugh Crombie, assuming a look of tender anxiety. 'The young gentlemen are affrighted for your valuable life. Fear deprives them of utterance: permit me to relieve you of these dangerous garments.'

'Trouble not yourself, honest man," replied the Doctor, who was one of the most gullible of mortals. 'I trust I am in no danger, my dwelling being near at hand. But for these young men —'

'Would your reverence but honor my Sunday suit — the gray broadcloth coat, and the black velvet small-clothes, that have covered my unworthy legs but once? Dame Crombie shall have them ready in a moment,' continued Hugh, beginning to divest the Doctor of his garments.

'I pray you to appease your anxiety,' cried Doctor Melmoth, retaining a firm hold on such parts of his dress as yet remained to him. 'Fear not for my health. I will but speak a word to those misguided youth, and begone.'

'Misguided youth, did your reverence say?' echoed Hugh, in a tone of utter astonishment. 'Never were they better guided, than when they entered my poor house. Oh! had your reverence but seen them, when I heard their cries, and rushed forth to their assistance. Dripping with wet were they, like three drowned men at the resurrec — ahem!' interrupted Hugh, recollecting that the comparison he meditated might not suit the Doctor's ideas of propriety.

'But why were they abroad on such a night?' inquired the President.

'Ah! doctor, you little know the love these good young gentlemen bear for you,' replied the landlord. 'Your absence — your long absence — had alarmed them; and they rushed forth through the rain and darkness to seek you.'

'And was this indeed so?' asked the doctor, in a softened tone, and casting a tender and grateful look upon the three students. They, it is but justice to mention, had simultaneously made a step forward, in order to contradict the egregious falsehoods, of which Hugh's fancy was so fertile; but he assumed an expression of such ludicrous entreaty, that it was irresistible.

'But methinks their anxiety was not of long continuance,' observed doctor Melmoth, looking at the wine, and remembering the song that his entrance had interrupted.

'Ah! your reverence disapproves of the wine, I see,' answered Hugh Crombie. 'I did but offer them a drop, to keep the life in their poor young hearts. My dame advised strong waters; but, dame Crombie, says I, would ye corrupt their youth? And in my zeal for their good, doctor, I was delighting them, just at your entrance, with a pious little melody of my own, against the sin of drunkenness.'

'Truly, I remember something of the kind,' observed doctor Melmoth; 'and, as I think, it seemed to meet with good acceptance.'

'Aye, that it did!' said the landlord. 'Will it please your reverence to hear it?'

King Solomon of old, boys, (a wise man I 'm thinking,)
Has warned you to beware of the horrid vice of drinking — "

But why I talk of drinking, foolish man that I am! and all this time, doctor, you have not sipped a drop of my

wine. Now, I entreat your reverence, as you value
your health, and the peace and quiet of these youth.'

Doctor Melmoth drank a glass of wine, with the
benevolent intention of allaying the anxiety of Hugh
Crombie and the students. He then prepared to de-
part; for a strong wind had partially dispersed the
clouds, and occasioned an interval in the cataract of
rain. There was, perhaps, a little suspicion yet remaining in the good man's mind respecting the truth of the
landlord's story ; — at least, it was his evident intention,
to see the students fairly out of the inn, before he quitted
it himself. They therefore proceeded along the passage
way in a body. — The lamp that Hugh Crombie held,
but dimly enlightened them, and the number and conti-
guity of the doors, caused doctor Melmoth to lay his
hand upon the wrong one.

'Not there, not there, doctor! It is Dame Crombie's
bedchamber,' shouted Hugh, most energetically. 'Now
Beelzebub defend me,' he muttered to himself, perceiving that his exclamation had been a moment too late.

'Heavens! what do I see?' ejaculated doctor Melmoth, lifting his hands, and starting back from the
entrance of the room. The three students pressed forward ; — Mrs. Crombie and the servant-girl had been
drawn to the spot by the sound of Hugh's voice ; and all
their wondering eyes were fixed on poor Ellen Langton.

The apartment in the midst of which she stood, was
dimly lighted by a solitary candle, at the farther extremity ; but Ellen was exposed to the glare of the three
lamps, held by Hugh, his wife, and the servant-girl.
Their combined rays seemed to form a focus exactly at
the point where they reached her ; and the beholders,
had any been sufficiently calm, might have watched her
features in their agitated workings, and frequent change
of expression, as perfectly as by the broad light of day.
Terror had at first blanched her as white as a lily, or as
a marble statue, which for a moment she resembled, as
she stood motionless in the centre of the room. Shame
next bore sway ; and her blushing countenance, covered
by her slender white fingers, might fantastically be com-

pared to a variegated rose, with its alternate stripes of white and red. The next instant, a sense of her pure and innocent intentions gave her strength and courage; and her attitude and look had now something of pride and dignity. These, however, in their turn, gave way; for Edward Walcott pressed forward, and attempted to address her.

'Ellen, Ellen!' he said, in an agitated and quivering whisper;—but what was to follow cannot be known, for his emotion checked his utterance. His tone, and look, however, again overcame Ellen Langton, and she burst to tears. Fanshawe advanced, and took Edward's arm; 'she has been deceived,' he whispered—'She is innocent. You are unworthy of her if you doubt it.'

'Why do you interfere, Sir?' demanded Edward, whose passions, thoroughly excited, would willingly have wreaked themselves on any one. 'What right have you to speak of her innocence? Perhaps,' he continued, an undefined and ridiculous suspicion arising in his mind, 'perhaps you are acquainted with her intentions. Perhaps you are the deceiver.'

Fanshawe's temper was not naturally of the meekest character; and having had a thousand bitter feelings of his own to overcome, before he could attempt to console Edward, this rude repulse had almost aroused him to fierceness. But his pride, of which a more moderate degree would have had a less peaceable effect, came to his assistance; and he turned calmly and contemptuously away.

Ellen, in the mean time, had been restored to some degree of composure. To this effect, a feeling of pique against Edward Walcott had contributed. She had distinguished his voice in the neighbouring apartment,— had heard his mirth and wild laughter, without being aware of the state of feeling that produced them. She had supposed that the terms on which they parted in the morning, (which had been very grievous to herself,) would have produced a corresponding sadness in him. But while she sat in loneliness and in tears, her bosom distracted by a thousand anxieties and sorrows, of many of which Edward was the object, his reckless gaiety had seemed to prove the slight regard in which he held her. After the first outbreak of emotion, therefore, she called up her pride (of which, on proper occasions, she had a reasonable share,) and sustained his upbraiding glance with a passive composure, which women have more readily at command than men.

Doctor Melmoth's surprise had, during this time, kept him silent and inactive. He gazed alternately from one to another, of those who stood around him, as if to seek some explanation of so strange an event. But the faces of all were as perplexed as his own; — even Hugh Crombie had assumed a look of speechless wonder, — speechless, because his imagination, prolific as it was, could not supply a plausible falsehood.

'Ellen, dearest child,' at length said the doctor, 'what is the meaning of this?'

Ellen endeavored to reply; but, as her composure was merely external, she was unable to render her words audible. Fanshawe spoke in a low voice to doctor Melmoth, who appeared grateful for his advice.

'True, it will be the better way,' he replied. 'My wits are utterly confounded, or I should not have remained thus long. Come, my dear child,' he continued, advancing to Ellen, and taking her hand, 'let us return home, and defer the explanation till the morrow. There, there; only dry your eyes, and we will say no more about it.'

'And that will be your wisest way, old gentleman,' muttered Hugh Crombie.

Ellen at first exhibited but little desire — or, rather, an evident reluctance — to accompany her guardian. She hung back, while her glance passed almost imperceptibly over the faces that gazed so eagerly at her; but the one she sought was not visible among them. She had no alternative, and suffered herself to be led from the inn.

Edward Walcott, alone, remained behind, — the most wretched being, (at least such was his own opinion,) that breathed the vital air. He felt a sinking and sickness

of the heart, and alternately a feverish frenzy, neither
of which his short and cloudless existence had heretofore occasioned him to experience. He was jealous of,
he knew not whom, and he knew not what. He was
ungenerous enough to believe that Ellen — his pure and
lovely Ellen — had degraded herself; though from what
motive, or by whose agency, he could not conjecture.
When Doctor Melmoth had taken her in charge, Edward
returned to the apartment where he had spent the evening. The wine was still upon the table, and, in the
desperate hope of stupifying his faculties, he unwisely
swallowed huge successive draughts. The effect of his
imprudence was not long in manifesting itself; though
insensibility, which at another time would have been the
result, did not now follow. Acting upon his previous
agitation, the wine seemed to set his blood in a flame;
and for the time being, he was a perfect madman.

A phrenologist would probably have found the organ
of destructiveness in strong development, just then, upon
Edward's cranium; for he certainly manifested an impulse to break and destroy whatever chanced to be
within his reach. He commenced his operations by
upsetting the table, and breaking the bottles and glasses.
Then, seizing a tall heavy chair in each hand, he hurled
them, with prodigious force, one through the window,
and the other against a large looking-glass, the most
valuable article of furniture in Hugh Crombie's inn.
The crash and clatter of these outrageous proceedings,
soon brought the master, mistress, and maid-servant to
the scene of action; but the two latter, at the first sight
of Edward's wild demeanor and gleaming eyes, retreated
with all imaginable expedition. Hugh chose a position
behind the door, from whence, protruding his head, he
endeavored to mollify his inebriated guest. His interference, however, had nearly been productive of most
unfortunate consequences; for a massive andiron, with
round brazen head, whizzed past him, within a hair's
breadth of his ear.

‘I might as safely take my chance in a battle,’ exclaimed Hugh, withdrawing his head, and speaking to

a man who stood in the passageway. 'A little twist of
his hand to the left would have served my turn, as well
as if I stood in the path of a forty-two pound ball. And
here comes another broadside,' he added, as some other
article of furniture rattled against the door.

'Let us return his fire, Hugh,' said the person whom
he addressed, composedly lifting the andiron. 'He is
in want of ammunition; let us send him back his own.'

The sound of this man's voice produced a most
singular effect upon Edward. The moment before,
his actions had been those of a raving maniac; but,
when the words struck his ear, he paused, put his hand
to his forehead, seemed to recollect himself, and finally
advanced with a firm and steady step. His countenance
was dark and angry, but no longer wild.

'I have found you, villain!" he said to the angler.
'It is you who have done this.'

'And, having done it, the wrath of a boy — his
drunken wrath — will not induce me to deny it,' replied
the other scornfully.

'The boy will require a man's satisfaction,' returned
Edward; — 'and that speedily.'

'Will you take it now?' inquired the angler, with a
cool, derisive smile, and almost in a whisper. At the
same time he produced a brace of pistols, and held them
towards the young man.

'Willingly,' answered Edward, taking one of the
weapons. 'Choose your distance.'

The angler stepped back a pace; but before their
deadly intentions, so suddenly conceived, could be executed, Hugh Crombie interposed himself between them.

'Do you take my best parlor for the cabin of the
Black Andrew, where a pistol shot was a nightly pas-
time?' he inquired of his comrade. 'And you, master
Edward, with what sort of a face will you walk into the
chapel, to morning prayers, after putting a ball through
this man's head, or receiving one through your own? —
Though, in this last case, you will be past praying for,
or praying either.'

'Stand aside: I will take the risk. Make way, or I

will put the ball through your own head,' exclaimed Edward, fiercely; for the interval of rationality, that circumstances had produced, was again giving way to intoxication.

'You see how it is,' said Hugh to his companion, unheard by Edward. 'You shall take a shot at me, sooner than at the poor lad in his present state. You have done him harm enough already, and intend him more. I propose,' he continued aloud, and with a peculiar glance towards the angler, 'that this affair be decided to-morrow, at nine o'clock, under the old oak, on the bank of the stream. In the mean time, I will take charge of these pop-guns, for fear of accidents.'

'Well, mine host, be it as you wish,' said his comrade. 'A shot more or less is of little consequence to me.' He accordingly delivered his weapon to Hugh Crombie, and walked carelessly away.

'Come, master Walcott, the enemy has retreated. Victoria! And now, I see, the sooner I get you to your chamber, the better,' added he aside; for the wine was at last beginning to produce its legitimate effect, in stupefying the young man's mental and bodily faculties.

Hugh Crombie's assistance, though not, perhaps, quite indispensable, was certainly very convenient to our unfortunate hero, in the course of the short walk that brought him to his chamber. When arrived there, and in bed, he was soon locked in a sleep, scarcely less deep than that of death.

The weather, during the last hour, had appeared to be on the point of changing; — indeed, there were, every few minutes, most rapid changes. A strong breeze sometimes drove the clouds from the brow of heaven, so as to disclose a few of the stars; but, immediately after, the darkness would again become Egyptian, and the rain rush like a torrent from the sky.

CHAPTER VI.

About her neck a packet-mail
Fraught with advice, some fresh, some stale,
Of men that walked when they were dead.

HUDIBRAS.

Scarcely a word had passed between doctor Melmoth and Ellen Langton, on their way home; for, though the former was aware that his duty towards his ward would compel him to inquire into the motives of her conduct, the tenderness of his heart prompted him to defer the scrutiny to the latest moment. The same tenderness induced him to connive at Ellen's stealing secretly up to her chamber, unseen by Mrs. Melmoth; to render which measure practicable, he opened the house door very softly, and stood before his half-sleeping spouse (who waited his arrival in the parlor,) without any previous notice. This act of the doctor's benevolence was not destitute of heroism; for he was well assured, that, should the affair come to the lady's knowledge through any other channel, her vengeance would descend not less heavily on him for concealing, than on Ellen for perpetrating the elopement. That she had, thus far, no suspicion of the fact, was evident from her composure, as well as from the reply to a question, which, with more than his usual art, her husband put to her respecting the non-appearance of his ward. Mrs. Melmoth answered, that Ellen had complained of indisposition, and after drinking, by her prescription, a large cup of herb-tea, had retired to her chamber early in the evening. Thankful that all was yet safe, the doctor laid his head upon his pillow; but, late as was the hour, his many anxious thoughts long drove sleep from his eyelids.

The diminution in the quantity of his natural rest, did not, however, prevent doctor Melmoth from rising at his usual hour, which, at all seasons of the year, was an early one. He found, on descending to the parlor, that breakfast was nearly in readiness; for the lady of the house, (and, as a corollary, her servant-girl,) was not accustomed to await the rising of the sun, in order to commence her domestic labors. Ellen Langton, however, who had heretofore assimilated her habits to those of the family, was this morning invisible, — a circumstance imputed by Mrs. Melmoth to her indisposition of the preceding evening, and by the doctor, to mortification, on account of her elopement and its discovery.

'I think I will step into Ellen's bedchamber,' said Mrs. Melmoth, 'and inquire how she feels herself. The morning is delightful after the storm, and the air will do her good.'

'Had we not better proceed with our breakfast? If the poor child is sleeping, it were a pity to disturb her,' observed the doctor; for, besides his sympathy with Ellen's feelings, he was reluctant, as if he were the guilty one, to meet her face.

'Well, be it so. And now sit down, doctor, for the hot cakes are cooling fast. I suppose you will say they are not so good as those Ellen made, yesterday morning. I know not how you will bear to part with her; though the thing must soon be.'

'It will be a sore trial, doubtless,' replied doctor Melmoth — 'like tearing away a branch that is grafted on an old tree. And yet there will be a satisfaction in delivering her safe into her father's hands.'

'A satisfaction for which you may thank me, doctor,' observed the lady, 'If there had been none but you to look after the poor thing's doings, she would have been enticed away long ere this, for the sake of her money.'

Doctor Melmoth's prudence could scarcely restrain a smile at the thought, that an elopement, as he had reason to believe, had been plotted, and partly carried into execution, while Ellen was under the sole care of his lady; and had been frustrated only by his own despised agency. He was not accustomed, however, — nor was this an eligible occasion, — to dispute any of Mrs. Melmoth's claims to superior wisdom.

The breakfast proceeded in silence, — or, at least, without any conversation material to the tale. At its conclusion, Mrs. Melmoth was again meditating on the propriety of entering Ellen's chamber; but she was now prevented by an incident, that always excited much interest both in herself and her husband.

This was the entrance of the servant, bearing the letters and newspaper, with which, once a fortnight, the mail-carrier journeyed up the valley. Doctor Melmoth's situation, at the head of a respectable seminary, and his character as a scholar, had procured him an extensive correspondence among the learned men of his own country; and he had even exchanged epistles with one or two of the most distinguished dissenting clergymen of Great Britain. But, unless when some fond mother enclosed a one-pound note, to defray the private expenses of her son at College, — it was frequently the case, that the packets addressed to the doctor, were the sole contents of the mail-bag. In the present instance, his letters were very numerous, and, to judge from the one he chanced first to open, of an unconscionable length. While he was engaged in their perusal, Mrs. Melmoth amused herself with the newspaper, — a little sheet of about twelve inches square, which had but one rival in the country. — Commencing with the title, she labored on, through advertisements old and new, through poetry, lamentably deficient in rhythm and rhymes — through essays, the ideas of which had been trite since the first week of the creation; — till she finally arrived at the department that, a fortnight before, had contained the latest news from all quarters. Making such remarks upon these items as to her seemed good, the dame's notice was at length attracted by an article, which her sudden exclamation proved to possess uncommon interest. Casting her eye hastily over it, she immediately began to read aloud to her husband; but he, deeply engaged in a long and learned letter, instead of listening to what she wished to communicate, exerted his own lungs in opposition to hers — as is the custom of abstracted men when disturbed. The result was as follows.

'A brig just arrived in the outer harbor,' began Mrs.

Melmoth, 'reports, that on the morning of the 25th ult.' here the doctor broke in, 'wherefore I am compelled to differ from your exposition of the said passage, for those reasons, of the which I have given you a taste; provided' — the lady's voice was now most audible — 'ship bottom upward, discovered by the name on her stern to be the Ellen of' — 'and in the same opinion are Hooker, Cotton, and divers learned divines of a later date.'

The doctor's lungs were deep and strong, and victory seemed to incline toward him; but Mrs. Melmoth now made use of a tone whose peculiar shrillness, as long experience had taught her husband, argued a mood of mind not to be trifled with.

'On my word, doctor,' she exclaimed, 'this is most unfeeling and unchristian conduct! Here am I, endeavoring to inform you of the death of an old friend, and you continue as deaf as a post.'

Doctor Melmoth, who had heard the sound, without receiving the sense, of these words, now laid aside the letter in despair, and submissively requested to be informed of her pleasure.

'There, — read for yourself,' she replied, handing him the paper, and pointing to the passage containing the important intelligence. 'Read, and then finish your letter, if you have a mind.'

'He took the paper, unable to conjecture how the dame could be so much interested in any part of its contents; but, before he had read many words, he grew pale as death. 'Good Heavens! what is this?' he exclaimed. He then read on, 'being the vessel wherein that eminent son of New-England, John Langton, Esquire, had taken passage for his native country after an absence of many years.'

'Our poor Ellen, his orphan child!' said doctor Melmoth, dropping the paper. 'How shall we break the intelligence to her? Alas! her share of the affliction causes me to forget my own.'

'It is a heavy misfortune, doubtless, and Ellen will grieve as a daughter should,' replied Mrs. Melmoth, speaking with the good sense of which she had a competent share. 'But she has never known her father, and her sorrow must arise from a sense of duty, more than from strong affection. I will go and inform her of her loss. It is late, and I wonder if she be still asleep?'

'Be cautious, dearest wife,' said the doctor — 'Ellen has strong feelings, and a sudden shock might be dangerous.'

'I think I may be trusted, doctor Melmoth,' replied the lady, who had a high opinion of her own abilities as a comforter, and was not averse to exercise them.

Her husband, after her departure, sat listlessly turning over the letters, that yet remained unopened, feeling little curiosity, after such melancholy intelligence, respecting their contents. But by the handwriting of the direction on one of them, his attention was gradually arrested, till he found himself gazing earnestly on those strong, firm, regular characters. They were perfectly familiar to his eye; but from what hand they came, he could not conjecture. Suddenly, however, the truth burst upon him; and after noticing the date, and reading a few lines, he rushed hastily in pursuit of his wife. He had arrived at the top of his speed, and at the middle of the stair-case, when his course was arrested by the lady whom he sought, who came, with a velocity equal to his own, in an opposite direction. The consequence was, a concussion between the two meeting masses, by which Mrs. Melmoth was seated securely on the stairs, while the doctor was only preserved from precipitation to the bottom, by clinging desperately to the balustrade. As soon as the pair discovered that they had sustained no material injury by their contact, they began eagerly to explain the cause of their mutual haste, without those reproaches, which, on the lady's part, would, at another time, have followed such an accident.

'You have not told her the bad news, I trust?' cried doctor Melmoth, after each had communicated his and her intelligence, without obtaining audience of the other.

'Would you have me tell it to the bare walls?' inquired the lady, in her shrillest tone. 'Have I not just
informed you that she has gone, fled, eloped? Her
chamber is empty, and her bed has not been occupied.'

'Gone!' repeated the doctor — 'and, when her father
comes to demand his daughter of me, what answer shall
I make?'

'Now, heaven defend us from the visits of the dead
and drowned!' cried Mrs. Melmoth. 'This is a serious
affair, doctor; but not, I trust, sufficient to raise a
ghost.'

'Mr. Langton is yet no ghost,' answered he; 'though
this event will go near to make him one. He was fortunately prevented, after he had made every preparation,
from taking passage in the vessel that was lost.'

'And where is he now?' she inquired.

'He is in New England. Perhaps he is at this
moment, on his way to us,' replied her husband. 'His
letter is dated nearly a fortnight back, and he expresses
an intention of being with us in a few days.'

'Well, I thank heaven for his safety,' said Mrs.
Melmoth; 'but truly, the poor gentleman could not
have chosen a better time to be drowned, nor a worse
one to come to life, than this. What we shall do, doctor,
I know not; but had you locked the doors, and fastened
the windows, as I advised, the misfortune could not
have happened.'

'Why, the whole country would have flouted us,'
answered the doctor. 'Is there a door in all the province, that is barred or bolted, night or day? Nevertheless, it might have been advisable last night, had it
occurred to me.'

'And why at that time, more than at all times?' she
inquired. 'We had surely no reason to fear this event.'

Doctor Melmoth was silent; for his worldly wisdom
was sufficient to deter him from giving his lady the
opportunity, which she would not fail to use to the
utmost, of laying the blame of the elopement at his door.
He now proceeded, with a heavy heart, to Ellen's
chamber, to satisfy himself with his own eyes, of the

state of affairs. It was deserted, too truly; and the wild flowers with which it was the maiden's custom daily, to decorate her premises, were drooping, as if in sorrow for her who had placed them there. Mrs. Melmoth, on this second visit, discovered on the table a note, addressed to her husband, and containing a few words of gratitude from Ellen, but no explanation of her mysterious flight. The doctor gazed long on the tiny letters, which had evidently been traced with a trembling hand, and blotted with many tears.

'There is a mystery in this — a mystery that I cannot fathom,' he said. 'And now, I would I knew what measures it would be proper to take.'

'Get you on horseback, doctor Melmoth, and proceed as speedily as may be, down the valley to the town,' said the dame, the influence of whose firmer mind was sometimes, as in the present case, most beneficially exerted over his own. 'You must not spare for trouble — no, nor for danger — now — oh! if I were a man' —

'Oh, that you were,' murmured the doctor, in a perfectly inaudible voice. 'Well, and when I reach the town, what then?'

'As I am a christian woman, my patience cannot endure you,' exclaimed Mrs. Melmoth — 'oh, I love to see a man with the spirit of a man; but you —' and she turned away in utter scorn.

'But, dearest wife,' remonstrated the husband, who was really at a loss how to proceed, and anxious for her advice, 'your worldly experience is greater than mine, and I desire to profit by it. What should be my next measure after arriving at the town?'

Mrs. Melmoth was appeased by the submission with which the doctor asked her counsel; though, if the truth must be told, she heartily despised him for needing it. She condescended, however, to instruct him in the proper method of pursuing the runaway maiden, and directed him, before his departure, to put strict inquiries to Hugh Crombie, respecting any stranger who might lately have visited his inn. That there would be wisdom in this, doctor Melmoth had his own reasons for believing; and, still without imparting them to his lady, he proceeded to do as he had been bid.

The veracious landlord acknowledged that a stranger had spent a night and day at his inn, and was missing that morning; but he utterly denied all acquaintance with his character, or privity to his purposes. Had Mrs. Melmoth, instead of her husband, conducted the examination, the result might have been different. As the case was, the doctor returned to his dwelling but little wiser than he went forth; and, ordering his steed to be saddled, he began a journey, of which he knew not what would be the end.

In the mean time, the intelligence of Ellen's disappearance circulated rapidly, and soon sent forth hunters more fit to follow the chase than doctor Melmoth.

CHAPTER VII.

"There was racing and chacing o'er Cannobie Lee."
                                        WALTER SCOTT.

When Edward Walcott awoke, the next morning, from his deep slumber, his first consciousness was, of a heavy weight upon his mind, the cause of which, he was unable, immediately to recollect. One by one, however, by means of the association of ideas, the events of the preceding night came back to his memory; though those of latest occurrence were dim as dreams. But one circumstance was only too well remembered — the discovery of Ellen Langton. By a strong effort, he next attained to an uncertain recollection, of a scene of madness and violence, followed, as he at first thought, by a duel. A little farther reflection, however, informed him that this event was yet among the things of futurity; but he could by no means recall the appointed time or place. As he had not the slightest intention (praiseworthy and prudent as it would unquestionably have been) to give up the chance of avenging Ellen's wrongs, and his own.

He immediately arose and began to dress, meaning to learn from Hugh Crombie those particulars which his own memory had not retained. His chief apprehension was, that the appointed time had already elapsed; for the early sun-beams of a glorious morning were now peeping into his chamber.

More than once, during the progress of dressing, he was inclined to believe that the duel had actually taken place, and been fatal to him, and that he was now in those regions, to which, his conscience told him, such an event would be likely to send him. This idea resulted from his bodily sensations, which were in the highest degree uncomfortable. He was tormented by a raging thirst, that seemed to have absorbed all the moisture of his throat and stomach; and in his present agitation, a cup of icy water would have been his first wish, had all the treasures of earth and sea been at his command. His head, too, throbbed almost to bursting, and the whirl of his brain, at every movement, promised little accuracy in the aim of his pistol when he should meet the angler. These feelings, together with the deep degradation of his mind, made him resolve that no circumstances should again, draw him into an excess of wine. In the meantime, his head was perhaps still too much confused to allow him fully to realize his unpleasant situation.

Before Edward was prepared to leave his chamber, the door was opened by one of the College bed-makers, who, perceiving that he was nearly dressed, entered and began to set the apartment in order. There were two of these officials pertaining to Harley College; each of them being, and, for obvious reasons, this was an indispensable qualification, a model of perfect ugliness in her own way. One was a tall, raw-boned, huge-jointed, double-fisted giantess, admirably fitted to sustain the part of Gleardallen, in the tragedy of Tom Thumb. Her features were as excellent as her form, appearing to have been rough hewn with a broad axe, and left unpolished. The other was a short, squat figure, about two thirds the height and three times the circumference

of ordinary females. Her hair was gray, her complexion
of a deep yellow, and her most remarkable feature was
a short snub nose, just discernible amid the broad im-
mensity of her face. This latter lady was she who now
entered Edward's chamber. Notwithstanding her deficiency in personal attractions, she was rather a favorite
of the students, being good-natured, anxious for their
comfort, and, when duly encouraged, very communicative. Edward perceived, as soon as she appeared, that
she only waited his assistance in order to disburden herself of some extraordinary information ; and, more from
compassion than curiosity, he began to question her.

'Well, Dolly, what news this morning ?'

'Why, let me see, — oh, yes. It had almost slipped
my memory,' replied the bed-maker. 'Poor widow Butler died last night, after her long sickness. Poor woman !
I remember her forty years ago, or so, as rosy a lass as
you could set eyes on.'

'Ah! has she gone ?' said Edward, recollecting the
sick woman of the cottage, which he had entered with
Ellen and Fanshawe. 'Was she not out of her right
mind, Dolly ?'

'Yes ; this seven years,' she answered. 'They say
she came to her senses, a bit, when doctor Melmoth
visited her yesterday, but was raving mad when she
died. Ah ! That son of hers, if he is yet alive.—
Well Well.'

'She had a son, then ?' inquired Edward.

'Yes, such as he was. The Lord preserve me from
such a one,' said Dolly. 'It was thought he went off
with Hugh Crombie, that keeps the tavern now. That
was fifteen years ago.'

'And have they heard nothing of him since ?' asked
Edward.'

'Nothing good, nothing good,' said the bed-maker.
'Stories did travel up the valley, now and then ; but
for five years there has been no word of him. They
say Merchant Langton, Ellen's father, met him in foreign parts and would have made a man of him ; but
there was too much of the wicked one in him for that.

Well, poor woman! I wonder who'll preach her funeral sermon.'

'Doctor Melmoth, probably,' observed the student.

'No, no! The Doctor will never finish his journey in time. And who knows but his own funeral will be the end of it,' said Dolly with a sagacious shake of her head.

'Doctor Melmoth gone a journey!' repeated Edward, 'What do you mean? For what purpose?'

'For a good purpose enough, I may say,' replied she. 'To search out Miss Ellen, that was run away with, last night.'

'In the devil's name, woman, of what are you speaking?' shouted Edward, seizing the affrighted bed-maker forcibly by the arm.

Poor Dolly had chosen this circuitous method of communicating her intelligence, because she was well aware, that, if she first told of Ellen's flight, she should find no ear for her account of the widow Butler's death. She had not calculated, however, that the news would produce so violent an effect upon her auditor; and her voice faltered as she recounted what she knew of the affair. She had hardly concluded, before Edward, who, as she proceeded, had been making hasty preparations, rushed from his chamber, and took the way towards Hugh Crombie's Inn. He had no difficulty in finding the Landlord; who had already occupied his accustomed seat, and was smoking his accustomed pipe, under the elm-tree.

'Well, Master Walcott, you have come to take a stomach-reliever, this morning, I suppose,' said Hugh, taking the pipe from his mouth. 'What shall it be? a bumper of wine with an egg? — or a glass of smooth, old, oily brandy, such as dame Crombie and I keep for our own drinking? Come, that will do it, I know.'

'No, no; — neither;' replied Edward, shuddering, involuntarily, at the bare mention of wine and strong drink. 'You know well, Hugh Crombie, the errand on which I come.'

'Well, perhaps I do,' said the landlord. '**You come**

to order me to saddle my best horse.   You are for a
ride, this fine morning.'

'True, and I must learn of you in what direction to
turn my horse's head,' replied Edward Walcott.

'I understand you,' said Hugh, nodding and smiling.
'And now, Master Edward, I really have taken a
strong liking to you; and, if you please to hearken to
it, you shall have some of my best advice.'

'Speak,' said the young man, expecting to be told in
what direction to pursue the chase.

"I advise you, then," continued Hugh Crombie, in a
tone in which some real feeling mingled with assumed
carelessness, — 'I advise you to forget that you have
ever known this girl, — that she has ever existed; for
she is as much lost to you, as if she never had been
born, or as if the grave had covered her.   Come, come,
man ; — toss off a quart of my old wine, and keep up a
merry heart.   This has been my way, in many a heavier
sorrow than ever you have felt ; and you see I am alive
and merry yet.'   But Hugh's merriment had failed him
just as he was making his boast of it ; for Edward saw
a tear in the corner of his eye.

'Forget her ?   Never, never !' said the student, while
his heart sank within him, at the hopelessness of pursuit
which Hugh's words implied.   'I will follow her to the
ends of the earth.'

'Then so much the worse for you, and for my poor
nag, — on whose back you shall be in three minutes,'
rejoined the landlord.   'I have spoken to you as I
would to my own son, if I had such an incumbrance.
Here you ragamuffin, saddle the gray, and lead him
round to the door.'

'The gray ?   I will ride the black,' said Edward, 'I
know your best horse, as well as you do yourself,
Hugh.'

There is no black horse in my stable ; I have parted
with him to an old comrade of mine,' answered the landlord, with a wink of acknowledgment to what he saw
were Edward's suspicions.   'The gray is a stout nag,
and will carry you a round pace, though not so fast as

to bring you up with them you seek. I reserved him for you, and put Mr. Fanshawe off with the old white, on which I travelled hitherward a year or two since.'

'Fanshawe! Has he, then, the start of me?' asked Edward.

'He rode off about twenty minutes ago,' replied Hugh; 'but you will overtake him within ten miles, at farthest. But if mortal man could recover the girl, that fellow would do it, — even if he had no better nag than a broomstick, like the witches of old times.'

'Did he obtain any information from you as to the course?' inquired the student.

'I could give him only this much,' said Hugh, pointing down the road, in the direction of the town. 'My old comrade, trust no man farther than is needful, and I ask no unnecessary questions.'

The ostler now led up to the door the horse which Edward was to ride. The young man mounted with all expedition; but, as he was about to apply the spurs, his thirst, which the bed-maker's intelligence had caused him to forget, returned most powerfully upon him.

'For Heaven's sake, Hugh, a mug of your sharpest cider, — and let it be a large one,' he exclaimed. 'My tongue rattles in my mouth like, — '

'Like the bones in a dice-box,' said the landlord, finishing the comparison, and hastening to obey Edward's directions. Indeed, he rather exceeded them, by mingling with the juice of the apple, a jill of his old brandy, which, his own experience told him, would at that time have a most desirable effect upon the young man's internal system.

'It is powerful stuff, mine host, and I feel like a new man already,' observed Edward, after draining the mug to the bottom.

'He is a fine lad, and sits his horse most gallantly,' said Hugh Crombie to himself, as the student rode off, 'I heartily wish him success. I wish to Heaven my conscience had suffered me to betray the plot before it was too late. Well, well, — a man must keep his mite of honesty.'

The morning was now one of the most bright and glorious, that ever shone for mortals; and, under other circumstances, Edward's bosom would have been as light, and his spirit would have sung as cheerfully, as one of the many birds that warbled around him. The rain-drops of the preceding night hung like glittering diamonds on every leaf of every tree, shaken and rendered more brilliant, by occasional sighs of wind, that removed from the traveller the superfluous heat of an unclouded sun. In spite of the adventure, so mysterious and vexatious, in which he was engaged, Edward's elastic spirit (assisted, perhaps, by the brandy he had unwittingly swallowed) rose higher as he rode on, and he soon found himself endeavoring to accommodate the tune of one of Hugh Crombie's ballads to the motion of the horse. Nor did this reviving cheerfulness argue anything against his unwavering faith, and pure and fervent love for Ellen Langton. A sorrowful and repining disposition is not the necessary accompaniment of a 'leal and loving heart;' and Edward's spirits were cheered, not by forgetfulness, but by hope, which would not permit him to doubt of the ultimate success of his pursuit. The uncertainty itself, and the probable danger of the expedition, were not without their charm to a youthful and adventurous spirit. In fact, Edward would not have been altogether satisfied to recover the errant damsel, without first doing battle in her behalf.

He had proceeded but a few miles, before he came in sight of Fanshawe, who had been accommodated by the landlord with a horse much inferior to his own. The speed to which he had been put, had almost exhausted the poor animal, whose best pace was now but little beyond a walk. Edward drew his bridle, as he came up with Fanshawe.

'I have been anxious to apologize,' he said to him, 'for the hasty and unjust expressions of which I made use last evening. May I hope, that in consideration of my mental distraction, and the causes of it, you will forget what has past?'

'I had already forgotten it,' replied Fanshawe, freely

offering his hand. 'I saw your disturbed state of feeling, and it would have been unjust, both to you and to myself, to remember the errors it occasioned.'

'A wild expedition this,' observed Edward, after shaking warmly the offered hand. 'Unless we obtain some farther information at the town, we shall hardly know which way to continue the pursuit.'

'We can scarcely fail, I think, of lighting upon some trace of them,' said Fanshawe. 'Their flight must have commenced after the storm subsided, which would give them but a few hours the start of us. May I beg,' he continued, noticing the superior condition of his rival's horse, 'that you will not attempt to accommodate your pace to mine?'

Edward bowed, and rode on, wondering at the change which a few months had wrought in Fanshawe's character. On this occasion, especially, the energy of his mind had communicated itself to his frame. The color was strong and high in his cheek, and his whole appearance was that of a gallant and manly youth, whom a lady might love, or a fool might fear. Edward had not been so slow as his mistress in discovering the student's affection, and he could not but acknowledge in his heart that he was a rival not to be despised, and might yet be a successful one, if by his means Ellen Langton were restored to her friends. This consideration caused him to spur forward with increased ardour; but all his speed could not divest him of the idea, that Fanshawe would finally overtake him, and attain the object of their mutual pursuit. There was certainly no apparent ground for this imagination; for every step of his horse increased the advantage which Edward had gained, and he soon lost sight of his rival.

Shortly after overtaking Fanshawe, the young man passed the lonely cottage, formerly the residence of the Widow Butler, who now lay dead within. He was at first inclined to alight and make inquiries respecting the fugitives; for he observed, through the windows, the faces of several persons, whom curiosity, or some better feeling had led to the house of mourning. Recollecting, however, that this portion of the road must have been passed by the angler and Ellen at too early an hour to attract notice, he forbore to waste time by a fruitless delay.

Edward proceeded on his journey, meeting with no other noticeable event, till, arriving at the summit of a hill, he beheld, a few hundred yards before him, the Rev. Doctor Melmoth. The worthy President was toiling onward, at a rate unexampled in the history either of himself or his steed, the excellence of the latter consisting in sure-footedness, rather than rapidity. The rider looked round, seemingly in some apprehension, at the sound of hoof-tramps behind him, but was unable to conceal his satisfaction on recognizing Edward Walcott.

In the whole course of his life, Doctor Melmoth had never been placed in circumstances so embarrassing as the present. He was altogether a child in the ways of the world, having spent his youth and early manhood in abstracted study, and his maturity in the solitude of these hills. The expedition, therefore, on which fate had now thrust him, was an entire deviation from the quiet pathway of all his former years, and he felt like one who sets forth over the broad ocean without chart or compass. The affair would undoubtedly have been perplexing to a man of far more experience than he; but the Doctor pictured to himself a thousand difficulties and dangers, which, except in his imagination, had no existence. The perturbation of his spirit had compelled him, more than once since his departure, to regret that he had not invited Mrs. Melmoth to a share in the adventure; this being an occasion where her firmness, decision, and confident sagacity — which made her a sort of domestic hedge-hog — would have been peculiarly appropriate. In the absence of such a counsellor, even Edward Walcott — young as he was, and indiscreet as the Doctor thought him — was a substitute not to be despised; and it was singular and rather ludicrous to observe how the grey-haired man unconsciously became as a child to the beardless youth. He addressed Edward with an assumption of dignity, through which his pleasure at the meeting was very obvious.

'Young gentleman, this is not well,' he said. 'By what authority have you absented yourself from the walls of Alma Mater, during term-time?'

'I conceived that it was unnecessary to ask leave, at such a conjuncture, and when the head of the institution was himself in the saddle,' replied Edward.

'It was a fault, it was a fault,' said Doctor Melmoth, shaking his head; 'but, in consideration of the motive, I may pass it over. And now, my dear Edward, I advise that we continue our journey together, as your youth and inexperience will stand in need of the wisdom of my grey head. Nay, I pray you, lay not the lash to your steed. You have ridden fast and far, and a slower place is requisite for a season.'

And, in order to keep up with his young companion, the Doctor smote his own grey nag; which unhappy beast, wondering what strange concatenation of events had procured him such treatment, endeavoured to obey his master's wishes. Edward had sufficient compassion for Doctor Melmoth (especially as his own horse now exhibited signs of weariness) to moderate his pace to one attainable by the former.

'Alas, youth! These are strange times,' observed the President, 'when a Doctor of Divinity and an under graduate set forth, like a knight-errant and his squire, in search of a stray damsel. Methinks I am an epitome of the church militant, or a new species of polemical divinity. Pray Heaven, however, there be no encounter in store for us: for I utterly forgot to provide myself with weapons.'

'I took some thought for that matter, reverend knight,' replied Edward, whose imagination was highly tickled by Dr. Melmoth's chivalrous comparison.

'Ay, I see that you have girded on a sword,' said the Divine. 'But wherewith shall I defend myself? — My hand being empty, except of this golden-headed staff, the gift of Mr. Langton?'

'One of these, if you will accept it,' answered Edward,

exhibiting a brace of pistols, 'will serve to begin the conflict, before you join the battle hand to hand.'

'Nay, I shall find little safety in meddling with that deadly instrument, since I know not accurately from which end proceeds the bullet,' said Doctor Melmoth. 'But were it not better, seeing we are so well provided with artillery, to betake ourselves, in the event of an encounter, to some stone wall or other place of strength ?'

'If I may presume to advise,' said the squire, 'you, as being most valiant and experienced, should ride forward, lance in hand, (your long staff serving for a lance) while I annoy the enemy from afar.'

'Like Teucer behind the shield of Ajax,' interrupted Doctor Melmoth, 'or David with his stone and sling. No, no, young man ; I have left unfinished in my study a learned treatise, important not only to the present age, but to posterity, for whose sakes I must take heed to my safety. But, lo! who ride yonder ?' he exclaimed, in manifest alarm, pointing to some horsemen upon the brow of a hill, at a short distance before them.

'Fear not, gallant leader,' said Edward Walcott, who had already discovered the objects of the Doctor's terror. 'They are men of peace, as we shall shortly see. The foremost is somewhere near your own years, and rides like a grave, substantial citizen, — though what he does here, I know not. Behind come two servants, men likewise of sober age and pacific appearance.'

'Truly your eyes are better than mine own. Of a verity, you are in the right,' acquiesced Doctor Melmoth, recovering his usual quantum of intrepidity. 'We will ride forward courageously, as those who, in a just cause, fear neither death nor bonds.'

The reverend knight-errant and his squire, at the time of discovering the three horsemen, were within a very short distance of the town, which was, however, concealed from their view by the hill, that the strangers were descending. The road from Harley College, through almost its whole extent, had been rough and wild, and the country thin of population ; but now, standing frequent amid fertile fields on each side of the way, were neat little cottages, from which groups of white-headed children rushed forth to gaze upon the travellers. The three strangers, as well as the Doctor and Edward, were surrounded, as they approached each other, by a crowd of this kind, plying their little bare legs most pertinaciously, in order to keep pace with the horses.

As Edward gained a nearer view of the foremost rider, his grave aspect and stately demeanour struck him with involuntary respect. There were deep lines of thought across his brow, and his calm yet bright grey eye betokened a steadfast soul. There was also an air of conscious importance, even in the manner in which the stranger sat his horse, which a man's good opinion of himself, unassisted by the concurrence of the world in general, seldom bestows. The two servants rode at a respectable distance in the rear; and the heavy portmanteaus at their backs intimated that the party had journeyed from afar. Doctor Melmoth endeavored to assume the dignity that became him as the head of Harley College; and with a gentle stroke of his staff upon his wearied steed, and a grave nod to the principal stranger, was about to commence the ascent of the hill, at the foot of which they were. The gentleman, however, made a halt.

'Doctor Melmoth, am I so fortunate as to meet you?' he exclaimed, in accents expressive of as much surprise and pleasure, as were consistent with his staid demeanour. 'Have you then forgotten your old friend?'

'Mr. Langton! Can it be?' said the Doctor, after looking him in the face a moment. 'Yes, it is my old friend indeed! Welcome, welcome! Though you come at an unfortunate time.'

'What say you? How is my child? Ellen, I trust, is well?' cried Mr. Langton; a father's anxiety overcoming the coldness and reserve that were natural to him, or that long habit had made a second nature.

'She is well in health. She was so, at least, last night,' replied Doctor Melmoth, unable to meet the eye of his friend. 'But, — but I have been a careless

shepherd, and the lamb has strayed from the fold while
I slept.'

Edward Walcott, who was a deeply interested observer
of this scene, had anticipated that a burst of passionate
grief would follow the disclosure. He was, however,
altogether mistaken. There was a momentary convul-
sion of Mr. Langton's strong features, as quick to come
and go as a flash of lightning; and then his countenance
was as composed — though, perhaps, a little sterner —
as before. He seemed about to inquire into the particulars of what so nearly concerned him; but changed
his purpose on observing the crowd of children, who,
with one or two of their parents, were endeavouring to
catch the words that passed between the Doctor and
himself.

'I will turn back with you to the village,' he said, in
a steady voice; 'and, at your leisure, I shall desire to
hear the particulars of this unfortunate affair.'

He wheeled his horse accordingly, and, side by side
with Doctor Melmoth, began to ascend the hill. On
reaching the summit, the little country town lay before
them, presenting a cheerful and busy spectacle. It
consisted of one long, regular street, extending parallel
to, and at a short distance from, the river; which here,
enlarged by a junction with another stream, became
navigable, not indeed for vessels of burthen, but for
rafts of lumber and boats of considerable size. The
houses, with peaked roofs and pitting stories, stood at
wide intervals along the street; and the commercial
character of the place was manifested by the shop door
and windows, that occupied the front of almost every
dwelling. One or two mansions, however, surrounded
by trees and standing back at a haughty distance from
the road, were evidently the abodes of the aristocracy
of the village. It was not difficult to distinguish the
owners of these, — self-important personages, with canes
and well-powdered periwigs, — among the crowd of
meaner men, who bestowed their attention upon Doctor
Melmoth and his friend, as they rode by. The town
being the nearest mart of a large extent of back coun-

try, there were many rough farmers and woodsmen, to whom the cavalcade was an object of curiosity and admiration. The former feeling, indeed, was general throughout the village. The shop-keepers left their customers, and looked forth from the doors, — the female portion of the community thrust their heads from the windows, — and the people in the street formed a lane, through which, with all eyes concentrated upon them, the party rode onward to the tavern. The general aptitude that pervades the populace of a small country town, to meddle with affairs not legitimately concerning them, was increased on this occasion, by the sudden return of Mr. Langton, after passing through the village. Many conjectures were afloat respecting the cause of this retrograde movement; and, by degrees, something like the truth, though much distorted, spread generally among the crowd, — communicated, probably, from Mr. Langton's servants. Edward Walcott, incensed at the uncourteous curiosity of which he, as well as his companions, was the object, felt a frequent impulse (though fortunately for himself, resisted,) to make use of his riding switch in clearing a passage.

On arriving at the tavern, Doctor Melmoth recounted to his friend the little he knew beyond the bare fact of Ellen's disappearance. Had Edward Walcott been called to their conference, he might, by disclosing the adventure of the angler, have thrown a portion of light upon the affair; but, since his first introduction, the cold and stately merchant had honoured him with no sort of notice.

Edward, on his part, was not well pleased at the sudden appearance of Ellen's father, and was little inclined to co-operate in any measures that he might adopt for her recovery. It was his wish to pursue the chase on his own responsibility, and as his own wisdom dictated: he chose to be an independent ally, rather than a subordinate assistant. But, as a step preliminary to his proceedings of every other kind, he found it absolutely necessary, having journeyed far and fasting, to call upon the landlord for a supply of food. The viands that were set before him, were homely, but abundant; nor were Edward's griefs and perplexities so absorbing, as to overcome the appetite of youth and health.

Doctor Melmoth, and Mr. Langton, after a short private conversation, had summoned the landlord, in the hope of obtaining some clue to the developement of the mystery. But no young lady, nor any stranger answering to the description the doctor had received from Hugh Crombie (which was indeed a false one) had been seen to pass through the village since day-break. Here, therefore, the friends were entirely at a loss in what direction to continue the pursuit. The village was the focus of several roads, diverging to widely distant portions of the country; and which of these the fugitives had taken, it was impossible to determine. One point, however, might be considered certain, — that the village was the first stage of their flight; for it commanded the only outlet from the valley, except a rugged path among the hills, utterly impassable by horse. In this dilemma, expresses were sent by each of the different roads; and poor Ellen's imprudence, the tale nowise decreasing as it rolled along, became known to a wide extent of country. Having thus done everything in his power to recover his daughter, the merchant exhibited a composure which doctor Melmoth admired, but could not equal. His own mind, however, was in a far more comfortable state, than when the responsibility of the pursuit had rested upon himself.

Edward Walcott, in the meantime, had employed but a very few moments in satisfying his hunger; after which his active intellect alternately formed and relinquished a thousand plans for the recovery of Ellen. — Fanshawe's observation, that her flight must have commenced after the subsiding of the storm, recurred to him. On inquiry, he was informed that the violence of the rain had continued, with a few momentary intermissions, till near day light. The fugitives must, therefore, have passed through the village, long after its inhabitants were abroad; and how, without the gift of invisibility, they had contrived to elude notice, Edward could not conceive.

'Fifty years ago,' thought Edward, 'my sweet Ellen would have been deemed a witch for this trackless journey. Truly, I could wish I were a wizard, that I might bestride a broom-stick, and follow her.'

While the young man, involved in these perplexing thoughts, looked forth from the open window of the apartment, his attention was drawn to an individual, evidently of a different, though not of a higher class, than the countrymen among whom he stood. Edward now recollected that he had noticed his rough, dark face, among the most earnest of those who had watched the arrival of the party. He had then taken him for one of the boatmen, of whom there were many in the village, and who had much of a sailor-like dress and appearance. A second and more attentive observation, however, convinced Edward that this man's life had not been spent upon fresh water; and had any stronger evidence, than the nameless marks which the ocean impresses upon its sons, been necessary, it would have been found in his mode of locomotion. While Edward was observing him, he beat slowly up to one of Mr. Langton's servants, who was standing near the door of the inn. He seemed to question the man with affected carelessness; but his countenance was dark and perplexed, when he turned to mingle again with the crowd. Edward lost no time in ascertaining from the servant the nature of his inquiries. They had related to the elopement of Mr. Langton's daughter; which was, indeed, the prevailing, if not the sole subject of conversation in the village.

The grounds for supposing that this man was in any way connected with the angler, were, perhaps, very slight; yet, in the perplexity of the whole affair, they induced Edward to resolve to get at the heart of his mystery. To attain this end, he took the most direct method, — by applying to the man himself.

He had now retired apart from the throng and bustle

of the village, and was seated upon a condemned boat, that was drawn up to rot upon the banks of the river. His arms were folded, and his hat drawn over his brows. The lower part of his face, which alone was visible, evinced gloom and depression, as did also the deep sighs, which, because he thought no one was near him, he did not attempt to restrain.

'Friend, I must speak with you,' said Edward Walcott, laying his hand upon his shoulder, after contemplating the man a moment, himself unseen.

He started at once from his abstraction and his seat, apparently expecting violence, and prepared to resist it; but perceiving the youthful and solitary intruder upon his privacy, he composed his features with much quickness.

'What would you with me?' he asked.

'They tarry long, — or you have kept a careless watch,' said Edward, speaking at a venture.

For a moment, there seemed a probability of obtaining such a reply to this observation, as the youth had intended to elicit. If any trust could be put in the language of the stranger's countenance, a set of words, different from those to which he subsequently gave utterance, had risen to his lips. But he seemed naturally slow of speech; and this defect was now, as is frequently the case, advantageous in giving him space for reflection.

'Look you, youngster; — crack no jokes on me,' he at length said, contemptuously. 'Away! — back whence you came, or — ' and he slightly waved a small rattan that he held in his right hand.

Edward's eyes sparkled, and his color rose. 'You must change this tone, fellow, and that speedily,' he observed. 'I order you to lower your hand, and answer the questions that I shall put to you.'

The man gazed dubiously at him; but finally adopted a more conciliatory mode of speech

'Well, master; and what is your business with me?' he inquired. 'I am a boatman out of employ. Any commands in my line?'

'Pshaw! I know you, my good friend, and you cannot deceive me,' replied Edward Walcott. 'We are private here,' he continued, looking around. 'I have no desire or intention to do you harm; and, if you act according to my directions, you shall have no cause to repent it.'

'And what if I refuse to put myself under your orders?' inquired the man. 'You are but a young captain, for such an old hulk as mine.'

'The ill consequences of a refusal would all be on your own side,' replied Edward. 'I shall, in that case, deliver you up to justice; if I have not the means of capturing you myself,' he continued, observing the seaman's eye to wander rather scornfully over his youthful and slender figure, 'there are hundreds within call whom it will be in vain to resist. Besides, it requires little strength to use this,' he added, laying his hand on a pistol.

'If that were all, I could suit you there, my lad,' muttered the stranger. He continued aloud, 'well, what is your will with me? D——d ungenteel treatment, this!—But put your questions; and, to oblige you, I may answer them;—if so be that I know anything of the matter.'

'You will do wisely,' observed the young man. 'And now to business. What reason have you to suppose that the persons for whom you watch are not already beyond the village?'

The seaman paused long before he answered, and gazed earnestly at Edward, apparently endeavoring to ascertain from his countenance, the amount of his knowledge. This he probably overrated, but, nevertheless, hazarded a falsehood.

'I doubt not they passed before midnight,' he said. 'I warrant you they are many a league towards the seacoast, ere this.'

'You have kept watch, then, since midnight?' asked Edward.

'Ay, that have I. And a dark and rough one it was,' answered the stranger.

'And you are certain that if they passed at all, it must have been before that hour?'

'I kept my walk across the road, till the village was all astir,' said the seaman. 'They could not have missed me. So, you see, your best way is to give chase; for they have a long start of you, and you have no time to lose.'

'Your information is sufficient, my good friend,' said Edward, with a smile. 'I have reason to know that they did not commence their flight before midnight. You have made it evident that they have not passed since. Ergo, they have not passed at all. An indisputable syllogism. And now will I retrace my footsteps.'

'Stay, young man,' said the stranger, placing himself full in Edward's way, as he was about to hasten to the inn. 'You have drawn me in to betray my comrade; but before you leave this place, you must answer a question or two of mine. Do you mean to take the law with you? — or will you right your wrongs, if you have any, with your own right hand?'

'It is my intention to take the latter method. But if I choose the former, what then?' demanded Edward.

'Nay, nothing; — only, you or I might not have gone hence alive,' replied the stranger. 'But as you say he shall have fair play——'

'On my word, friend,' interrupted the young man, 'I fear your intelligence has come too late to do either good or harm. Look towards the inn; my companions are getting to horse, and my life on it, they know whither to ride.'

So saying, he hastened away, followed by the stranger. It was indeed evident that news, of some kind or other, had reached the village. The people were gathered in groups, conversing eagerly; and the pale cheeks, uplifted eyebrows, and outspread hands of some of the female sex filled Edward's mind with undefined, but intolerable apprehensions. He forced his way to doctor Melmoth, who had just mounted, and, seizing his bridle, peremptorily demanded if he knew aught of Ellen Langton.

CHAPTER VIII.

"Full many a miserable year hath past —
  She knows him as one dead, — or worse than dead ;
  And many a change her varied life hath known,
  But her heart none."   MATURIN.

Since her interview with the angler, which was interrupted by the appearance of Fanshawe, Ellen Langton's
hitherto calm and peaceful mind, had been in a state of
insufferable doubt and dismay. She was imperatively
called upon — at least, she so conceived, to break through
the rules which nature and education impose upon her
sex, to quit the protection of those whose desire for her
welfare was true and strong, — and to trust herself, for
what purpose she scarcely knew, to a stranger, from
whom the instinctive purity of her mind would involuntarily have shrunk, under whatever circumstances she
had met him. The letter which she had received from
the hands of the angler, had seemed to her inexperience,
to prove beyond a doubt, that the bearer was the friend
of her father, and authorized by him, if her duty and
affection were stronger than her fears, to guide her to
his retreat. The letter spoke vaguely of losses and
misfortunes, and of a necessity for concealment on her
father's part, and secrecy on her's ; and, to the credit
of Ellen's not very romantic understanding, it must be
acknowledged that the mystery of the plot had nearly
prevented its success. She did not, indeed, doubt that
the letter was from her father's hand ; for every line
and stroke, and even many of its phrases, were familiar
to her. Her apprehension was, that his misfortunes,
of what nature soever they were, had affected his intellect, and that, under such an influence, he had commanded her to take a step, which nothing less than such
a command could justify. Ellen did not, however,
remain long in this opinion ; for when she re-perused
the letter, and considered the firm, regular characters,
and the style, — calm and cold, even in requesting such
a sacrifice — she felt that there was nothing like insanity

here. In fine, she came gradually to the belief, that there were strong reasons, though incomprehensible by her, for the secrecy that her father had enjoined.

Having arrived at this conviction, her decision lay plain before her. Her affection for Mr. Langton was not, indeed — nor was it possible — so strong as that she would have felt for a parent who had watched over her from her infancy. Neither was the conception, she had unavoidably formed of his character, such as to promise, that in him she would find an equivalent for all she must sacrifice. On the contrary, her gentle nature and loving heart, which otherwise would have rejoiced in a new object of affection, now shrank with something like dread from the idea of meeting her father, — stately, cold, and stern, as she could not but imagine him. A sense of duty was, therefore Ellen's only support, in resolving to tread the dark path that lay before her.

Had there been any person of her own sex, in whom Ellen felt confidence, there is little doubt that she would so far have disobeyed her father's letter, as to communicate its contents, and take counsel as to her proceedings. But Mrs. Melmoth was the only female — excepting, indeed, the maid-servant — to whom it was possible to make the communication; and though Ellen at first thought of such a step, her timidity and her knowledge of the lady's character, did not permit her to venture upon it. She next reviewed her acquaintances of the other sex; and doctor Melmoth first presented himself, as, in every respect but one, an unexceptionable confidant. But the single exception was equivalent to many. The maiden, with the highest opinion of the doctor's learning and talents, had sufficient penetration to know, that in the ways of the world, she was herself the better skilled of the two. For a moment she thought of Edward Walcott; but he was light and wild, and — which her delicacy made an insurmountable objection — there was an untold love between them. Her thoughts finally centered on Fanshawe. In his judgment, young and inexperienced though he was, she would have placed a firm trust, and his zeal, from whatever cause it arose, she could not doubt.

If, in the short time allowed her for reflection, an opportunity had occurred for consulting him, she would, in all probability, have taken advantage of it. But the terms on which they had parted, the preceding evening, had afforded him no reason to hope for her confidence; and he felt that there were others who had a better right to it than himself. He did not, therefore, throw himself in her way, and poor Ellen was consequently left without an adviser.

The determination that resulted from her own unassisted wisdom, has been seen. When discovered by doctor Melmoth at Hugh Crombie's inn, she was wholly prepared for flight, and but for the intervention of the storm, would, ere then, have been far away.

The firmness of resolve, that had impelled a timid maiden upon such a step, was not likely to be broken by one defeat; and Ellen, accordingly, confident that the stranger would make a second attempt, determined that no effort on her part should be wanting to its success. On reaching her chamber, therefore, instead of retiring to rest (of which, from her sleepless thoughts of the preceding night, she stood greatly in need,) she sat watching for the abatement of the storm. Her meditations were now calmer, than at any time since her first meeting with the angler. She felt as if her fate was decided. The stain had fallen upon her reputation, — she was no longer the same pure being in the opinion of those whose approbation she most valued.

One obstacle to her flight — and, to a woman's mind, a most powerful one — had thus been removed. Dark and intricate as was the way, it was easier, now, to proceed, than to pause; and her desperate and forlorn situation gave her a strength, which hitherto she had not felt.

At every cessation in the torrent of rain that beat against the house, Ellen flew to the window, expecting to see the stranger form beneath it. But the clouds would again thicken, and the storm recommence, with its former violence ; and she began to fear, that the approach of morning would compel her to meet the now dreaded face of Doctor Melmoth. At length, however, a strong and steady wind, supplying the place of the fitful gusts of the preceding part of the night, broke and scattered the clouds from the broad expanse of the sky. The moon, commencing her late voyage not long before the sun, was now visible, setting forth like a lonely ship from the dark line of the horizon, and touching at many a little silver cloud, the islands of that aerial deep. Ellen felt that now the time was come ; and, with a calmness, wonderful to herself, she prepared for her final departure.

She had not long to wait, ere she saw between the vacancies of the trees, the angler, advancing along the shady avenue that led to the principal entrance of Doctor Melmoth's dwelling. He had no need to summon her, either by word or signal ; for she had descended, emerged from the door, and stood before him, while he was yet at some distance from the house.

'You have watched well,' he observed, in a low, strange tone. ' As saith the scripture, many daughters have done virtuously, but thou excellest them all.'

He took her arm, and they hastened down the avenue. Then, leaving Hugh Crombie's Inn on their right, they found its master, in a spot so shaded that the moonbeams could not enlighten it. He held by the bridle two horses, one of which the angler assisted Ellen to mount. Then, turning to the landlord, he pressed a purse into his hand ; but Hugh drew back, and it fell to the ground.

'No ; this would not have tempted me, nor will it reward me, he said. If you have gold to spare, there are some that need it more than I.'

'I understand you, mine host. I shall take thought for them, and enough will remain for you and me,' replied his comrade. 'I have seen the day when such a purse would not have slipped between your fingers. Well, be it so. And now, Hugh, my old friend, a shake of your hand ; for we are seeing our last of each other.'

'Pray Heaven it be so; though I wish you no ill,' said the landlord, giving his hand. He then seemed about to approach Ellen, who had been unable to distinguish the words of this brief conversation; but his comrade prevented him. 'There is no time to lose,' he observed. 'The moon is growing pale already, and we should have been many a mile beyond the valley, ere this.' He mounted, as he spoke, and guiding Ellen's rein till they reached the road, they dashed away.

It was now that she felt herself completely in his power; and with that consciousness, there came a sudden change of feeling, and an altered view of her conduct. A thousand reasons forced themselves upon her mind, seeming to prove that she had been deceived; while the motives, so powerful with her but a moment before, had either vanished from her memory, or lost all their efficacy. Her companion, who gazed searchingly into her face, where the moonlight, coming down between the pines, allowed him to read its expression, probably discerned somewhat of the state of her thoughts.

'Do you repent so soon?' he inquired. 'We have a weary way before us. Faint not ere we have well entered upon it.'

'I have left dear friends behind me, and am going I know not whither,' replied Ellen, tremblingly.

'You have a faithful guide,' he observed; turning away his head, and speaking in the tone of one who endeavours to smother a laugh.

Ellen had no heart to continue the conversation; and they rode on in silence, and through a wild and gloomy scene. The wind roared heavily through the forest, and the trees shed their rain drops upon the travellers. The road, at all times rough, was now broken into deep gullies, through which streams went murmuring down, to mingle with the river. The pale moonlight combined with the grey of the morning to give a ghastly and unsubstantial appearance to every object.

The difficulties of the road had been so much increased by the storm, that the purple eastern clouds

gave notice of the near approach of the sun, just as the
travellers reached the little lonesome cottage which
Ellen remembered to have visited several months before.
On arriving opposite to it, her companion checked his
horse, and gazed with a wild earnestness at the wretched
habitation.   Then, stifling a groan that would not altogether be repressed, he was about to pass on, but at
that moment, the cottage door opened, and a woman,
whose sour, unpleasant countenance Ellen recognized,
came hastily forth.   She seemed not to heed the travellers ; but the angler, his voice thrilling and quivering
with indescribable emotion, addressed her.

'Woman, whither do you go ?' he inquired.

She started ; but, after a momentary pause, replied,
'There is one within at the point of death.   She strug-
gles fearfully ; and I cannot endure to watch alone by
her bedside.   If you are christians, come in with me.'

Ellen's companion leaped hastily from his horse, assisted her also to dismount, and followed the woman
into the cottage, having first thrown the bridles of the
horses carelessly over the branch of a tree.   Ellen
trembled at the awful scene she would be compelled to
witness ; but, when death was so near at hand, it was
more terrible to stand alone in the dim morning light,
than even to watch the parting of soul and body.   She
therefore entered the cottage.

Her guide, his face muffled in his cloak, had taken
his stand at a distance from the death-bed, in a part of
the room, which neither the increasing daylight nor the
dim rays of a solitary lamp, had yet enlightened.   At
Ellen's entrance, the dying woman lay still, and apparently calm, except that a plaintive, half articulate sound
occasionally wandered through her lips.

'Hush ! For mercy's sake, silence !' whispered the
other woman to the strangers.   'There is good hope
now, that she will die a peaceful death ; but, if she is
disturbed, the boldest of us will not dare to stand by her
bed-side.'

The whisper by which her sister endeavoured to preserve quiet, perhaps reached the ears of the dying

female; for she now raised herself in bed, slowly, but with a strength superior to what her situation promised. Her face was ghastly and wild, from long illness, approaching death, and disturbed intellect; and a disembodied spirit could scarcely be a more fearful object, than one whose soul was just struggling forth. Her sister, approaching with the soft and stealing step appropriate to the chamber of sickness and death, attempted to replace the covering around her, and to compose her again upon the pillow. 'Lie down and sleep, sister,' she said; 'and when the day breaks, I will waken you. Methinks your breath comes freer, already. A little more slumber, and tomorrow you will be well.'

'My illness is gone, I am well,' said the dying woman, gasping for breath. 'I wander where the fresh breeze comes sweetly over my face, but a close and stifled air has choked my lungs.'

'Yet a little while, and you will no longer draw your breath in pain,' observed her sister, again replacing the bed-clothes, which she continued to throw off.

'My husband is with me,' murmured the widow. 'He walks by my side, and speaks to me as in old times; but his words come faintly on my ear; cheer me and comfort me, my husband; for there is a terror in those dim, motionless eyes, and in that shadowy voice.'

As she spoke thus, she seemed to gaze upon some object that stood by her bed-side, and the eyes of those who witnessed this scene could not but follow the direction of hers. They observed that the dying woman's own shadow was marked upon the wall, receiving a tremulous motion from the fitful rays of the lamp, and from her own convulsive efforts. 'My husband stands gazing on me,' she said, again; 'but my son, — where is he? — and, as I ask, the father turns away his face. Where is our son? For his sake, I have longed to come to this land of rest. For him I have sorrowed many years. Will he not comfort me now?'

At these words, the stranger made a few hasty steps towards the bed; but, ere he reached it, he conquered the impulse that drew him thither, and, shrouding his face more deeply in his cloak, returned to his former position. The dying woman, in the meantime, had thrown herself back upon the bed; and her sobbing and wailing, imaginary as was their cause, were inexpressibly affecting.

'Take me back to earth,' she said; 'for its griefs have followed me hither.'

The stranger advanced, and, seizing the lamp, knelt down by the bed-side, throwing the light full upon his pale and convulsed features.

'Mother, here is your son;' he exclaimed.

At that unforgotten voice, the darkness burst away at once from her soul. She arose in bed, her eyes and her whole countenance beaming with joy, and threw her arms about his neck. A multitude of words seemed struggling for utterance; but they gave place to a low moaning sound, and then to the silence of death. The one moment of happiness, that recompensed years of sorrow, had been her last. Her son laid the lifeless form upon the pillow, and gazed with fixed eyes on his mother's face.

As he looked, the expression of enthusiastic joy, that parting life had left upon the features, faded gradually away, and the countenance, though no longer wild, assumed the sadness which it had worn through a long course of grief and pain. On beholding this natural consequence of death, the thought perhaps occurred to him, that her soul, no longer dependent on the imperfect means of intercourse possessed by mortals, had communed with his own, and become acquainted with all its guilt and misery. He started from the bed-side, and covered his face with his hands, as if to hide it from those dead eyes.

Such a scene as has been described could not but have a powerful effect upon any one, who retained aught of humanity; and the grief of the son, whose natural feelings had been blunted, but not destroyed, by an evil life, was much more violent than his outward demeanor would have expressed. But his deep repentance for the misery he had brought upon his parent, did not produce

in him a resolution to do wrong no more. The sudden
consciousness of accumulated guilt made him desperate.
He felt as if no one had thenceforth a claim to justice or
compassion at his hands, when his neglect and cruelty
had poisoned his mother's life, and hastened her death.
Thus it was that the Devil wrought with him to his
own destruction, reversing the salutary effect, which his
mother would have died, exultingly, to produce upon
his mind. He now turned to Ellen Langton, with a
demeanour singularly calm and composed.

'We must resume our journey,' he said, in his usual
tone of voice. 'The sun is on the point of rising, though
but little light finds its way into this hovel.'

Ellen's previous suspicions as to the character of her
companion had now become certainty, so far as to con-
vince her that she was in the power of a lawless and
guilty man; though what fate he intended for her, she
was unable to conjecture. An open opposition to his
will, however, could not be ventured upon; especially as
she discovered, on looking round the apartment, that,
with the exception of the corpse, they were alone.

'Will you not attend your mother's funeral?' she
asked, trembling, and conscious that he would discover
her fears.

'The dead must bury their dead,' he replied; 'I have
brought my mother to her grave; — and what can a son
do more? This purse, however, will serve to lay her in
the earth, and leave something for the old hag. Whither
is she gone?' interrupted he, casting a glance round the
room in search of the old woman. 'Nay, then, we must
speedily to horse. I know her of old.'

Thus saying, he threw the purse upon the table, and,
without trusting himself to look again towards the dead,
conducted Ellen out of the cottage. The first rays of
the sun at that moment gilded the tallest trees of the
forest.

On looking towards the spot where the horses had
stood, Ellen thought that Providence, in answer to her
prayers, had taken care for her deliverance. They were
no longer there, — a circumstance easily accounted for,

by the haste with which the bridles had been thrown over the branch of the tree. Her companion, however, imputed it to another cause.

'The hag! She would sell her own flesh and blood by weight and measure,' he muttered to himself. 'This is some plot of hers, I know well.'

He put his hand to his forehead, for a moment's space, seeming to reflect on the course most advisable to be pursued. Ellen, perhaps unwisely, interposed.

'Would it not be well to return?' she asked, timidly. 'There is now no hope of escaping; but I might yet reach home undiscovered.'

'Return!' repeated her guide, with a look and smile from which she turned away her face. 'Have you forgotten your father and his misfortunes? No, no, sweet Ellen; it is too late for such thoughts as these.'

He took her hand, and led her towards the forest, in the rear of the cottage. She would fain have resisted; but they were all alone, and the attempt must have been both fruitless and dangerous. She therefore trod with him a path so devious, so faintly traced, and so overgrown with bushes and young trees, that only a most accurate acquaintance in his early days could have enabled her guide to retain it. To him, however, it seemed so perfectly familiar, that he was not once compelled to pause, though the numerous windings soon deprived Ellen of all knowledge of the situation of the cottage. They descended a steep hill, and proceeding parallel to the river — as Ellen judged by its rushing sound — at length found themselves at what proved to be the termination of their walk.

Ellen now recollected a remark of Edward Walcott's respecting the wild and rude scenery through which the river here kept its way; and, in less agitating circumstances, her pleasure and admiration would have been great. They stood beneath a precipice, so high that the loftiest pine tops (and many of them seemed to soar to Heaven) scarcely surmounted it. This line of rock has a considerable extent, at unequal heights and with many interruptions, along the course of the river, and it seems probable, that, at some former period, it was the boundary of the waters, though they are now confined within far less ambitious limits. The inferior portion of the crag, beneath which Ellen and her guide were standing, varies so far from the perpendicular as not to be inaccessible by a careful footstep; but only one person has been known to attempt the ascent of the superior half, and only one the descent, yet, steep as is the height, trees and bushes of various kinds have clung to the rock, wherever their roots could gain the slightest hold, — thus seeming to prefer the scanty and difficult nourishment of the cliff, to a more luxurious life in the rich interval that extends from its base to the river. But, whether or no these hardy vegetables have voluntarily chosen their rude resting place, the cliff is indebted to them for much of the beauty that tempers its sublimity. When the eye is pained and wearied by the bold nakedness of the rock, it rests with pleasure on the cheerful foliage of the birch, or upon the darker green of the funereal fire. Just at the termination of the accessible portion of the crag, these trees are so numerous, and their foliage so dense, that they completely shroud from view a considerable excavation, formed, probably, hundreds of years since, by the fall of a portion of the rock. The detached fragment still lies at a little distance from the base, grey and moss-grown, but corresponding, in its general outline, to the cavity from which it was rent.

But the most singular and beautiful object in all this scene, is a tiny fount of chrystal water, that gushes forth from the high, smooth forehead of the cliff. Its perpendicular descent is of many feet; after which it finds its way, with a sweet, diminutive murmur, to the level ground.

It is not easy to conceive, whence the barren rock procures even the small supply of water, that is necessary to the existence of this stream; it is as unaccountable, as the gush of gentle feeling which sometimes proceeds from the hardest heart; but there it continues to flow and fall, undiminished and unincreased. The stream is so slender, that the gentlest breeze suffices to disturb its descent, and to scatter its pure sweet waters over the face of the cliff. But in that deep forest, there is seldom a breath of wind : so that, plashing continually upon one spot, the fount has worn its own little channel of white sand, by which it finds its way to the river. Alas, that the Naiades have lost their old authority ; for what a Deity of tiny loveliness must once have presided here !

Ellen's companion paused not to gaze either upon the loveliness or the sublimity of this scene, but assisting her where it was requisite, began the steep and difficult ascent of the lower part of the cliff. The maiden's ingenuity in vain endeavoured to assign reasons for this movement; but when they reached the tuft of trees, which, as has been noticed, grew at the ultimate point where mortal footstep might safely tread, she perceived through their thick branches the recess in the rock. Here they entered ; and her guide pointed to a mossy seat, in the formation of which, to judge from its regularity, art had probably a share.

'Here you may remain in safety,' he observed, 'till I obtain the means of proceeding, In this spot you need fear no intruder ; but it will be dangerous to venture beyond its bounds.'

The meaning glance that accompanied these words, intimated to poor Ellen, that, in warning her against danger, he alluded to the vengeance with which he would visit any attempt to escape. To leave her thus alone, trusting to the influence of such a threat, was a bold, yet a necessary and by no means a hopeless measure. On Ellen it produced the desired effect; and she sat in the cave as motionless, for a time, as if she had herself been a part of the rock. In other circumstances, this shady recess would have been a delightful retreat, during the sultry warmth of a summer's day. The dewy coolness of the rock kept the air always fresh, and the sun beams never thrust themselves so as to dissipate the mellow twilight through the green trees with which the chamber was curtained. Ellen's sleeplessness and agitation, for many preceding hours, had perhaps deadened her feelings; for she now felt a sort of indifference creeping upon her, an inability to realize the evils of her situation, at the same time that she was perfectly aware of them all. This torpor of mind increased, till her eyelids began to grow heavy, and the cave and trees to swim before her sight. In a few moments more, she would probably have been in dreamless slumber; but, rousing herself by a strong effort, she looked round the narrow limits of the cave, in search of objects to excite her worn-out mind.

She now perceived, wherever the smooth rock afforded place for them, the initials, or the full length names, of former visitants of the cave. What wanderer on mountain-tops or in deep solitudes, has not felt the influence of these records of humanity, telling him, when such a conviction is soothing to his heart, that he is not alone in the world? It was singular, that, when her own mysterious situation had almost lost its power to engage her thoughts, Ellen perused these barren memorials with a certain degree of interest. She went on repeating them aloud, and starting at the sound of her own voice, till at length, as one name passed through her lips, she paused, and then, leaning her forehead against the letters, burst into tears. It was the name of Edward Walcott; and it struck upon her heart, arousing her to a full sense of her present misfortunes and dangers, and, more painful still, of her past happiness. Her tears had, however, a soothing, and at the same time a strengthening effect upon her mind; for, when their gush was over, she raised her head and began to meditate on the means of escape. She wondered at the species of fascination that had kept her, as if chained to the rock, so long, when there was, in reality, nothing to bar her path-way. She determined, late as it was, to attempt her own deliverance; and for that purpose began slowly and cautiously to emerge from the cave.

Peeping out from among the trees, she looked and listened with most painful anxiety, to discover if any living thing were in that seeming solitude, or if any sound disturbed the heavy stillness. But she saw only nature in her wildest forms, and heard only the plash and murmur (almost inaudible, because continual) of the little waterfall, and the quick, short throbbing of her own heart, against which she pressed her hand, as if to hush it. Gathering courage, therefore, she began to descend; and, starting often at the loose stones that even her light footstep displaced and sent rattling down, she at length reached the base of the crag in safety. She then made a few steps in the direction, as nearly as she could judge, by which she arrived at the spot; but paused, with a sudden revulsion of the blood to her heart, as her guide emerged from behind a projecting part of the rock. He approached her deliberately, an ironical smile writhing his features into a most disagreeable expression, while in his eyes there was something that seemed a wild, fierce joy. By a species of sophistry, of which oppressors often make use, he had brought himself to believe that he was now the injured one, and that Ellen, by her distrust of him, had fairly subjected herself to whatever evil it consisted with his will and power to inflict upon her. Her only restraining influence over him, the consciousness in his own mind that he possessed her confidence, was now done away. Ellen, as well as her enemy, felt that this was the case. She knew not what to dread; but she was well aware that danger was at hand, and that, in the deep wilderness, there was none to help her, except that Being, with whose inscrutable purposes it might consist, to allow the wicked to triumph for a season, and the innocent to be brought low.

'Are you so soon weary of this quiet retreat?' demanded her guide, continuing to wear the same sneering smile. 'Or has your anxiety for your father induced you to set forth alone, in quest of the afflicted old man?'

'O, if I were but with him!' exclaimed Ellen. 'But this place is lonely and fearful, and I cannot endure to remain here.'

'Lonely, is it, sweet Ellen?' he rejoined, 'am I not with you? Yes, it is lonely — lonely as guilt could wish. Cry aloud, Ellen, and spare not. Shriek, and see if there be any among these rocks and woods to hearken to you!'

'There is — there is one,' exclaimed Ellen, shuddering, and affrighted at the fearful meaning of his countenance. 'He is here — He is there!' And she pointed to heaven.

'It may be so, dearest,' he replied. 'But if there be an ear that hears, and an eye that sees all the evil of the earth, yet the arm is slow to avenge. Else why do I stand before you, a living man?'

'His vengeance may be delayed for a time, but not forever,' she answered, gathering a desperate courage from the extremity of her fear.

'You say true, lovely Ellen; and I have done enough, ere now, to insure its heaviest weight. There is a pass, when evil deeds can add nothing to guilt, nor good ones take anything from it.'

'Think of your mother, — of her sorrow through life, and perhaps even after death,' Ellen began to say. But as she spoke these words, the expression of his face was changed, becoming suddenly so dark and fiend-like, that she clasped her hands, and fell on her knees before him.

'I have thought of my mother,' he replied, speaking very low, and putting his face close to hers. 'I remember the neglect — the wrong — the lingering and miserable death, that she received at my hands. By what claim can either man or woman henceforth expect mercy from me? If God will help you, be it so; but by those words you have turned my heart to stone.'

At this period of their conversation, when Ellen's peril seemed most imminent, the attention of both was attracted by a fragment of rock, which, falling from the summit of the crag, struck very near them. Ellen started from her knees, and, with her false guide, gazed eagerly upward; he in the fear of interruption, she in the hope of deliverance.

CHAPTER IX.

At length, he cries, behold the fated spring !
Yon rugged cliff conceals the fountain blest,
Dark rocks its chrystal source o'ershadowing.

                                        PSYCHE.

The tale now returns to Fanshawe, who, as will be
recollected, after being overtaken by Edward Walcott,
was left with little apparent prospect of aiding in the
deliverance of Ellen Langton.

It would be difficult to analyze the feelings with
which the student pursued the chase, or to decide
whether he was influenced and animated by the same
hopes of successful love, that cheered his rival. That
he was conscious of such hopes, there is little reason to
suppose; for the most powerful minds are not always
the best acquainted with their own feelings. Had Fanshawe, moreover, acknowledged to himself the possibility
of gaining Ellen's affections, his generosity would have
induced him to refrain from her society, before it was
too late. He had read her character with accuracy, and
had seen how fit she was to love, and to be loved by
a man who could find his happiness in the common
occupations of the world; and Fanshawe never deceived
himself so far, as to suppose that this would be the case
with him. Indeed, he often wondered at the passion,
with which Ellen's simple loveliness of mind and person
had inspired him, and which seemed to be founded on
the principle of contrariety, rather than of sympathy.
It was the yearning of a soul, formed by Nature in a
peculiar mould, for communion with those to whom it
bore a resemblance, yet of whom it was not. But there
was no reason to suppose that Ellen, who differed from
the multitude only as being purer and better, would cast
away her affections on the one, of all who surrounded
her least fitted to make her happy. Thus Fanshawe
reasoned with himself, and of this he believed that he
was convinced. Yet, ever and anon, he found himself
involved in a dream of bliss, of which Ellen was to be

the giver and the sharer. Then would he rouse himself, and press upon his mind the chilling consciousness, that it was, and could be, but a dream. There was also another feeling, apparently discordant with those which have been enumerated. It was a longing for rest, — for his old retirement, that came at intervals so powerfully upon him, as he rode on, that his heart sickened of the active exertion on which fate had thrust him.

After being overtaken by Edward Walcott, Fanshawe continued his journey with as much speed as was attainable by his wearied horse, but at a pace infinitely too slow for his earnest thoughts. These had carried him far away, leaving him only such a consciousness of his present situation as to make diligent use of the spur, when a horse's tread, at no great distance, struck upon his ear. He looked forward, and behind; but, though a considerable extent of the narrow, rocky, and grass-grown road was visible, he was the only traveller there. Yet again he heard the sound, which, he now discovered, proceeded from among the trees that lined the roadside. Alighting, he entered the forest, with the intention, if the steed proved to be disengaged and superior to his own, of appropriating him to his own use. He soon gained a view of the object he sought; but the animal rendered a closer acquaintance unattainable, by immediately taking to his heels. Fanshawe had however made a most interesting discovery; for the horse was accoutred with a side-saddle; and who, but Ellen Langton, could have been his rider? At this conclusion, though his perplexity was thereby in no degree diminished, the student immediately arrived. Returning to the road, and perceiving on the summit of the hill a cottage, which he recognized as the one he had entered with Ellen and Edward Walcott, he determined there to make inquiry respecting the objects of his pursuit.

On reaching the door of the poverty-stricken dwelling, he saw that it was not now so desolate of inmates as on his previous visit. In the single inhabitable apartment were several elderly women, clad evidently in their well-worn and well-saved Sunday clothes, and all wearing a deep-grievous expression of countenance. Fanshawe was not long in deciding, that death was within the cottage, and that these aged females were of the class who love the house of mourning, because to them it is a house of feasting. It is a fact, disgusting and lamentable, that the disposition which heaven for the best of purposes has implanted in the female breast — to watch by the sick and comfort the afflicted, frequently becomes depraved into an odious love of scenes of pain, and death, and sorrow. Such women are like the Gouls of the Arabian Tales, whose feasting was among tombstones, and upon dead carcasses.

(It is sometimes, though less frequently, the case, that this disposition to make a 'joy of grief' extends to individuals of the other sex. But in us it is even less excusable and more disgusting, because it is our nature to shun the sick and afflicted; and, unless restrained by principles other than we bring into the world with us, men might follow the example of many animals in destroying the infirm of their own species. Indeed, instances of this nature might be adduced among savage nations.) Sometimes, however, from an original *lusus naturæ*, or from the influence of circumstances, a man becomes a haunter of death-beds, — a tormentor of afflicted hearts, — and a follower of funerals. Such an abomination now appeared before Fanshawe, and beckoned him into the cottage. He was considerably beyond the middle age, rather corpulent, with a broad, fat, tallow complexioned countenance. The student obeyed his silent call, and entered the room, through the open door of which he had been gazing.

He now beheld, stretched out upon the bed, where she had so lately laid in life, though dying, the yet uncoffined corpse of the aged woman, whose death has been described. How frightful it seemed! — that fixed countenance of ashy paleness, amid its decorations of muslin and fine linen, — as if a bride were decked for the marriage chamber, — as if death were a bridegroom, and the coffin a bridal bed. Alas that the vanity of dress should extend even to the grave!

The female, who, as being the near and only relative of the deceased, was supposed to stand in need of comfort, was surrounded by five or six of her own sex. These continually poured into her ear the stale, trite maxims, which, where consolation is actually required, add torture insupportable to the wounded heart. Their present object, however, conducted herself with all due decorum, holding her handkerchief to her tearless eyes, and answering with very grievous groans to the words of her comforters. Who could have imagined that there was joy in her heart, because, since her sister's death, there was but one remaining obstacle between herself and the sole property of that wretched cottage?

While Fanshawe stood silently observing this scene, a low, monotonous voice was uttering some words in his ear, of the meaning of which his mind did not immediately take note. He turned, and saw that the speaker was the person who had invited him to enter.

'What is your pleasure with me, Sir?' demanded the student.

'I make bold to ask,' replied the man, 'whether you would choose to partake of some creature comfort, before joining in prayer with the family and friends of our deceased sister?' As he spoke, he pointed to a table, on which was a moderate sized stone jug, and two or three broken glasses; for then, as now, there were few occasions of joy or grief on which ardent spirits were not considered indispensable, to heighten the one, or to alleviate the other.

'I stand in no need of refreshment,' answered Fanshawe; 'and it is not my intention to pray at present.'

'I pray your pardon, reverend sir,' rejoined the other; 'but your face is pale, and you look wearied. A drop from yonder vessel is needful to recruit the outward man. And for the prayer, the sisters will expect it, and their souls are longing for the outpouring of the spirit. I was intending to open my own mouth, with such words as are given to my poor ignorance, but' —

Fanshawe was here about to interrupt this address, which proceeded on the supposition, arising from his black dress and thoughtful countenance, that he was a clergyman. But one of the females now approached him, and intimated that the sister of the deceased was desirous of the benefit of his conversation. He would have returned a negative to this request, but, looking towards the afflicted woman, he saw her withdraw her handkerchief from her eyes, and cast a brief, but penetrating and most intelligent, glance upon him. He immediately expressed his readiness to offer such consolation as might be in his power.

'And in the mean time,' observed the lay-preacher, 'I will give the sisters to expect a word of prayer and exhortation, either from you or from myself.'

These words were lost upon the supposed clergyman, who was already at the side of the mourner. The females withdrew out of ear-shot, to give place to a more legitimate comforter than themselves.

'What know you respecting my purpose?' inquired Fanshawe, bending towards her.

The woman gave a groan — the usual result of all efforts at consolation — for the edification of the company; and then replied in a whisper, which reached only the ear for which it was intended. 'I know whom you come to seek, — I can direct you to them. Speak low, for God's sake,' she continued, observing that Fanshawe was about to utter an exclamation. She then resumed her groans with greater zeal than before.

'Where — where are they?' asked the student, in a whisper which all his efforts could scarcely keep below his breath. 'I adjure you to tell me.'

'And, if I should, how am I like to be bettered by it?' inquired the old woman, her speech still preceded and followed by a groan.

'O God! — The 'auri sacra fames!' thought Fanshawe with a sickening heart, looking at the motionless corpse upon the bed, and then at the wretched being, whom the course of nature, in comparatively a moment of time, would reduce to the same condition.

He whispered again, however, putting his purse into the hag's hand. 'Take this. Make your own terms when they are discovered. Only tell me where I must seek them,—and speedily, or it may be too late.'

'I am a poor woman, and am afflicted,' said she, taking the purse, unseen by any who were in the room. 'It is little that worldly goods can do for me, and not long can I enjoy them,' and here she was delivered of a louder, and a more heartfelt groan than ever. She then continued, 'Follow the path behind the cottage, that leads to the river side. Walk along the foot of the rock, and search for them near the water-spout; keep a slow pace till you are out of sight,' she added, as the student started to his feet.

The guests of the cottage did not attempt to oppose Fanshawe's progress, when they saw him take the path towards the forest, imagining, probably, that he was retiring for the purpose of secret prayer. But the old woman laughed behind the handkerchief with which she veiled her face.

'Take heed of your steps, boy,' she muttered; 'for they are leading you whence you will not return. Death too, for the slayer. Be it so.'

Fanshawe, in the mean while, continued to discover, and, for a while, to retain, the narrow and winding path that led to the river side. But it was originally no more than a track, by which the cattle belonging to the cottage went down to their watering-place; and by these four-footed passengers it had long been deserted. The fern-bushes, therefore, had grown over it, and in several places, trees of considerable size had shot up in the midst. These difficulties could scarcely have been surmounted by the utmost caution; and as Fanshawe's thoughts were too deeply fixed upon the end, to pay a due regard to the means, he soon became desperately bewildered, both as to the locality of the river, and of the cottage. Had he known, however, in which direction to seek the latter, he would not, probably, have turned back; not that he was infected by any chivalrous desire to finish the adventure alone; but because he would expect little assistance from those he had left there. — Yet he could not but wonder — though he had not in his first eagerness taken notice of it — at the anxiety of the old woman that he should proceed singly, and without the knowledge of her guests, on the search. He nevertheless continued to wander on, — pausing often to listen for the rush of the river, and then starting forward, with fresh rapidity, to rid himself of the sting of his own thoughts, which became painfully intense, when undisturbed by bodily motion. His way was now frequently interrupted by rocks, that thrust their huge grey heads from the ground, compelling him to turn aside, and thus depriving him, fortunately perhaps, of all remaining idea of the direction he had intended to pursue.

Thus he went on — his head turned back, and taking little heed to his footsteps — when, perceiving that he trod upon a smooth, level rock, he looked forward, and found himself almost on the utmost verge of a precipice.

After the throbbing of the heart that followed this narrow escape had subsided, he stood gazing down where the sun-beams slept so pleasantly at the roots of the tall old trees, with whose highest tops he was upon a level. Suddenly he seemed to hear voices — one well remembered voice — ascending from beneath; and approaching to the edge of the cliff, he saw at its base the two whom he sought.

He saw and interpreted Ellen's look and attitude of entreaty, though the words with which she sought to soften the ruthless heart of her guide, became inaudible, ere they reached the height where Fanshawe stood. He felt that Heaven had sent him thither, at the moment of her utmost need, to be the preserver of all that was dear to him, and he paused only to consider the mode in which her deliverance was to be effected. Life he would have laid down willingly — exultingly; — his only care was, that the sacrifice should not be in vain.

At length, when Ellen fell upon her knees, he lifted a small fragment of rock, and threw it down the cliff. It struck so near the pair, that it immediately drew the attention of both.

When the betrayer — at the instant in which he had

almost defied the power of the Omnipotent to bring help to Ellen — became aware of Fanshawe's presence, his hardihood failed him for a time, and his knees actually tottered beneath him. There was something awful, to his apprehension, in the slight form that stood so far above him, like a being from another sphere, looking down upon his wickedness. But his half superstitious dread endured only a moment's space; and then, mustering the courage that in a thousand dangers had not deserted him, he prepared to revenge the intrusion by which Fanshawe had a second time interrupted his designs.

'By Heaven, I will cast him down at her feet!' he muttered through his closed teeth. 'There shall be no form nor likeness of man left in him. Then let him rise up, if he is able, and defend her.'

Thus resolving, and overlooking all hazard, in his eager hatred, and desire for vengeance, he began a desperate attempt to ascend the cliff. The space, which only had hitherto been deemed accessible, was quickly past, and in a moment more he was half way up the precipice, clinging to trees, shrubs, and projecting portions of the rock, and escaping through hazards which seemed to menace inevitable destruction.

Fanshawe, as he watched his upward progress, deemed that every step would be his last; but when he perceived that more than half, and apparently, the most difficult part, of the ascent was surmounted, his opinion changed. His courage, however, did not fail him, as the moment of need drew nigh. His spirits rose buoyantly, his limbs seemed to grow firm and strong, and he stood on the edge of the precipice, prepared for the death-struggle which would follow the success of his enemy's attempt.

But that attempt was not successful. When within a few feet of the summit, the adventurer grasped at a twig, too slenderly rooted to sustain his weight. It gave way in his hand, and he fell backward down the precipice. His head struck against the less perpendicular part of the rock, whence the body rolled heavily down to the detached fragment, of which mention has heretofore

been made. There was no life left in him. With all
the passions of hell alive in his heart, he had met the
fate that he intended for Fanshawe.

The student paused not, then, to shudder at the sudden and awful overthrow of his enemy, for he saw that
Ellen lay motionless at the foot of the cliff. She had,
indeed, fainted, at the moment she became aware of her
deliverer's presence, — and no stronger proof could she
have given of her firm reliance upon his protection.

Fanshawe was not deterred by the danger, of which
he had just received so fearful an evidence, from attempt-
ing to descend to her assistance; and, whether owing to
his advantage in lightness of frame, or to superior caution, he arrived safely at the base of the precipice.

He lifted the motionless form of Ellen in his arms,
and resting her head against his shoulder, gazed on her
cheek of lily paleness, with a joy — a triumph — that
rose almost to madness. It contained no mixture of
hope, it had no reference to the future, — it was the
perfect bliss of a moment, — an insulated point of happiness. He bent over her and pressed a kiss — the first,
and he knew it would be the last — on her pale lips;
then, bearing her to the fountain, he sprinkled its waters
profusely over her face, neck, and bosom. She at length
opened her eyes, slowly and heavily; but her mind was
evidently wandering, till Fanshawe spoke.

'Fear not, Ellen; you are safe,' he said.

At the sound of his voice, her arm, which was thrown
over his shoulder, involuntarily tightened its embrace,
telling him, by that mute motion, with how firm a trust
she confided in him. But, as a fuller sense of her situation returned, she raised herself to her feet, though still
retaining the support of his arm. It was singular, that,
although her insensibility had commenced before the
fall of her guide, she turned away her eyes, as if instinc-
tively, from the spot where the mangled body lay; nor
did she inquire of Fanshawe the manner of her
deliverance.

'Let us begone from this place,' she said in faint, low
accents, and with an inward shudder.

They walked along the precipice, seeking some passage by which they might gain its summit, and at length arrived at that by which Ellen and her guide had descended. Chance, — for neither Ellen nor Fanshawe could have discovered the path, — led them, after but little wandering, to the cottage. A messenger was sent forward to the town, to inform Dr. Melmoth of the recovery of his ward; and the intelligence thus received had interrupted Edward Walcott's conversation with the seaman.

It would have been impossible, in the mangled remains of Ellen's guide, to discover the son of the widow Butler, except from the evidence of her sister, who became, by his death, the sole inheritrix of the cottage. The history of this evil and unfortunate man must be comprised within very narrow limits. A harsh father, and his own untameable disposition, had driven him from home in his boyhood, and chance had made him the temporary companion of Hugh Crombie. After two years of wandering, when in a foreign country and in circumstances of utmost need, he attracted the notice of Mr. Langton. The merchant took his young countryman under his protection, afforded him advantages of education, and, as his capacity was above mediocrity, gradually trusted him in many affairs of importance. During this period, there was no evidence of dishonesty on his part. On the contrary, he manifested a zeal for Mr. Langton's interest, and a respect for his person, that proved his strong sense of the benefits he had received. But he unfortunately fell into certain youthful indiscretions, which, if not entirely pardonable, might have been palliated by many considerations that would have occurred to a merciful man. Mr. Langton's justice, however, was seldom tempered by mercy; and on this occasion, he shut the door of repentance against his erring protegé, and left him in a situation not less desperate than that from which he had relieved him. The goodness and the nobleness, of which his heart was not destitute, turned, from that time, wholly to evil, and he became irrecoverably ruined and irreclaim-

ably depraved. His wandering life had led him, shortly
before the period of this tale, to his native country.
Here the erroneous intelligence of Mr. Langton's death
had reached him, and suggested the scheme, which circumstances seemed to render practicable, but the fatal
termination of which has been related.

The body was buried where it had fallen, close by
the huge, gray, moss-grown fragment of rock, — a monument on which centuries can work little change. The
eighty years that have elapsed since the death of the
widow's son have, however, been sufficient to obliterate
an inscription, which some one was at the pains to cut
in the smooth surface of the stone. Traces of letters
are still discernible; but the writer's many efforts could
never discover a connected meaning. The grave, also,
is overgrown with fern bushes, and sunk to a level with
the surrounding soil. But the legend, though my ver-
sion of it may be forgotten, will long be traditionary in
that lonely spot, and give to the rock and the precipice,
and the fountain, an interest thrilling to the bosom of
the romantic wanderer.

CHAPTER X.

Sitting then in shelter shady,
To observe and mark his mone,
Suddenly I saw a Lady
Hasting to him all alone,
Clad in maiden-white and green,
Whom I judg'd the Forrest Queen.
THE WOODMAN'S BEAR.

DURING several weeks succeeding her danger and
deliverance, Ellen Langton was confined to her chamber, by illness, resulting from the agitation she had
endured. Her father embraced the earliest opportunity to express his deep gratitude to Fanshawe for the
inestimable service he had rendered, and to intimate a
desire to requite it, to the utmost of his power. He had

understood that the student's circumstances were not prosperous, and, with the feeling of one who was habituated to give and receive a 'quid pro quo,' he would have rejoiced to share his abundance with the deliverer of his daughter. But Fanshawe's flushed brow and haughty eye, when he perceived the thought that was stirring in Mr. Langton's mind, sufficiently proved to the discerning merchant, that money was not in the present instance a circulating medium. His penetration, in fact, very soon informed him of the motives by which the young man had been actuated, in risking his life for Ellen Langton; but he made no allusion to the subject, — concealing his intentions, if any he had, in his own bosom.

During Ellen's illness, Edward Walcott had manifested the deepest anxiety respecting her; he had wandered around and within the house, like a restless ghost, informing himself of the slightest fluctuation in her health, and thereby graduating his happiness or misery. He was at length informed that her convalescence had so far progressed, that, on the succeeding day, she would venture below. From that time, Edward's visits to Doctor Melmoth's mansion were relinquished; — his cheek grew pale, and his eye lost its merry light, — but he resolutely kept himself a banished man. Multifarious were the conjectures to which this course of conduct gave rise; but Ellen understood and approved his motives. The maiden must have been far more blind than ever woman was, in such a matter, if the late events had not convinced her of Fanshawe's devoted attachment; and she saw that Edward Walcott, feeling the superior, the irresistible strength of his rival's claim, had retired from the field. Fanshawe, however, discovered no intention to pursue his advantage. He paid her no voluntary visit, and even declined an invitation to tea, with which Mrs. Melmoth, after extensive preparations, had favoured him. He seemed to have resumed all the habits of seclusion, by which he was distinguished previous to his acquaintance with Ellen, — except that he still took his sunset walk, on the banks of the stream.

On one of these occasions, he stayed his footsteps by the old leafless oak, which had witnessed Ellen's first meeting with the angler. Here he mused upon the circumstances that had resulted from that event, and upon the rights and privileges — for he was well aware of them all — which those circumstances had given him. Perhaps the loveliness of the scene and the recollections connected with it, — perhaps the warm and mellow sunset, — perhaps a temporary weakness in himself, had softened his feelings, and shaken the firmness of his resolution, to leave Ellen to be happy with his rival. His strong affections rose up against his reason, whispering that bliss, — on earth and in Heaven, through time and Eternity, — might yet be his lot with her. It is impossible to conceive of the flood of momentary joy, which the bare admission of such a possibility sent through his frame; and, just when the tide was highest in his heart, a soft little hand was laid upon his own, and, starting, he beheld Ellen at his side.

Her illness, since the commencement of which, Fanshawe had not seen her, had wrought a considerable, but not a disadvantageous change in her appearance. She was paler and thinner, — her countenance was more intellectual — more spiritual, — and a spirit did the student almost deem her, appearing so suddenly in that solitude. There was a quick vibration of the delicate blood in her cheek, yet never brightening to the glow of perfect health; a tear was glittering on each of her long dark eyelashes; and there was a gentle tremor through all her frame, which compelled her, for a little space, to support herself against the oak. Fanshawe's first impulse was, to address her in words of rapturous delight; but he checked himself, and attempted — vainly, indeed — to clothe his voice in tones of calm courtesy. His remark merely expressed pleasure at her restoration to health; and Ellen's low and indistinct reply had as little relation to the feelings that agitated her.

'Yet I fear,' continued Fanshawe, recovering a degree of composure, and desirous of assigning a motive (which

he felt was not the true one) for Ellen's agitation, —
'I fear that your walk has extended too far for your
strength.'

'It would have borne me farther, with such a motive,'
she replied, still trembling, — 'to express my gratitude
to my preserver.'

'It was needless Ellen, it was needless; for the deed
brought with it its own reward,' exclaimed Fanshawe,
with a vehemence that he could not repress. 'It was
dangerous, for' —

Here he interrupted himself, and turned his face
away.

'And wherefore was it dangerous?' inquired Ellen,
laying her hand gently on his arm; for he seemed about
to leave her.

'Because you have a tender and generous heart, and
I a weak one,' he replied.

'Not so,' answered she, with animation. 'Yours is a
heart full of strength and nobleness; and if it have a
weakness' —

'You know well that it has, Ellen, — one that has
swallowed up all its strength,' said Fanshawe. 'Was it
wise, then, to tempt it thus — when, if it yield, the result
must be your own misery?'

Ellen did not affect to misunderstand his meaning.
On the contrary, with a noble frankness, she answered
to what was implied rather than expressed.

'Do me not this wrong,' she said, blushing, yet earnestly. 'Can it be misery — will it not be happiness to
form the tie that shall connect you to the world? — to
be your guide — a humble one, it is true, but the one of
your choice — to the quiet paths, from which your proud
and lonely thoughts have estranged you? Oh! I know
that there will be happiness in such a lot, from these and
a thousand other sources.'

The animation with which Ellen spoke, and, at the
same time, a sense of the singular course to which her
gratitude had impelled her, caused her beauty to grow
brighter and more enchanting with every word. And
when, as she concluded, she extended her hand to Fan-

shawe, to refuse it was like turning from an angel, who would have guided him to heaven. But, had he been capable of making the woman he loved a sacrifice to her own generosity, that act would have rendered him unworthy of her. Yet the struggle was a severe one, ere he could reply.

'You have spoken generously and nobly, Ellen,' he said. 'I have no way to prove that I deserve your generosity, but by refusing to take advantage of it. Even if your heart were yet untouched, — if no being, more happily constituted than myself, had made an impression there, — even then, I trust, a selfish passion would not be stronger than my integrity. But now,' — He would have proceeded, but the firmness, which had hitherto sustained him, gave way. He turned aside to hide the tears, which all the pride of his nature could not restrain, and which, instead of relieving, added to his anguish. At length he resumed. 'No, Ellen, we must part now and forever. Your life will be long and happy. Mine will be short, but not altogether wretched, — nor shorter than if we had never met. When you hear that I am in my grave, do not imagine that you have hastened me thither. Think that you scattered bright dreams around my path-way, — an ideal happiness, that you would have sacrificed your own to realize.'

He ceased; and Ellen felt that his determination was unalterable. She could not speak; but, taking his hand, she pressed it to her lips; and they saw each other no more. Mr. Langton and his daughter, shortly after returned to the sea-port, which, for several succeeding years, was their residence.

After Ellen's departure, Fanshawe returned to his studies with the same absorbing ardour, that had formerly characterized him. His face was as seldom seen among the young and gay; — the pure breeze and the blessed sun-shine as seldom refreshed his pale and weary brow; and his lamp burned as constantly from the first shade of evening till the grey morning light began to dim its beams. Nor did he, as weak men will, treasure up his love in a hidden chamber of his breast.

He was in reality the thoughtful and earnest student that he seemed. He had exerted the whole might of his spirit over itself, — and he was a conqueror. Perhaps, indeed, a summer breeze of sad and gentle thoughts would sometimes visit him; but, in these brief memories of his love, he did not wish that it should be revived, or mourn over its event.

There were many who felt an interest in Fanshawe; but the influence of none could prevail upon him to lay aside the habits, mental and physical, by which he was bringing himself to the grave. His passage thither was consequently rapid, — terminating just as he reached his twentieth year. His fellow students erected to his memory a monument of rough-hewn granite, with a white marble slab, for the inscription. This was borrowed from the grave of Nathanael Mather, whom, in his almost insane eagerness for knowledge and in his early death, Fanshawe resembled.

THE ASHES OF A HARD STUDENT AND A GOOD SCHOLAR.

MANY tears were shed over his grave; but the thoughtful and the wise, though turf never covered a nobler heart, could not lament that it was so soon at rest. He left a world for which he was unfit; and we trust, that, among the innumerable stars of heaven, there is one where he has found happiness.

Of the other personages of this tale, — Hugh Crombie, being exposed to no strong temptations, lived and died an honest man. Concerning Doctor Melmoth, it is unnecessary here to speak. The reader, if he have any curiosity upon the subject, is referred to his life, which, together with several sermons and other productions of the Doctor, was published by his successor in the Presidency of Harley College, about the year 1768.

It was not till four years after Fanshawe's death, that Edward Walcott was united to Ellen Langton. Their future lives were uncommonly happy. Ellen's gentle, almost imperceptible, but powerful influence, drew her husband away from the passions and pursuits that would have interfered with domestic felicity; and he never regretted the worldly distinction of which she thus deprived him. Theirs was a long life of calm and quiet bliss; — and what matters it, that, except in these pages, they have left no name behind them?

ERRATA.

The author requests the reader's favourable construction of several errors, chiefly of orthography and punctuation, which have escaped the press. The following effect the sense.

Page 36 lines 33–34, for 'atmosphere of the Sun' read 'atmosphere of an Inn.' Page 69, line 36, for 'Gleardallen' read 'Glumdalea.' Page 75, line 21, for 'fool' read 'foe.' Page 80, line 28, for 'pitting' read 'jutting.' Page 107, line 22, for 'continued' read 'contrived.'

THE WHOLE HISTORY

OF

GRANDFATHER'S CHAIR

CONTENTS

GRANDFATHER'S CHAIR

PART I

PART II

CONTENTS

iv

INTRODUCTION

This volume comprises the four books for children issued by Hawthorne in 1841 and 1842. The first (1841) was entitled *Grandfather's Chair: A History for Youth*. Two others appeared in 1841, entitled respectively — *Famous Old People: Being the Second Epoch of Grandfather's Chair;* and *Liberty Tree, with the Last Words of Grandfather's Chair. Biographical Stories for Children* came out in 1842. These four books were also published together, in two volumes, in 1842, with the title *Historical Tales for Youth* printed upon the backs of the covers. In 1851 the four were issued again, by Ticknor, Reed and Fields of Boston, as *True Stories from History and Biography*. In 1853 a London edition was brought out, under the same title, by the house of Sampson Low, Son, & Co. These later editions do not deviate from the first, except in title-page and in the dropping of the prefaces to *Famous Old People* and *Liberty Tree*. It is true that the second edition of *Grandfather's Chair*, issued by Tappan and Dennet of Boston, in 1842, announces itself as "Revised and Enlarged," but the text follows, paragraph by paragraph, that of the original edition. An artist has been called in, however, to supply a frontispiece representing an old-fashioned, claw-footed chair, most gloriously foliaged and figured, and, later on, a picture of Lady Arbella drooping in its carven arms, the lion's head above wearing a sympathetic and solicitous expression. Even in the frontispiece it is only a courtesy lion, his "savage grin" having been much mollified, presumably by listening to the stories.

We owe these books, in a sense, to Samuel G. Goodrich, "Peter Parley," to whose Boston annual, *The Token*, Hawthorne contributed tales and essays from 1831 (possibly from 1830) on through 1838, with the exception of

1834.   *Twice-Told Tales*, *Mosses from an Old Manse*, and *The Snow Image* now bear immortal witness to the beauty of those anonymous and ill-paid contributions. Hawthorne, in the opinion of his friend Horatio Bridge, was more grateful to Goodrich for such initiation into the literary arena than was at all necessary, although when Bridge met the publisher, he liked him better than he had intended.

"Peter Parley" was the son of a Connecticut minister, so shrewd a parson that, in those frugal times, he reared a family of eight children on a salary which never exceeded five hundred dollars a year, and left an estate valued at four thousand. The son Samuel was thought to be of a mechanical turn, and his early education was limited to the three R's. He was not an imaginative child. He resented nursery rhymes and fairy stories, and the first book that he read with "real enthusiasm" was Hannah More's *Moral Repository*. As a clerk in a country store, his opportunities for culture did not increase with his growth, although he picked up for himself a few odds and ends of Latin, French, and mathematics. At the age of twenty-three he went into the bookselling and publishing business at Hartford and promptly showed his faith in American literature by bringing out Trumbull's poems, — a venture in which he lost a thousand dollars. His growing resolution to develop a line of American books for children was confirmed by a trip to England and a call on Hannah More, — a visit, as he termed it, "almost like a pilgrimage to the shrine of some divinity." In the course of his conversation with her, he says, he "first formed the conception of the Parley Tales, the general idea of which was to make nursery books reasonable and truthful." In 1826 Mr. Goodrich removed his business to Boston, where he did his best to promote the interests of American letters, publishing an edition of the novels of Charles Brockden Brown, a volume of *Sketches* by N. P. Willis, and various periodicals. The two volumes of *The Legendary* led the way, consisting, as he says, of "original pieces in prose and verse, principally illustrative of American history, scenery, and manners." *The Token*, consolidated in 1836 with *The Atlantic Souvenir*, followed. Here comes the first point of contact between Hawthorne and Goodrich, men who could not have been expected to find each other congenial. Goodrich valued Willis and Mrs. Sigourney most among the contributors to *The Token*. What he has to say of Hawthorne indicates little penetration into either genius or character : —

" It is not easy to conceive of a stronger contrast than is presented by comparing Nathaniel Hawthorne with N. P. Willis. The former was for a time one of the principal writers for *The Token*, and his admirable sketches were published side by side with those of the latter. Yet it is curious to remark that everything Willis wrote attracted immediate attention, and excited ready praise, while the productions of Hawthorne were almost entirely unnoticed.

" The personal appearance and demeanor of these two gifted young men, at the early period of which I speak, was also in striking contrast. Willis was slender, his hair sunny and silken, his cheek ruddy, his aspect cheerful and confident. He met society with a ready and welcome hand, and was received readily and with welcome. Hawthorne, on the contrary, was of a rather sturdy form, his hair dark and bushy, his eye steel-gray, his brow thick, his mouth sarcastic, his complexion stony, his whole aspect cold, moody, distrustful. He stood aloof, and surveyed the world from shy and sheltered positions.

" There was a corresponding difference in the writings of these two persons. Willis was all sunshine and summer, the other chill, dark, and wintry ; the one was full of love and hope, the other of doubt and distrust ; the one sought the open daylight—sunshine, flowers, music, and found them everywhere—the other plunged into the dim caverns of the mind, and studied the grisly spectres of jealousy, remorse, despair. It is, perhaps, neither a subject of surprise nor regret, that the larger portion of the world is so happily constituted as to have been more ready to flirt with the gay muse of the one, than to descend into the spiritual charnelhouse, and assist at the psychological dissections of the other.

"I had seen some anonymous publication which seemed to me to indicate extraordinary powers. I inquired of the publishers as to the writer, and through them a correspondence ensued between me and 'N. Hawthorne.' This name I considered a disguise, and it was not till after many letters had passed, that I met the author, and found it to be a true title, representing a very substantial personage. At this period he was unsettled as to his views; he had tried his hand in literature, and considered himself to have met with a fatal rebuff from the reading world. His mind vacillated between various projects, verging, I think, toward a mercantile profession. I combated his despondence, and assured him of triumph, if he would persevere in a literary career.

" He wrote numerous articles, which appeared in *The Token;* occasionally an astute critic seemed to see through them, and to discover the soul that was in them; but in general they passed without notice. Such articles as *Sights from a Steeple, Sketches beneath an Umbrella, The Wives of the Dead, The Prophetic Pictures*, now universally acknowledged to be productions of extraordinary depth, meaning, and power, extorted hardly a word of either praise or blame, while columns were given to pieces since totally forgotten. I felt annoyed, almost angry indeed, at this. I wrote several articles in the papers, directing attention to these productions, and finding no echo of my views, I recollect to have asked John Pickering to read some of them, and give me his opinion of them. He did as I requested; his answer was that they displayed a wonderful beauty of style, with a kind of double vision, a sort of second sight, which revealed, beyond the outward forms of life and being, a sort of spirit world, somewhat as a lake reflects the earth around it and the sky above it : yet he deemed them too mystical to be popular. He was right, no doubt, at that period, but, ere long, a portion of mankind, a large portion of the reading world, obtained a new sense — how or where or whence, is not easily determined — which led them to study the mystical, to dive beneath and beyond the senses, and to discern, gather, and cherish gems and pearls of price in the hidden depths of the soul. Hawthorne was, in fact, a kind of Wordsworth in prose — less kindly, less genial toward mankind, but deeper and more philosophical. His fate was similar: at first he was neglected, at last he had worshippers.

"In 1837, I recommended Mr. Hawthorne to publish a volume, comprising his various pieces, which had appeared in *The Token* and elsewhere. He consented, but as I had ceased to be a publisher it was difficult to find anyone who would undertake to bring out the work. I applied to the agent of the Stationers' Company, but he refused, until at last I relinquished my copyrights on such of the tales as I had published, to Mr. Hawthorne, and joined a friend of his in a bond to indemnify them against loss; and thus the work was published by the Stationers' Company, under the title of *Twice-Told Tales*, and for the author's benefit. It was deemed a failure for more than a year, when a breeze seemed to rise and fill its sails, and with it the author was carried on to fame and fortune."

This account of Goodrich's relations with Hawthorne was published (in Goodrich's *Recollections of a Lifetime*, vol. 2, pp. 269–273) in 1856, while Hawthorne was abroad, holding the Liverpool consulate. That Peter Parley told the truth as he saw it, need not be doubted, but the coloring of his report is self-complacent, and his statements are occasionally vague. What was that "anonymous publication" which caught his discerning eye, — *Fanshawe*, or a fantasy in *The Salem Gazette?* In what papers did he publish those generous articles in praise of the contributions to his own annual? Other statements are confusing, for we have Horatio Bridge's testimony, on which no shadow of doubt has ever been cast, to the effect that it was he who took the initiative in the publication of *Twice-Told Tales* and assumed the full financial risk. As for Goodrich's magnanimous relinquishment of the copyrights, his letter to Hawthorne, under date of January 19, 1830, implies that Haw-thorne, in selling Goodrich "the privilege of inserting" these tales in *The Token,* had been accustomed to reserve book rights; yet the evidence is not conclusive.

Hawthorne's comment on the reference to himself in Goodrich's autobiography was made in a letter to his sister-in-law, Miss Elizabeth Peabody : —

"As regards Goodrich's account of the relations be-tween him and me, it is funny enough to see him taking the airs of a patron; but I do not mind it in the least, nor feel the slightest inclination to defend myself, or be defended.   I should as soon think of controverting his statement about my personal appearance (of which he draws no very lovely picture) as about anything else that he says.   So pray do not take up the cudgels on my behalf; especially as I perceive that your recollections are rather inaccurate.   For instance, it was Park Benjamin, not Goodrich, who cut up the 'Story-teller.'   As for Goodrich, I have rather a kindly feeling towards him, and he himself is a not unkindly man, in spite of his propensity to feed and fatten himself on better brains than his own.   Only let him do that, and he will really some-times put himself to some trouble to do a goodnatured act.   His quarrel with me was, that I broke away from him before he had quite finished his meal, and while a portion of my brain was left; and I have not the slightest doubt that he really felt himself wronged by my so doing. Really, I half think so too.   He was born to do what he did, as maggots to feed on rich cheese."

The amount of hack work which Goodrich got out of Hawthorne is not accurately known.   Goodrich opened his long series of children's books in 1827 with the *Tales of Peter Parley about America.*   By 1856 he could say that he was the author and editor of about one hundred and seventy volumes, one hundred and sixteen bearing the name of Peter Parley.   Of all these, seven million had then been sold.   Meanwhile, several spurious Peter Parleys had sprung up and, in defending himself against these, Goodrich admitted the coöperation of a dozen named authors, including Hawthorne, besides "others," including Hawthorne's elder sister. In the course of this explanation, we have: "As to *Parley's Historical Compends* — some nine or ten volumes — I had the assistance of N. Hawthorne, and J. O. Sargent, Esqs., and others."

What Goodrich meant by "assistance" we may understand by referring to some published correspondence. Hawthorne wrote to his sister Elizabeth, from Boston, May 5, 1836: "I saw Mr. Goodrich yesterday. . . . He wants me to undertake a *Universal History*. . . . If you are willing to write any part of it, . . . I shall agree to do it." Six days later he added: "Our pay as historians of the universe will be about one hundred dollars, the whole of which you may have. It is a poor compensation." On September 23, 1836, Goodrich wrote to Hawthorne: "Your letter and the two folios of *Universal History* were received some days ago. I like the History pretty well, — I shall make it do."

This was quick work. The *Universal History* had a great sale, and Goodrich could congratulate himself on a good bargain. The narrative, sprinkled with small wood-cuts, succinctly sketches the progress of the universe from Noah's Ark to the steamboat. The fiction of Peter Parley is faithfully kept up. After a graphic account of the death of the Chinese Emperor Chaus, who, "to the great joy of his subjects, . . . went down among the fishes and never again came a-hunting in the rice-fields," we have three impressive paragraphs concerning Ching.

"8. The emperor Ching, who reigned about two thousand years ago, built a great wall, in order to protect his dominions against the Tartars. It was forty-five feet high, and eighteen feet thick, and it extended over mountains and valleys, a distance of fifteen hundred miles. This wall still remains.

"9. When Ching had completed the wall, he thought himself so very great an emperor, that none of his predecessors were worth remembering. He therefore ordered all historical writings and public records to be burnt. He also caused four hundred learned men, who were addicted to writing histories, to be buried alive.

"10. If the emperor Ching could have caught poor old Peter Parley, he certainly would have buried him likewise, with his four hundred learned brethren; and so the world would have lost this *Universal History!*"

It is like Hawthorne to note in regard to another Chinese emperor, Vati, that he "was desirous of reigning till the world should come to an end, and perhaps longer. He therefore spent his time in endeavoring to brew a liquor that would make him immortal. But, unfortunately, before the liquor was fit to drink, the emperor died." It is like Hawthorne, too, to linger over the Spanish search for the fountain of youth: —

"8. Another thing which the Spaniards expected to find in America, was the fountain of youth. Far away beneath the shadows of the forest, they believed that there was a fountain, the bright waters of which would wash away wrinkles, and turn gray hair dark again.

"9. Oh, if there were any such fountain, old Peter Parley would journey thither, lame as he is, and plunge head foremost into its bosom! After a while the children of America would ask — 'Where is that lame old gentleman who used to tell us stories?'

"10. And there would be a little rosy boy among them, a stranger whom they had never seen before. He would cry out, 'I was old Peter Parley; but I have been bathing in the fountain of youth, and now I am a boy again! Come, let us see which will hop farthest!'"

Among the various good features of this sprightly compendium is its interest in the life of the people. Kings are often dismissed with scant ceremony. Louis XVIII of France was "chiefly distinguished for his love of oysters"; Richard II of England "was not half so good a ruler as the blacksmith [Wat Tyler] would probably have been"; Henry VIII was a "royal villain"; George IV had a great deal of taste in dress "and it was a pity that he was a king, because he might otherwise have been an excellent tailor."

American history, especially the Revolutionary War, is related with patriotic fervor.

While Hawthorne, under Peter Parley's shadow, was in this "historical compend," and perhaps in others, learning how to talk to children in print, he was also, still with Goodrich at his elbow, working on the subjects which were presently to be treated in *Grandfather's Chair*.

Mr. Goodrich, Mr. Bowen of Charlestown, who was an engraver, and several other gentlemen, were associated in what was known as the Boston Bewick Company. The name Bewick was in compliment to an Englishman who had restored the art of wood engraving. The company was formed ,for the purpose of publishing the *American Magazine of Useful and Entertaining Knowledge*, where illustrations were to be the leading feature. This dismal periodical, which managed to live from 1834 to September, 1837, passed through the hands of several editors. In 1836 Goodrich induced Hawthorne to undertake the editorship at a salary of five hundred dollars a year. He edited six numbers of the magazine, from March through August, and then, unable to get his meagre salary paid, seems to have thrown up the task in disgust. Meanwhile, with the help of his elder sister, he had done all the literary work for every number, writing articles to fit the rude woodcuts furnished by the Bewick Company, and ransacking books old and new, current newspapers, reports of legislative committees, Lyceum addresses, even the encyclopædia, for detachable bits of "useful and entertaining knowledge."

The *American Magazine* had declared itself, at the outset, emphatically patriotic. It condemned what it avowed to be the custom of the American periodicals of the day — the giving nine-tenths of their space to foreign subjects — and promised on its own behalf to supply the public with "*a work descriptive not merely of subjects, scenes, places, and persons existing in distant climes*, BUT ALSO OF THOSE WHICH ARE TO BE FOUND IN OUR OWN FINE AND NATIVE COUNTRY." Its plan was to supply a limited amount of original editorial matter in connection with the largest and worst wood-cuts, and fill up the remaining pages with extracts and condensations, exclusive of fiction. The failure of the Bewick Company, however inconvenient for Hawthorne and their other creditors, was to the honor of contemporary taste.

Hawthorne's first number, March, opens with a crude engraving presenting the bust of Washington in a nimbus of star-spangled banners, cannon, shot, bayonets, drums, and battle-smoke, with the passage of the Delaware in the distance. This number is made up of biographies of American worthies, a historical sketch of Jerusalem, a description of New York, a meditative account by Hawthorne of his experiences on *An Ontario Steamboat*, and the usual miscellany of clippings. The opening article on Washington strikes a note familiar to the readers of *Grandfather's Chair:*—

"What American has not beheld the majestic features of WASHINGTON!—A generation has been born, and arrived at middle age, since he departed. Yet, were it possible that his illustrious shade should return, to mark the mighty growth of the country which he made a nation—were he to walk, in visible shape, the streets of our cities, not one among the crowd but would know Washington; were he to enter the most solitary farmhouse, its inmates would at once recognize their awful guest; were he to visit that far western region, which he left a wilderness, the population of its busy towns would bow before him; or were he to pause near a New England school-house, the group of children round the door would gaze at him, and whisper—'It is Washington, our Father!'"

The April number, which Hawthorne thought better, contained some characteristic columns from his pen on *The Boston Tea-Party*, *April Fools*, and *Martha's Vineyard*, and his hand is perceptible in the May number, especially in the account of *Wolfe on the Heights of Abraham*, and the pioneer experiences of *The Duston Family*. In June the lack of salary—for by the middle

of May Hawthorne had received only twenty dollars —
seems to have dulled editorial enthusiasm. There is no
original work of consequence in that month's issue,
nor is the July number much better; but the August
magazine, whose frontispiece is a bust of John Adams
on a pedestal of mingled flags and folios, has the
Hawthorne touch again, most noticeable in a review of
the *Life of Eliot*, apostle to the Indians.

In this number, Hawthorne takes a laconic leave of
his editorship : —

"Owing to circumstances unforeseen when we assumed
the charge of this periodical, (in March last,) the present
Number will probably terminate our connection with it.
The brevity of our continuance in the Chair Editorial
will excuse us from any lengthened ceremony in resign-
ing it. In truth, there is very little to be said on the
occasion. We have endeavored to fill our pages with a
pleasant variety of wholesome matter. The reader must
judge how far the attempt has been successful. It is
proper to remark that we have not had the full control
over the contents of the Magazine; inasmuch as the
embellishments have chiefly been selected by the exec-
utive officers of the Boston Bewick Company or by the
engravers themselves, and our humble duty has consisted
merely in preparing the literary illustrations."

Hawthorne's connection with Peter Parley, then, had
accustomed him to writing for children in a simple,
straightforward style, and to drawing popular material
from the standard books of American history and biography. The only surprising thing about the appearance
of his four little volumes of "historical tales for youth"
is that they were not issued earlier than 1841, but the
lack of a publisher probably accounts for this. His
enterprising sister-in-law elect, Miss Elizabeth Peabody,
was by that time in the book business herself, and she
published the three parts of *Grandfather's Chair* in
Boston, Wiley & Putnam of New York appearing on the
same title-page. These first editions are veritable child-
books, 32mo., in cloth covers of brown, lavender, and
green respectively. Little oblong black labels, pasted

in the middle of the front cover, bear, in the two latter cases, the title in gilt within a gay gilt border. As to the first part, the two copies which I have chanced to see have their black labels blank, as if Miss Peabody's gilder had not done his full duty. The well-known preface to this first volume is dated Boston, November, 1840. The preface to *Famous Old People*, written in Boston, December 30, 1840, is as follows: —

"Grandfather again shoves his great Chair before the youthful public, and desires to make them acquainted with a new dynasty of occupants. The iron race of Puritans, whose rigid figures sat bolt upright against its oaken back, in the first Epoch of our History, have now given place to quite a different set of men.

"It is true, we have here a venerable School-master, who was a contemporary of the early Puritans, and preserved their moral characteristics, as he did his own white beard, at a period when both were out of fashion. We have likewise a shadow of Dr. Cotton Mather, who, setting aside many individual peculiarities, may be looked upon as an exaggeration of those pious and potent Divines, whom he reverenced as the great men of the preceding age.

"But then come a succession of Governors, holding up the royal commission as the source of their authority. These dignitaries are illuminated by a ray, although faint and distant, yet gleaming upon them from the splendor of the British throne. Our old Chair, itself, loses the severe simplicity, which was in keeping with the habits of its earliest possessors, and is gilded and varnished, and gorgeously cushioned, so as to make it a fitting seat for vice-regal pomp. It is now occupied by Rulers, whose position compels them to regard the interests of the people as, in some degree, hostile to those of the Monarch, and therefore to their own. It is surrounded by ambitious Politicians, Soldiers, and Adventurers, having no pretension to that high religious and moral principle, which gave to our first Epoch a character of the truest and loftiest romance.

"This Epoch presents enough of military and worldly

adventure to please our little friend Charley, in whom
we discern the traits, which may hereafter render him a
man of power among actual affairs, and in all the business of life. Laurence, in whom we represent a more
ideal nature, probably feels a greater sympathy with
the unworldly Pilgrims, and especially with the Apostle
Eliot, who joined to their high excellences a spirit of
love, that scarcely any other man of his day possessed.
Perhaps, in a third Epoch, we shall find in individuals,
and the people at large, a combination of ideal principle
and adventurous action, that may attract the interest
both of Laurence and Charley.

"This little book presents a slight historic sketch of
the period, when Massachusetts had ceased to be a
Republic, and was strictly a Province of England. It
is therefore sufficiently complete in itself, to make it
independent of our preceding volume. Should we be
encouraged to conclude the adventures of our old Chair,
the remaining part, beginning with the first movement
of the Revolution, will also include a period of history,
that may be read in disconnection with the past. But
the Author's desire is, in the three numbers that will
compose the entire history of GRANDFATHER'S CHAIR,
to give the youthful reader a rounded outline of the
whole period, during which this piece of furniture was so
prominent an object."

The preface to *Liberty Tree*, dated Boston, February
27, 1841, runs thus: —

"Has the youthful reader grown weary of Grandfather's stories about his Chair? Will he not come, this
once more, to our fire-side, and be received as an own
grandchild, and as brother, sister, or cousin to Laurence,
Clara, Charley, and little Alice? Come, do not be bash-
ful, nor afraid. You will find Grandfather a kindly old
man, with a cheerful spirit, and a heart that has grown
mellow, instead of becoming dry and wilted, with age.

"He will tell you how King George, trusting in the
might of his armies and navies, sought to establish a tyranny over our fathers. Then you shall hear about Liberty
Tree, and what crowds used to assemble within the cir-

cumference of its shadow. Grandfather must speak, also, about riots and disorders, and how an angry multitude broke into the mansion of the lieutenant governor. Next, he will show you the proud array of British soldiers, in their uniforms of scarlet and gold, landing at Long Wharf, and marching to take possession of the Common, and Faneuil Hall, and the Old State House. Then you must listen to the dismal tale of the Boston Massacre. Next comes the marvellous story of the tea ships, and of that band of Indian figures who made their appearance in the dusk of evening, and vanished before the dawn of day. Now come more and more regiments of soldiers. Their tents whiten the Common like untimely snow. Their war-horses prance and neigh, within the walls of the Old South Church. Hark! that faint echo comes from Lexington, where the British soldiers have fired a volley that begins the war of the Revolution. The people are up in arms. Gage, Howe, Burgoyne, Lord Percy and many another haughty Englishman, are beleaguered within the peninsula of Boston. The Americans build batteries on every hill; and look! a warlike figure, on a white horse, rides majestically from height to height, and directs the progress of the siege. Can it be WASHINGTON?

"Then Grandfather will call up the shadow of a devoted loyalist, and strive to paint him to your eyes and heart, as he takes his farewell walk through Boston. We will trace his melancholy steps from Faneuil Hall to Liberty Tree. That famous tree! The axes of the British soldiers have hewn it down, but not before its wind-strewn leaves had scattered the spirit of freedom far and wide — not before its roots had sprouted, even in the distant soil of Georgia.

"Amid all these wonderful matters, we shall not lose sight of Grandfather's Chair. On its sturdy oaken legs, it trudges diligently from one scene to another, and seems always to thrust itself in the way, with most benign complacency, whenever an historical personage happens to be looking round for a seat. The excellent old chair! Let the reader make much of it, while he may; for with this little volume Grandfather concludes its history, and withdraws it from the public eye."

Hawthorne was so well pleased with the second sentence of this last paragraph that he added it to the first paragraph of the preface to *Grandfather's Chair*. That preface, with this one sentence added and with two or three verbal alterations, was then pressed into service for *True Stories*.

The *Biographical Tales*, whose brief preface is dated Boston, January 17, 1842, found publishers in the Boston firm of Tappan and Dennet. Of the six worthies honored in that plain, brown-clad little volume only two are Americans, — our illustrious Benjamins, Franklin and West; but it was the American in Hawthorne that selected Oliver Cromwell. Hawthorne's special feeling for Samuel Johnson is made evident by the chapter on *Lichfield and Uttoxeter* in *Our Old Home*. The author admits that Queen Christina is a concession to the "little girls among our readers," and Sir Isaac Newton promises, at least, something genuine in the way of "useful and entertaining knowledge."

In regard to the reception given these successive booklets, we may rest content with the testimony, a trifle forgetful in details, of Miss Elizabeth Peabody : —

"In 1840 he [Hawthorne] went to Brook Farm, and left it in six months, and then published the 'Grandfather's Chair' in three parts. I was keeping bookstore then and published it. This was a great success; and Tappan and Dutton made him a great offer for it, and also engaged him to write 'True Stories for Children.'"

If it were *Grandfather's Chair* only for which we have to thank Peter Parley, our gratitude would be sincere; but *Grandfather's Chair* has a higher value than its own. It led the way to those children's classics, *A Wonder-Book* and *Tanglewood Tales*.

KATHARINE LEE BATES.

PREFACE

In writing this ponderous tome, the author's desire has been to describe the eminent characters and remarkable events of our early annals, in such a form and style that the *young* might make acquaintance with them of their own accord. For this purpose, while ostensibly relating the adventures of a chair, he has endeavored to keep a distinct and unbroken thread of authentic history. The chair is made to pass from one to another of those personages of whom he thought it most desirable for the young reader to have vivid and familiar ideas, and whose lives and actions would best enable him to give picturesque sketches of the times.

There is certainly no method, by which the shadowy outlines of departed men and women can be made to assume the hues of life more effectually than by connecting their images with the substantial and homely reality of a fireside chair. It causes us to feel at once that these characters of history had a private and familiar existence, and were not wholly contained within that cold array of outward action which we are compelled to receive as the adequate representation of their lives. If this impression can be given, much is accomplished.

Setting aside Grandfather and his auditors, and excepting the adventures of the chair, which form the machinery of the work, nothing in the ensuing pages can be termed fictitious. The author, it is true, has sometimes assumed the license of filling up the outline of history with details, for which he has none but imaginative authority, but which, he hopes, do not violate nor give a false coloring to the truth. He believes that, in this respect, his narrative will not be found to convey ideas and impressions of which the reader may hereafter find it necessary to purge his mind.

The author's great doubt is whether he has succeeded in writing a book which will be readable by the class for whom he intends it. To make a lively and entertaining narrative for children, with such unmalleable material as is presented by the sombre, stern, and rigid characteristics of the Puritans, is quite as difficult an attempt as to manufacture delicate playthings out of the granite rocks on which New England is founded.

BOSTON, November, 1840.

GRANDFATHER'S CHAIR

PART I

CHAPTER I

GRANDFATHER had been sitting in his old arm-chair all that pleasant afternoon, while the children were pursuing their various sports, far off or near at hand. Sometimes you would have said, " Grandfather is asleep;" but still, even when his eyes were closed, his thoughts were with the young people, playing among the flowers and shrubbery of the garden.

He heard the voice of Laurence, who had taken pos-session of a heap of decayed branches which the gar-dener had lopped from the fruit-trees, and was building a little hut for his cousin Clara and himself. He heard Clara's gladsome voice, too, as she weeded and watered the flower-bed which had been given her for her own. He could have counted every footstep that Charley took, as he trundled his wheelbarrow along the gravel walk. And though Grandfather was old and gray-haired, yet his heart leaped with joy whenever little Alice came fluttering, like a butterfly, into the room. She had made each of the children her playmate in turn, and now made Grandfather her playmate too, and thought him the merriest of them all.

At last the children grew weary of their sports; because a summer afternoon is like a long lifetime to the young. So they came into the room together, and clustered round Grandfather's great chair. Little Alice, who was hardly five years old, took the privilege of the youngest, and climbed his knee. It was a pleasant thing to behold that fair and golden-haired child in the lap of the old man, and to think that, different as they were, the hearts of both could be gladdened with the same joys.

"Grandfather," said little Alice, laying her head back upon his arm, "I am very tired now. You must tell me a story to make me go to sleep."

"That is not what story-tellers like," answered Grandfather, smiling. "They are better satisfied when they can keep their auditors awake."

"But here are Laurence, and Charley, and I," cried cousin Clara, who was twice as old as little Alice. "We will all three keep wide awake. And pray, Grandfather, tell us a story about this strange-looking old chair."

Now, the chair in which Grandfather sat was made of oak, which had grown dark with age, but had been rubbed and polished till it shone as bright as mahogany. It was very large and heavy, and had a back that rose high above Grandfather's white head. This back was curiously carved in open-work, so as to represent flowers and foliage and other devices; which the children had often gazed at, but could never understand what they meant. On the very tiptop of the chair, over the head of Grandfather himself, was a likeness of a lion's head, which had such a savage grin, that you would almost expect to hear it growl and snarl.

The children had seen Grandfather sitting in this chair ever since they could remember anything. Perhaps the younger of them supposed that he and the chair had come into the world together, and that both had always been as old as they were now. At this time, however, it happened to be the fashion for ladies to adorn their drawing-rooms with the oldest and oddest chairs that could be found. It seemed to cousin Clara that if these ladies could have seen Grandfather's old chair, they would have thought it worth all the rest together. She wondered if it were not even older than Grandfather himself, and longed to know all about its history.

"Do, Grandfather, talk to us about this chair," she repeated.

"Well, child," said Grandfather, patting Clara's cheek, "I can tell you a great many stories of my chair. Perhaps your cousin Laurence would like to hear them too. They would teach him something about the history and distinguished people of his country, which he has never read in any of his school-books."

Cousin Laurence was a boy of twelve, a bright scholar, in whom an early thoughtfulness and sensibility began to show themselves. His young fancy kindled at the idea of knowing all the adventures of this venerable chair. He looked eagerly in Grandfather's face; and even Charley, a bold, brisk, restless little fellow of nine, sat himself down on the carpet, and resolved to be quiet for at least ten minutes, should the story last so long.

Meantime, little Alice was already asleep; so Grandfather, being much pleased with such an attentive audience, began to talk about matters that happened long ago.

CHAPTER II

B UT, before relating the adventures of the chair, Grandfather found it necessary to speak of the circumstances that caused the first settlement of New England. For it will soon be perceived that the story of this remarkable chair cannot be told without telling a great deal of the history of the country.

So, Grandfather talked about the Puritans, as those persons were called who thought it sinful to practise the religious forms and ceremonies which the Church of England had borrowed from the Roman Catholics. These Puritans suffered so much persecution in England that, in 1607, many of them went over to Holland, and lived ten or twelve years at Amsterdam and Leyden. But they feared that, if they continued there much longer, they should cease to be English, and should adopt all the manners and ideas and feelings of the Dutch. For this and other reasons, in the year 1620, they embarked on board of the ship Mayflower, and crossed the ocean to the shores of Cape Cod. There they made a settlement, and called it Plymouth, which, though now a part of Massachusetts, was for a long time a colony by itself. And thus was formed the earliest settlement of the Puritans in America.

Meantime, those of the Puritans who remained in England continued to suffer grievous persecution on account of their religious opinions. They began to look around them for some spot where they might worship God, not as the king and bishops thought fit, but according to the dictates of their own consciences. When their brethren had gone from Holland to America, they bethought themselves that they likewise might find refuge from persecution there. Several gentlemen among them purchased a tract of country

4

on the coast of Massachusetts Bay, and obtained a charter from King Charles, which authorized them to make laws for the settlers. In the year 1628, they sent over a few people, with John Endicott at their head, to commence a plantation at Salem. Peter Palfrey, Roger Conant, and one or two more, had built houses there in 1626, and may be considered as the first settlers of that ancient town. Many other Puritans prepared to follow Endicott.

"And now we come to the chair, my dear children," said Grandfather. "This chair is supposed to have been made of an oak-tree which grew in the park of the English earl of Lincoln, between two and three centuries ago. In its younger days it used, probably, to stand in the hall of the earl's castle. Do not you see the coat of arms of the family of Lincoln, carved in the open-work of the back? But when his daughter, the Lady Arbella, was married to a certain Mr. Johnson, the earl gave her this valuable chair."

"Who was Mr. Johnson?" inquired Clara.

"He was a gentleman of great wealth, who agreed with the Puritans in their religious opinions," answered Grandfather. " And as his belief was the same as theirs, he resolved that he would live and die with them. Accordingly, in the month of April, 1630, he left his pleasant abode and all his comforts in England, and embarked with the Lady Arbella, on board of a ship bound for America."

As Grandfather was frequently impeded by the questions and observations of his young auditors, we deem it advisable to omit all such prattle as is not essential to the story. We have taken some pains to find out exactly what Grandfather said, and here offer to our readers, as nearly as possible in his own words, the story of

THE LADY ARBELLA

The ship in which Mr. Johnson and his lady embarked, taking Grandfather's chair along with them, was called the Arbella, in honor of the lady herself. A fleet of ten or twelve vessels, with many hundred passengers, left England about the same time; for a multitude of people, who were discontented with the king's government, and oppressed by the bishops, were flocking over to the new world. One of the vessels in the fleet was that same Mayflower which had carried the Puritan pilgrims to Plymouth. And now, my children, I would have you fancy yourselves in the cabin of the good ship Arbella; because if you could behold the passengers aboard that vessel, you would feel what a blessing and honor it was for New England to have such settlers. They were the best men and women of their day.

Among the passengers was John Winthrop, who had sold the estate of his forefathers, and was going to prepare a new home for his wife and children in the wilderness. He had the king's charter in his keeping, and was appointed the first Governor of Massachusetts. Imagine him a person of grave and benevolent aspect, dressed in a black velvet suit, with a broad ruff around his neck and a peaked beard upon his chin. There was likewise a minister of the Gospel, whom the English bishops had forbidden to preach, but who knew that he should have liberty both to preach and pray in the forests of America. He wore a black cloak, called a Geneva cloak, and had a black velvet cap, fitting close to his head, as was the fashion of almost all the Puritan clergymen. In their company came Sir Richard Saltonstall, who had been one of the five first projectors of the new colony. He soon returned to his native country. But his descendants still remain in New England; and the good old family name is as much respected in our days as it was in those of Sir Richard.

Not only these, but several other men of wealth, and pious ministers, were in the cabin of the Arbella. One had banished himself forever from the old hall where his ancestors had lived for hundreds of years. Another had left his quiet parsonage, in a country town of England. Others had come from the universities of Oxford or Cambridge, where they had gained great fame for their learning. And here they all were, tossing upon the uncertain and dangerous sea, and bound for a home that was more dangerous than even the sea itself. In the cabin, likewise, sat the Lady Arbella in her chair, with a gentle and sweet expression on her face, but looking too pale and feeble to endure the hardships of the wilderness.

Every morning and evening the Lady Arbella gave up her great chair to one of the ministers, who took his place in it and read passages from the Bible to his companions. And thus, with prayers and pious conversation, and frequent singing of hymns, which the breezes caught from their lips and scattered far over the desolate waves, they prosecuted their voyage, and sailed into the harbor of Salem in the month of June.

At that period there were but six or eight dwellings in the town; and these were miserable hovels, with roofs of straw and wooden chimneys. The passengers in the fleet either built huts with bark and branches of trees, or erected tents of cloth till they could provide themselves with better shelter. Many of them went to form a settlement at Charlestown. It was thought fit that the Lady Arbella should tarry in Salem for a time; she was probably received as a guest into the family of John Endicott. He was the chief person in the plantation, and had the only comfortable house which the newcomers had beheld since they left England. So now, children, you must imagine Grandfather's chair in the midst of a new scene.

Suppose it a hot summer's day, and the lattice-windows of a chamber in Mr. Endicott's house thrown wide open. The Lady Arbella, looking paler than she did on shipboard, is sitting in her chair, and thinking mournfully of far-off England. She rises and goes to the window. There, amid patches of garden ground and corn-field, she sees the few wretched hovels of the settlers, with the still ruder wigwams and cloth tents of the passengers who had arrived in the same fleet with herself. Far and near stretches the dismal forest of pine-trees, which throw their black shadows over the whole land, and likewise over the heart of this poor lady.

All the inhabitants of the little village are busy. One is clearing a spot on the verge of the forest for his homestead; another is hewing the trunk of a fallen pine-tree, in order to build himself a dwelling; a third is hoeing in his field of Indian corn. Here comes a huntsman out of the woods, dragging a bear which he has shot, and shouting to the neighbors to lend him a hand. There goes a man to the seashore, with a spade and a bucket, to dig a mess of clams, which were a principal article of food with the first settlers. Scattered here and there are two or three dusky figures, clad in mantles of fur, with ornaments of bone hanging from their ears, and the feathers of wild birds in their coal-black hair. They have belts of shell-work slung across their shoulders, and are armed with bows and arrows and flint-headed spears. These are an Indian Sagamore and his attendants, who have come to gaze at the labors of the white men. And now rises a cry, that a pack of wolves have seized a young calf in the pasture, and every man snatches up his gun or pike, and runs in chase of the marauding beasts.

Poor Lady Arbella watches all these sights, and feels that this new world is fit only for rough and hardy people. None should be here but those who can struggle with wild beasts and wild men, and can toil in the heat or cold, and can keep their hearts firm against all difficulties and dangers. But she is not one of these. Her gentle and timid spirit sinks within her; and turning away from the window she sits down in the great chair, and wonders whereabouts in the wilderness her friends will dig her grave.

Mr. Johnson had gone, with Governor Winthrop and most of the other passengers, to Boston, where he intended to build a house for Lady Arbella and himself. Boston was then covered with wild woods, and had fewer inhabitants even than Salem. During her husband's absence, poor Lady Arbella felt herself growing ill, and was hardly able to stir from the great chair. Whenever John Endicott noticed her despondency, he doubtless addressed her with words of comfort. "Cheer up, my good lady!" he would say. "In a little time, you will love this rude life of the wilderness as I do." But Endicott's heart was as bold and resolute as iron, and he could not understand why a woman's heart should not be of iron too.

Still, however, he spoke kindly to the lady, and then hastened forth to till his corn-field and set out fruit-trees, or to bargain with the Indians for furs, or perchance to oversee the building of a fort. Also being a magistrate, he had often to punish some idler or evil-doer, by ordering him to be set in the stocks or scourged at the whipping-post. Often, too, as was the custom of the times, he and Mr. Higginson, the minister of Salem, held long religious talks together. Thus John Endicott was a man of multifarious business, and had no time to look back regretfully to his native land. He felt himself fit for the new world, and for the work that he had to do, and set himself resolutely to accomplish it.

What a contrast, my dear children, between this bold, rough, active man, and the gentle Lady Arbella, who was fading away, like a pale English flower, in the shadow of the forest! And now the great chair was often empty, because Lady Arbella grew too weak to arise from bed.

Meantime, her husband had pitched upon a spot for their new home. He returned from Boston to Salem, travelling through the woods on foot, and leaning on his pilgrim's staff. His heart yearned within him; for he was eager to tell his wife of the new home which he had chosen. But when he beheld her pale and hollow cheek, and found how her strength was wasted, he must have known that her appointed home was in a better land. Happy for him then, — happy both for him and her, — if they remembered that there was a path to heaven, as well from this heathen wilderness as from the Christian land whence they had come. And so, in one short month from her arrival, the gentle Lady Arbella faded away and died. They dug a grave for her in the new soil, where the roots of the pine-trees impeded their spades; and when her bones had rested

there nearly two hundred years, and a city had sprung
up around them, a church of stone was built upon the
spot.

Charley, almost at the commencement of the foregoing narrative, had galloped away with a prodigious
clatter, upon Grandfather's stick, and was not yet returned. So large a boy should have been ashamed to
ride upon a stick. But Laurence and Clara had listened attentively, and were affected by this true story
of the gentle lady, who had come so far to die so soon.
Grandfather had supposed that little Alice was asleep,
but, towards the close of the story, happening to look
down upon her, he saw that her blue eyes were wide
open, and fixed earnestly upon his face. The tears had
gathered in them, like dew upon a delicate flower; but
when Grandfather ceased to speak, the sunshine of her
smile broke forth again.

"Oh, the lady must have been so glad to get to
heaven!" exclaimed little Alice.

"Grandfather, what became of Mr. Johnson?" asked
Clara.

"His heart appears to have been quite broken,"
answered Grandfather; "for he died at Boston within
a month after the death of his wife. He was buried in
the very same tract of ground, where he had intended
to build a dwelling for Lady Arbella and himself.
Where their house would have stood, there was his
grave."

"I never heard anything so melancholy!" said Clara.

"The people loved and respected Mr. Johnson so
much," continued Grandfather, "that it was the last
request of many of them, when they died, that they
might be buried as near as possible to this good man's
grave. And so the field became the first burial-ground
in Boston. When you pass through Tremont street,
along by King's Chapel, you see a burial-ground, containing many old grave-stones and monuments. That
was Mr. Johnson's field."

"How sad is the thought," observed Clara, "that one

of the first things which the settlers had to do, when they came to the new world, was to set apart a burial-ground!"

"Perhaps," said Laurence, "if they had found no need of burial-grounds here, they would have been glad, after a few years, to go back to England."

Grandfather looked at Laurence, to discover whether he knew how profound and true a thing he had said.

CHAPTER III

NOT long after Grandfather had told the story of his great chair, there chanced to be a rainy day. Our friend Charley, after disturbing the household with beat of drum and riotous shouts, races up and down the staircase, overturning of chairs, and much other uproar, began to feel the quiet and confinement within doors intolerable. But as the rain came down in a flood, the little fellow was hopelessly a prisoner, and now stood with sullen aspect at a window, wondering whether the sun itself were not extinguished by so much moisture in the sky.

Charley had already exhausted the less eager activity of the other children; and they had betaken themselves to occupations that did not admit of his companionship. Laurence sat in a recess near the book-case, reading, not for the first time, the Midsummer Night's Dream. Clara was making a rosary of beads for a little figure of a Sister of Charity, who was to attend the Bunker Hill Fair, and lend her aid in erecting the Monument. Little Alice sat on Grandfather's footstool, with a picture-book in her hand; and, for every picture, the child was telling Grandfather a story. She did not read from the book (for little Alice had not much skill in reading), but told the story out of her own heart and mind.

Charley was too big a boy, of course, to care anything about little Alice's stories, although Grandfather appeared to listen with a good deal of interest. Often, in a young child's ideas and fancies, there is something which it requires the thought of a lifetime to comprehend. But Charley was of opinion, that if a story must be told, it had better be told by Grandfather, than little Alice.

"Grandfather, I want to hear more about your chair," said he.

Now Grandfather remembered that Charley had galloped away upon a stick, in the midst of the narrative of poor Lady Arbella, and I know not whether he would have thought it worth while to tell another story, merely to gratify such an inattentive auditor as Charley. But Laurence laid down his book and seconded the request. Clara drew her chair nearer to Grandfather, and little Alice immediately closed her picture-book, and looked up into his face. Grandfather had not the heart to disappoint them.

He mentioned several persons who had a share in the settlement of our country, and who would be well worthy of remembrance, if we could find room to tell about them all. Among the rest, Grandfather spoke of the famous Hugh Peters, a minister of the Gospel, who did much good to the inhabitants of Salem. Mr. Peters afterwards went back to England, and was chaplain to Oliver Cromwell; but Grandfather did not tell the children what became of this upright and zealous man, at last. In fact, his auditors were growing impatient to hear more about the history of the chair.

"After the death of Mr. Johnson," said he, "Grandfather's chair came into the possession of Roger Williams. He was a clergyman, who arrived at Salem, and settled there in 1631. Doubtless the good man has spent many a studious hour in this old chair, either penning a sermon, or reading some abstruse book of theology, till midnight came upon him unawares. At that period, as there were few lamps or candles to be had, people used to read or work by the light of pitchpine torches. These supplied the place of the 'midnight oil' to the learned men of New England."

Grandfather went on to talk about Roger Williams, and told the children several particulars, which we have not room to repeat. One incident, however, which was connected with his life, must be related, because it will give the reader an idea of the opinions and feelings of the first settlers of New England. It was as follows:—

THE RED CROSS

While Roger Williams sat in Grandfather's chair, at his humble residence in Salem, John Endicott would often come to visit him. As the clergy had great influence in temporal concerns, the minister and magistrate would talk over the occurrences of the day, and consult how the people might be governed according to scriptural laws.

One thing especially troubled them both. In the old national banner of England, under which her soldiers have fought for hundreds of years, there is a Red Cross, which has been there ever since the days when England was in subjection to the Pope. The Cross, though a holy symbol, was abhorred by the Puritans, because they considered it a relic of Popish idolatry. Now, whenever the train-band of Salem was mustered, the soldiers, with Endicott at their head, had no other flag to march under than this same old papistical banner of England, with the Red Cross in the midst of it. The banner of the Red Cross, likewise, was flying on the walls of the fort of Salem ; and a similar one was displayed in Boston harbor, from the fortress on Castle Island.

"I profess, brother Williams," Captain Endicott would say, after they had been talking of this matter, "it distresses a Christian man's heart to see this idolatrous Cross flying over our heads. A stranger, beholding it, would think that we had undergone all our hardships and dangers, by sea and in the wilderness, only to get new dominions for the Pope of Rome."

"Truly, good Mr. Endicott," Roger Williams would answer, "you speak as an honest man and Protestant Christian should. For mine own part, were it my business to draw a sword, I should reckon it sinful to fight under such a banner. Neither can I, in my pulpit, ask the blessing of Heaven upon it."

Such, probably, was the way in which Roger Williams and John Endicott used to talk about the banner of the Red Cross. Endicott, who was a prompt and resolute man, soon determined that Massachusetts, if she could not have a banner of her own, should at least be delivered from that of the Pope of Rome.

Not long afterwards there was a military muster at Salem. Every able-bodied man in the town and neighborhood was there. All were well armed, with steel caps upon their heads, plates of iron upon their breasts and at their backs, and gorgets of steel around their necks. When the sun shone upon these ranks of iron-clad men, they flashed and blazed with a splendor that bedazzled the wild Indians, who had come out of the woods to gaze at them. The soldiers had long pikes, swords, and muskets, which were fired with matches, and were almost as heavy as a small cannon.

These men had mostly a stern and rigid aspect. To judge by their looks, you might have supposed that there was as much iron in their hearts as there was upon their heads and breasts. They were all devoted Puritans, and of the same temper as those with whom Oliver Cromwell afterwards overthrew the throne of England. They hated all the relics of Popish superstition as much as Endicott himself; and yet, over their heads, was displayed the banner of the Red Cross.

Endicott was the captain of the company. While the soldiers were expecting his orders to begin their exercise, they saw him take the banner in one hand, holding his drawn sword in the other. Probably he addressed them in a speech, and explained how horrible a thing it was, that men, who had fled from Popish idolatry into the wilderness, should be compelled to fight under its symbols here. Perhaps he concluded his address somewhat in the following style : —

"And now, fellow-soldiers, you see this old banner of England. Some of you, I doubt not, may think it treason for a man to lay violent hands upon it. But whether or no it be treason to man, I have good assurance in my conscience that it is no treason to God. Wherefore I have resolved that we will rather be God's soldiers, than soldiers of the Pope of Rome;

and in that mind I now cut the Papal Cross out of this banner."

And so he did. And thus, in a province belonging to the crown of England, a captain was found bold enough to deface the King's banner with his sword.

When Winthrop and the other wise men of Massachusetts heard of it, they were disquieted, being afraid that Endicott's act would bring great trouble upon himself and them. An account of the matter was carried to King Charles ; but he was then so much engrossed by dissensions with his people, that he had no leisure to punish the offender. In other times, it might have cost Endicott his life, and Massachusetts her charter.

" I should like to know, Grandfather," said Laurence, when the story was ended, " whether, when Endicott cut the Red Cross out of the banner, he meant to imply that Massachusetts was independent of England ? "

" A sense of the independence of his adopted country must have been in that bold man's heart," answered Grandfather ; " but I doubt whether he had given the matter much consideration, except in its religious bearing. However, it was a very remarkable affair, and a very strong expression of Puritan character."

Grandfather proceeded to speak further of Roger Williams, and of other persons who sat in the great chair, as will be seen in the following chapter.

CHAPTER IV

"ROGER WILLIAMS," said Grandfather, "did not keep possession of the chair a great while. His opinions of civil and religious matters differed, in many respects, from those of the rulers and clergymen of Massachusetts. Now the wise men of those days believed that the country could not be safe, unless all the inhabitants thought and felt alike."

"Does anybody believe so in our days, Grandfather?" asked Laurence.

"Possibly there are some who believe it," said Grandfather; "but they have not so much power to act upon their belief, as the magistrates and ministers had, in the days of Roger Williams. They had the power to deprive this good man of his home, and to send him out from the midst of them, in search of a new place of rest. He was banished in 1634, and went first to Plymouth colony; but as the people there held the same opinions as those of Massachusetts, he was not suffered to remain among them. However, the wilderness was wide enough; so Roger Williams took his staff and travelled into the forest, and made treaties with the Indians, and began a plantation which he called Providence."

"I have been to Providence on the railroad," said Charley. "It is but a two hours' ride."

"Yes, Charley," replied Grandfather; "but when Roger Williams travelled thither, over hills and valleys, and through the tangled woods, and across swamps and streams, it was a journey of several days. Well, his little plantation is now grown to be a populous city; and the inhabitants have a great veneration for Roger Williams. His name is familiar in the mouths of all because they see it on their bank bills. How it would have perplexed this good clergyman, if he had been told that he should give his name to the ROGER WILLIAMS BANK!"

"When he was driven from Massachusetts," said Laurence, "and began his journey into the woods, he must have felt as if he were burying himself forever from the sight and knowledge of men. Yet the whole country has now heard of him, and will remember him forever."

"Yes," answered Grandfather, "it often happens, that the outcasts of one generation are those who are reverenced as the wisest and best of men by the next. The securest fame is that which comes after a man's death. But let us return to our story. When Roger Williams was banished, he appears to have given the chair to Mrs. Anne Hutchinson. At all events it was in her possession in 1637. She was a very sharp-witted and well-instructed lady, and was so conscious of her own wisdom and abilities, that she thought it a pity that the world should not have the benefit of them. She therefore used to hold lectures in Boston once or twice a week, at which most of the women attended. Mrs. Hutchinson presided at these meetings, sitting with great state and dignity in Grandfather's chair."

"Grandfather, was it positively this very chair?" demanded Clara, laying her hand upon its carved elbow.

"Why not, my dear Clara?" said Grandfather.

"Well, Mrs. Hutchinson's lectures soon caused a great disturbance; for the ministers of Boston did not think it safe and proper, that a woman should publicly instruct the people in religious doctrines. Moreover, she made the matter worse, by declaring that the Rev. Mr. Cotton was the only sincerely pious and holy clergyman in New England. Now the clergy of those days had quite as much share in the government of the country, though indirectly, as the magistrates themselves; so you may imagine what a host of powerful enemies were raised up against Mrs. Hutchinson. A synod was convened; that is to say, an assemblage of all the ministers in Massachusetts. They declared that there were eighty-two erroneous opinions on religious subjects, diffused among the people, and that Mrs. Hutchinson's opinions were of the number."

"If they had eighty-two wrong opinions," observed Charley, "I don't see how they could have any right ones."

"Mrs. Hutchinson had many zealous friends and converts," continued Grandfather. "She was favored by young Henry Vane, who had come over from England a year or two before, and had since been chosen governor of the colony, at the age of twenty-four. But Winthrop, and most of the other leading men, as well as the ministers, felt an abhorrence of her doctrines. Thus two opposite parties were formed; and so fierce were the dissensions, that it was feared the consequence would be civil war and bloodshed. But Winthrop and the ministers being the most powerful, they disarmed and imprisoned Mrs. Hutchinson's adherents. She, like Roger Williams, was banished."

"Dear Grandfather, did they drive the poor woman into the woods?" exclaimed little Alice, who contrived to feel a human interest even in these discords of polemic divinity.

"They did, my darling," replied Grandfather; "and the end of her life was so sad, you must not hear it. At her departure, it appears, from the best authorities, that she gave the great chair to her friend, Henry Vane. He was a young man of wonderful talents and great learning, who had imbibed the religious opinions of the Puritans, and left England with the intention of spending his life in Massachusetts. The people chose him governor; but the controversy about Mrs. Hutchinson, and other troubles, caused him to leave the country in 1637. You may read the subsequent events of his life in the History of England."

"Yes, Grandfather," cried Laurence; "and we may read them better in Mr. Upham's biography of Vane. And what a beautiful death he died, long afterwards! beautiful, though it was on a scaffold."

" Many of the most beautiful deaths have been there,"
said Grandfather. " The enemies of a great and good
man can in no other way make him so glorious, as by
giving him the crown of martyrdom."

In order that the children might fully understand the
all-important history of the chair, Grandfather now
thought fit to speak of the progress that was made in
settling several colonies. The settlement of Plymouth,
in 1620, has already been mentioned. In 1635, Mr.
Hooker and Mr. Stone, two ministers, went on foot
from Massachusetts to Connecticut, through the pathless
woods, taking their whole congregation along with them.
They founded the town of Hartford. In 1638, Mr.
Davenport, a very celebrated minister, went, with other
people, and began a plantation at New Haven. In the
same year, some persons who had been persecuted in
Massachusetts went to the Isle of Rhodes, since called
Rhode Island, and settled there. About this time, also,
many settlers had gone to Maine, and were living without any regular government. There were likewise settlers near Piscataqua River, in the region which is now
called New Hampshire.

Thus, at various points along the coast of New England, there were communities of Englishmen. Though
these communities were independent of one another, yet
they had a common dependence upon England; and, at
so vast a distance from their native home, the inhabitants must all have felt like brethren. They were fitted
to become one united people at a future period. Perhaps their feelings of brotherhood were the stronger,
because different nations had formed settlements to the
north and to the south. In Canada and Nova Scotia
were colonies of French. On the banks of the Hudson
River was a colony of Dutch, who had taken possession
of that region many years before, and called it New
Netherlands.

Grandfather, for aught I know, might have gone on
to speak of Maryland and Virginia; for the good old
gentleman really seemed to suppose that the whole surface of the United States was not too broad a founda-

tion to place the four legs of his chair upon. But, happening to glance at Charley, he perceived that this naughty boy was growing impatient, and meditating another ride upon a stick. So here, for the present, Grandfather suspended the history of his chair.

CHAPTER V

THE children had now learned to look upon the chair with an interest, which was almost the same as if it were a conscious being, and could remember the many famous people whom it had held within its arms.

Even Charley, lawless as he was, seemed to feel that this venerable chair must not be clambered upon nor overturned, although he had no scruple in taking such liberties with every other chair in the house. Clara treated it with still greater reverence, often taking occasion to smooth its cushion, and to brush the dust from the carved flowers and grotesque figures of its oaken back and arms. Laurence would sometimes sit a whole hour, especially at twilight, gazing at the chair, and, by the spell of his imaginations, summoning up its ancient occupants to appear in it again.

Little Alice evidently employed herself in a similar way; for once, when Grandfather had gone abroad, the child was heard talking with the gentle Lady Arbella, as if she were still sitting in the chair. So sweet a child as little Alice may fitly talk with angels, such as the Lady Arbella had long since become.

Grandfather was soon importuned for more stories about the chair. He had no difficulty in relating them; for it really seemed as if every person, noted in our early history, had, on some occasion or other, found repose within its comfortable arms. If Grandfather took pride in anything it was in being the possessor of such an honorable and historic elbow chair.

"I know not precisely who next got possession of the chair, after Governor Vane went back to England," said Grandfather. "But there is reason to believe that President Dunster sat in it, when he held the first commencement at Harvard College. You have often heard, children, how careful our forefathers were to give their

22

young people a good education. They had scarcely cut down trees enough to make room for their own dwellings, before they began to think of establishing a college. Their principal object was, to rear up pious and learned ministers; and hence old writers call Harvard College a school of the prophets."

"Is the college a school of the prophets now?" asked Charley.

"It is a long while since I took my degree, Charley. You must ask some of the recent graduates," answered Grandfather. "As I was telling you, President Dunster sat in Grandfather's chair in 1642, when he conferred the degree of bachelor of arts on nine young men. They were the first in America who had received that honor. And now, my dear auditors, I must confess that there are contradictory statements and some uncertainty about the adventures of the chair, for a period of almost ten years. Some say that it was occupied by your own ancestor, William Hawthorne, first Speaker of the House of Representatives. I have nearly satisfied myself, however, that, during most of this questionable period, it was literally the Chair of State. It gives me much pleasure to imagine, that several successive governors of Massachusetts sat in it at the council board."

"But, Grandfather," interposed Charley, who was a matter-of-fact little person, "what reason have you to imagine so?"

"Pray do imagine it, Grandfather," said Laurence.

"With Charley's permission, I will," replied Grandfather, smiling. "Let us consider it settled, therefore, that Winthrop, Bellingham, Dudley, and Endicott, each of them, when chosen governor, took his seat in our great chair on election day. In this chair, likewise, did those excellent governors preside, while holding consultations with the chief counsellors of the province, who were styled Assistants. The governor sat in this chair, too, whenever messages were brought to him from the chamber of Representatives."

And here Grandfather took occasion to talk, rather tediously, about the nature and forms of government that established themselves, almost spontaneously, in Massachusetts and the other New England colonies. Democracies were the natural growth of the new world. As to Massachusetts, it was at first intended that the colony should be governed by a council in London. But, in a little while, the people had the whole power in their own hands, and chose annually the governor, the counsellors, and the representatives. The people of old England had never enjoyed anything like the liberties and privileges, which the settlers of New England now possessed. And they did not adopt these modes of government after long study, but in simplicity, as if there were no other way for people to be ruled.

"But, Laurence," continued Grandfather, "when you want instruction on these points, you must seek it in Mr. Bancroft's History. I am merely telling the history of a chair. To proceed. The period during which the governors sat in our chair was not very full of striking incidents. The province was now established on a secure foundation ; but it did not increase so rapidly as at first, because the Puritans were no longer driven from England by persecution. However, there was still a quiet and natural growth. The legislature incorporated towns, and made new purchases of lands from the Indians. A very memorable event took place in 1643. The colonies of Massachusetts, Plymouth, Connecticut, and New Haven formed a union, for the purpose of assisting each other in difficulties, and for mutual defence against their enemies. They called themselves the United Colonies of New England."

"Were they under a government like that of the United States?" inquired Laurence.

"No," replied Grandfather, "the different colonies did not compose one nation together; it was merely a confederacy among the governments. It somewhat resembled the league of the Amphictyons, which you remember in Grecian history. But to return to our chair. In 1644 it was highly honored; for Governor Endicott sat in it, when he gave audience to an ambassador from the French governor of Acadie, or Nova

Scotia. A treaty of peace, between Massachusetts and the French colony, was then signed."

" Did England allow Massachusetts to make war and peace with foreign countries ? " asked Laurence.

" Massachusetts, and the whole of New England, was then almost independent of the mother country," said Grandfather. " There was now a civil war in England ; and the king, as you may well suppose, had his hands full at home, and could pay but little attention to these remote colonies. When the Parliament got the power into their hands, they likewise had enough to do in keeping down the Cavaliers. Thus New England, like a young and hardy lad, whose father and mother neglect it, was left to take care of itself. In 1649, King Charles was beheaded. Oliver Cromwell then became Protector of England ; and as he was a Puritan himself, and had risen by the valor of the English Puritans, he showed himself a loving and indulgent father to the Puritan colonies in America."

Grandfather might have continued to talk in this dull manner, nobody knows how long ; but, suspecting that Charley would find the subject rather dry, he looked sideways at that vivacious little fellow, and saw him give an involuntary yawn. Whereupon, Grandfather proceeded with the history of the chair, and related a very entertaining incident, which will be found in the next chapter.

CHAPTER VI

" ACCORDING to the most authentic records, my dear children," said Grandfather, "the chair, about this time, had the misfortune to break its leg. It was probably on account of this accident, that it ceased to be the seat of the governors of Massachusetts; for, assuredly, it would have been ominous of evil to the Commonwealth, if the Chair of State had tottered upon three legs. Being therefore sold at auction, — alas! what a vicissitude for a chair that had figured in such high company! — our venerable friend was knocked down to a certain Captain John Hull. This old gentleman, on carefully examining the maimed chair, discovered that its broken leg might be clamped with iron, and made as serviceable as ever."

"Here is the very leg that was broken!" exclaimed Charley, throwing himself down on the floor to look at it. "And here are the iron clamps. How well it was mended!"

When they had all sufficiently examined the broken leg, Grandfather told them a story about Captain John Hull and

THE PINE-TREE SHILLINGS

The Captain John Hull, aforesaid, was the mint-master of Massachusetts, and coined all the money that was made there. This was a new line of business; for, in the earlier days of the colony, the current coinage consisted of gold and silver money of England, Portugal, and Spain. These coins being scarce, the people were often forced to barter their commodities, instead of selling them.

For instance, if a man wanted to buy a coat, he perhaps exchanged a bear-skin for it. If he wished for a

26

barrel of molasses, he might purchase it with a pile of pine boards. Musket-bullets were used instead of farthings. The Indians had a sort of money, called wampum, which was made of clamshells; and this strange sort of specie was likewise taken in payment of debts, by the English settlers. Bank-bills had never been heard of. There was not money enough of any kind, in many parts of the country, to pay the salaries of the ministers; so that they sometimes had to take quintals of fish, bushels of corn, or cords of wood, instead of silver or gold.

As the people grew more numerous, and their trade one with another increased, the want of current money was still more sensibly felt. To supply the demand, the general court passed a law for establishing a coinage of shillings, sixpences, and threepences. Captain John Hull was appointed to manufacture this money, and was to have about one shilling out of every twenty to pay him for the trouble of making them.

Hereupon, all the old silver in the colony was handed over to Captain John Hull. The battered silver cans and tankards, I suppose, and silver buckles, and broken spoons, and silver buttons of worn-out coats, and silver hilts of swords that had figured at court, — all such curious old articles were doubtless thrown into the melting-pot together. But by far the greater part of the silver consisted of bullion from the mines of South America, which the English buccaneers — (who were little better than pirates) — had taken from the Spaniards, and brought to Massachusetts.

All this old and new silver being melted down and coined, the result was an immense amount of splendid shillings, sixpences, and threepences. Each had the date, 1652, on the one side, and the figure of a pine-tree on the other. Hence they were called pine-tree shillings, and for every twenty shillings that he coined, you will remember, Captain John Hull was entitled to put one shilling into his own pocket.

The magistrates soon began to suspect that the mintmaster would have the best of the bargain. **They**

offered him a large sum of money, if he would but give
up that twentieth shilling, which he was continually
dropping into his own pocket. But Captain Hull declared himself perfectly satisfied with the shilling. And
well he might be; for so diligently did he labor, that,
in a few years, his pockets, his money-bags, and his
strong-box were overflowing with pine-tree shillings.
This was probably the case when he came into possession of Grandfather's chair; and, as he had worked so
hard at the mint, it was certainly proper that he
should have a comfortable chair to rest himself in.

When the mint-master had grown very rich, a young
man, Samuel Sewell by name, came a-courting to his
only daughter. His daughter — whose name I do not
know, but we will call her Betsey — was a fine, hearty
damsel, by no means so slender as some young ladies of
our own days. On the contrary, having always fed
heartily on pumpkin pies, doughnuts, Indian puddings,
and other Puritan dainties, she was as round and plump
as a pudding herself. With this round, rosy Miss Betsey,
did Samuel Sewell fall in love. As he was a young man
of good character, industrious in his business, and a
member of the church, the mint-master very readily
gave his consent.

"Yes, you may take her," said he, in his rough way;
"and you'll find her a heavy burden enough!"

On the wedding-day, we may suppose that honest
John Hull dressed himself in a plum-colored coat, all the
buttons of which were made of pine-tree shillings. The
buttons of his waistcoat were sixpences; and the knees
of his small-clothes were buttoned with silver threepences.
Thus attired, he sat with great dignity in Grandfather's
chair; and being a portly old gentleman, he completely
filled it from elbow to elbow. On the opposite side of
the room, between her bridemaids, sat Miss Betsey.
She was blushing with all her might, and looked like
a full-blown pæony, or a great red apple.

There, too, was the bridegroom, dressed in a fine
purple coat, and gold lace waistcoat, with as much other
finery as the Puritan laws and customs would allow him

to put on. His hair was cropped close to his head, because Governor Endicott had forbidden any man to wear it below the ears.   But he was a very personable young man ; and so thought the bridemaids and Miss Betsey herself.

The mint-master also was pleased with his new son-in-law ; especially as he had courted Miss Betsey out of pure love, and had said nothing at all about her portion. So when the marriage ceremony was over, Captain Hull whispered a word to two of his men-servants, who immediately went out, and soon returned, lugging in a large pair of scales.   They were such a pair as wholesale merchants use for weighing bulky commodities ; and quite a bulky commodity was now to be weighed in them.

"Daughter Betsey," said the mint-master, "get into one side of these scales."

Miss Betsey, — or Mrs. Sewell, as we must now call her, — did as she was bid, like a dutiful child, without any question of the why and wherefore.   But what her father could mean, unless to make her husband pay for her by the pound, (in which case she would have been a dear bargain,) she had not the least idea.

"And now," said honest John Hull to the servants, " bring that box hither."

The box, to which the mint-master pointed, was a huge, square, iron-bound, oaken chest ; it was big enough, my children, for all four of you to play at hide-and-seek in.   The servants tugged with might and main, but could not lift this enormous receptacle, and were finally obliged to drag it across the floor.   Captain Hull then took a key from his girdle, unlocked the chest, and lifted its ponderous lid.   Behold ! it was full to the brim of bright pine-tree shillings, fresh from the mint ; and Samuel Sewell began to think that his father-in-law had got possession of all the money in the Massachusetts treasury.   But it was only the mint-master's honest share of the coinage.

Then the servants, at Captain Hull's command, heaped double handfuls of shillings into one side of the scales, while Betsey remained in the other.   Jingle, jingle went the shillings, as handful after handful was thrown in, till, plump and ponderous as she was, they fairly weighed the young lady from the floor.

"There, son Sewell!" cried the honest mint-master, resuming his seat in Grandfather's chair, "take these shillings for my daughter's portion.   Use her kindly, and thank Heaven for her.   It is not every wife that's worth her weight in silver!"

The children laughed heartily at this legend, and would hardly be convinced but that Grandfather had made it out of his own head.   He assured them faithfully, however, that he had found it in the pages of a grave historian, and had merely tried to tell it in a somewhat funnier style.   As for Samuel Sewell, he afterwards became Chief Justice of Massachusetts.

"Well, Grandfather," remarked Clara, "if wedding portions nowadays were paid as Miss Betsey's was, young ladies would not pride themselves upon an airy figure, as many of them do."

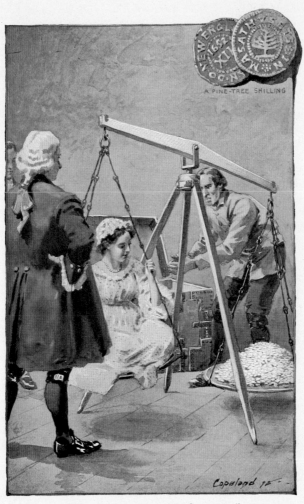

A PINE-TREE SHILLING

"JINGLE, JINGLE, WENT THE SHILLINGS."

CHAPTER VII

WHEN his little audience next assembled round the chair, Grandfather gave them a doleful history of the Quaker persecution, which began in 1656, and raged for about three years in Massachusetts.

He told them how, in the first place, twelve of the converts of George Fox, the first Quaker in the world, had come over from England. They seemed to be impelled by an earnest love for the souls of men, and a pure desire to make known what they considered a revelation from Heaven. But the rulers looked upon them as plotting the downfall of all government and religion. They were banished from the colony. In a little while, however, not only the first twelve had returned, but a multitude of other Quakers had come to rebuke the rulers, and to preach against the priests and steeple-houses.

Grandfather described the hatred and scorn with which these enthusiasts were received. They were thrown into dungeons; they were beaten with many stripes, women as well as men; they were driven forth into the wilderness, and left to the tender mercies of wild beasts and Indians. The children were amazed to hear, that, the more the Quakers were scourged, and imprisoned, and banished, the more did the sect increase, both by the influx of strangers, and by converts from among the Puritans. But Grandfather told them, that God had put something into the soul of man, which always turned the cruelties of the persecutor to naught.

He went on to relate, that, in 1659, two Quakers, named William Robinson and Marmaduke Stephenson, were hanged at Boston. A woman had been sentenced to die with them, but was reprieved, on condition of her leaving the colony. Her name was Mary Dyer. In the year 1660 she returned to Boston, although she knew

31

death awaited her there; and, if Grandfather had been correctly informed, an incident had then taken place, which connects her with our story. This Mary Dyer had entered the mint-master's dwelling, clothed in sackcloth and ashes, and seated herself in our great chair, with a sort of dignity and state. Then she proceeded to deliver what she called a message from Heaven; but in the midst of it, they dragged her to prison.

"And was she executed?" asked Laurence.

"She was," said Grandfather.

"Grandfather," cried Charley, clenching his fist, "I would have fought for that poor Quaker woman!"

"Ah! but if a sword had been drawn for her," said Laurence, "it would have taken away all the beauty of her death."

It seemed as if hardly any of the preceding stories had thrown such an interest around Grandfather's chair, as did the fact, that the poor, persecuted, wandering Quaker woman had rested in it for a moment. The children were so much excited, that Grandfather found it necessary to bring his account of the persecution to a close.

"In 1660, the same year in which Mary Dyer was executed," said he, "Charles the Second was restored to the throne of his fathers. This king had many vices; but he would not permit blood to be shed, under pretence of religion, in any part of his dominions. The Quakers in England told him what had been done to their brethren in Massachusetts; and he sent orders to Governor Endicott to forbear all such proceedings in future. And so ended the Quaker persecution, — one of the most mournful passages in the history of our forefathers."

Grandfather then told his auditors, that, shortly after the above incident, the great chair had been given by the mint-master to the Rev. Mr. John Eliot. He was the first minister of Roxbury. But besides attending to his pastoral duties there, he learned the language of the red men, and often went into the woods to preach to them. So earnestly did he labor for their conversion, that he has always been called the apostle to the Indians. The mention of this holy man suggested to Grandfather the propriety of giving a brief sketch of the history of the Indians, so far as they were connected with the English colonists.

A short period before the arrival of the first Pilgrims at Plymouth, there had been a very grievous plague among the red men; and the sages and ministers of that day were inclined to the opinion, that Providence had sent this mortality, in order to make room for the settlement of the English. But I know not why we should suppose that an Indian's life is less precious, in the eye of Heaven, than that of a white man. Be that as it may, death had certainly been very busy with the savage tribes.

In many places the English found the wigwams deserted, and the corn-fields growing to waste, with none to harvest the grain. There were heaps of earth also, which, being dug open, proved to be Indian graves, containing bows and flint-headed spears and arrows ; for the Indians buried the dead warrior's weapons along with him. In some spots, there were skulls and other human bones, lying unburied. In 1633, and the year afterwards, the small-pox broke out among the Massachusetts Indians, multitudes of whom died by this terrible disease of the old world. These misfortunes made them far less powerful than they had formerly been.

For nearly half a century after the arrival of the English, the red men showed themselves generally inclined to peace and amity. They often made submission, when they might have made successful war. The Plymouth settlers, led by the famous Captain Miles Standish, slew some of them in 1623, without any very evident necessity for so doing. In 1636, and the following year, there was the most dreadful war that had yet occurred between the Indians and the English. The Connecticut settlers, assisted by a celebrated Indian chief, named Uncas, bore the brunt of this war, with but little aid from Massachusetts. Many hundreds of the hostile Indians were slain, or burnt in their wigwams. Sassacus, their sachem, fled to another tribe,

after his own people were defeated; but he was mur-
dered by them, and his head was sent to his English
enemies.

From that period, down to the time of King Philip's
war, which will be mentioned hereafter, there was not
much trouble with the Indians. But the colonists were
always on their guard, and kept their weapons ready
for the conflict.

"I have sometimes doubted," said Grandfather, when
he had told these things to the children, " I have sometimes doubted whether there was more than a single
man, among our forefathers, who realized that an Indian
possesses a mind and a heart, and an immortal soul.
That single man was John Eliot. All the rest of the
early settlers seemed to think that the Indians were an
inferior race of beings, whom the Creator had merely
allowed to keep possession of this beautiful country, till
the white men should be in want of it."

"Did the pious men of those days never try to make
Christians of them?" asked Laurence.

"Sometimes, it is true," answered Grandfather, "the
magistrates and ministers would talk about civilizing and
converting the red people. But at the bottom of their
hearts, they would have had almost as much expectation
of civilizing a wild bear of the woods, and making him
fit for paradise. They felt no faith in the success of any
such attempts, because they had no love for the poor
Indians. Now Eliot was full of love for them, and
therefore so full of faith and hope, that he spent the
labor of a lifetime in their behalf."

"I would have conquered them first, and then converted then," said Charley.

"Ah, Charley, there spoke the very spirit of our forefathers!" replied Grandfather. "But Mr. Eliot had a
better spirit. He looked upon them as his brethren.
He persuaded as many of them as he could to leave off
their idle and wandering habits, and to build houses,
and cultivate the earth, as the English did. He established schools among them, and taught many of the
Indians how to read. He taught them, likewise, how

to pray. Hence they were called 'praying Indians.'
Finally, having spent the best years of his life for their
good, Mr. Eliot resolved to spend the remainder in doing
them a yet greater benefit."

" I know what that was ! " cried Laurence.

" He sat down in his study," continued Grandfather,
" and began a translation of the Bible into the Indian
tongue. It was while he was engaged in this pious
work, that the mint-master gave him our great chair.
His toil needed it, and deserved it."

"Oh, Grandfather, tell us all about that Indian Bible ! "
exclaimed Laurence. " I have seen it in the library of
the Athenæum ; and the tears came into my eyes, to
think that there were no Indians left to read it."

CHAPTER VIII

A S Grandfather was a great admirer of the Apostle Eliot, he was glad to comply with the earnest request which Laurence had made at the close of the last chapter. So he proceeded· to describe how good Mr. Eliot labored, while he was at work upon

The Indian Bible

My dear children, what a task would you think it, even with a long lifetime before you, were you bidden to copy every chapter and verse, and word, in yonder great family Bible! Would not this be a heavy toil? But if the task were, not to write off the English Bible, but to learn a language, utterly unlike all other tongues, — a language which hitherto had never been learned, except by the Indians themselves, from their mother's lips, — a language never written, and the strange words of which seemed inexpressible by letters; — if the task were, first to learn this new variety of speech, and then to translate the Bible into it, and to do it so carefully, that not one idea throughout the holy book should be changed, — what would induce you to undertake this toil? Yet this was what the Apostle Eliot did.

It was a mighty work for a man, now growing old, to take upon himself. And what earthly reward could he expect from it? None; no reward on earth. But he believed that the red men were the descendants of those lost tribes of Israel of whom history has been able to tell us nothing for thousands of years. He hoped that God had sent the English across the ocean, Gentiles as they were, to enlighten this benighted portion of His once chosen race. And when he should be summoned hence, he trusted to meet blessed spirits in another world, whose bliss would have been earned by his

36

patient toil, in translating the Word of God. This hope
and trust were far dearer to him than anything that
earth could offer.

Sometimes, while thus at work, he was visited by
learned men, who desired to know what literary undertaking Mr. Eliot had in hand. They, like himself, had
been bred in the studious cloisters of a university, and
were supposed to possess all the erudition which mankind has hoarded up from age to age. Greek and Latin
were as familiar to them as the babble of their childhood.
Hebrew was like their mother tongue. They had grown
gray in study; their eyes were bleared with poring over
print and manuscript by the light of the midnight lamp.

And yet, how much had they left unlearned! Mr.
Eliot would put into their hands some of the pages which
he had been writing; and behold! the gray-headed men
stammered over the long, strange words, like a little
child in his first attempts to read. Then would the
apostle call to him an Indian boy, one of his scholars,
and show him the manuscript, which had so puzzled the
learned Englishmen.

"Read this, my child," said he, "these are some brethren of mine, who would fain hear the sound of thy native
tongue."

Then would the Indian boy cast his eyes over the mysterious page, and read it so skilfully, that it sounded
like wild music. It seemed as if the forest leaves were
singing in the ears of his auditors, and as if the roar of
distant streams were poured through the young Indian's
voice. Such were the sounds amid which the language
of the red man had been formed; and they were still
heard to echo in it.

The lesson being over, Mr. Eliot would give the Indian boy an apple or a cake, and bid him leap forth into
the open air, which his free nature loved. The apostle
was kind to children, and even shared in their sports
sometimes. And when his visitors had bidden him farewell, the good man turned patiently to his toil again.

No other Englishman had ever understood the Indian
character so well, nor possessed so great an influence

over the New England tribes, as the apostle did. His advice and assistance must often have been valuable to his countrymen, in their transactions with the Indians. Occasionally, perhaps, the governor and some of the counsellors came to visit Mr. Eliot. Perchance they were seeking some method to circumvent the forest people. They inquired, it may be, how they could obtain possession of such and such a tract of their rich land. Or they talked of making the Indians their servants, as if God had destined them for perpetual bondage to the more powerful white man.

Perhaps, too, some warlike captain, dressed in his buff-coat, with a corslet beneath it, accompanied the governor and counsellors. Laying his hand upon his sword-hilt, he would declare, that the only method of dealing with the red men was to meet them with the sword drawn, and the musket presented.

But the apostle resisted both the craft of the politician, and the fierceness of the warrior.

"Treat these sons of the forest as men and brethren," he would say, "and let us endeavor to make them Christians. Their forefathers were of that chosen race, whom God delivered from Egyptian bondage. Perchance He has destined us to deliver, the children from the more cruel bondage of ignorance and idolatry. Chiefly for this end, it may be, we were directed across the ocean."

When these other visitors were gone, Mr. Eliot bent himself again over the half-written page. He dared hardly relax a moment from his toil. He felt that, in the book which he was translating, there was a deep human, as well as heavenly wisdom, which would of itself suffice to civilize and refine the savage tribes. Let the Bible be diffused among them, and all earthly good would follow. But how slight a consideration was this, when he reflected that the eternal welfare of a whole race of men depended upon his accomplishment of the task which he had set himself! What if his hands should be palsied? What if his mind should lose its vigor? What if death should come upon him, ere the work were done? Then must the red man wander in the dark wilderness of heathenism forever.

Impelled by such thoughts as these, he sat writing in the great chair, when the pleasant summer breeze came in through his open casement ; and also when the fire of forest logs sent up its blaze and smoke, through the broad stone chimney, into the wintry air. Before the earliest bird sang, in the morning, the apostle's lamp was kindled ; and, at midnight, his weary head was not yet upon its pillow. And at length, leaning back in the great chair, he could say to himself, with a holy triumph, — "The work is finished ! "

It was finished. Here was a Bible for the Indians. Those long-lost descendants of the ten tribes of Israel would now learn the history of their forefathers. That grace, which the ancient Israelites had forfeited, was offered anew to their children.

There is no impiety in believing that, when his long life was over, the apostle of the Indians was welcomed to the celestial abodes by the prophets of ancient days, and by those earliest apostles and evangelists, who had drawn their inspiration from the immediate presence of the Saviour. They first had preached truth and salvation to the world. And Eliot, separated from them by many centuries, yet full of the same spirit, had borne the like message to the new world of the West. Since the first days of Christianity, there has been no man more worthy to be numbered in the brotherhood of the apostles, than Eliot.

"My heart is not satisfied to think," observed Laurence, "that Mr. Eliot's labors have done no good, except to a few Indians of his own time. Doubtless, he would not have regretted his toil, if it were the means of saving but a single soul. But it is a grievous thing to me, that he should have toiled so hard to translate the Bible, and now the language and the people are gone! The Indian Bible itself is almost the only relic of both."

"Laurence," said his Grandfather, "if ever you

should doubt that man is capable of disinterested zeal
for his brother's good, then remember how the Apostle
Eliot toiled.   And if you should feel your own self-
interest pressing upon your heart too closely, then think
of Eliot's Indian Bible.   It is good for the world that
such a man has lived, and left this emblem of his life."

The tears gushed into the eyes of Laurence, and he
acknowledged that Eliot had not toiled in vain.   Little
Alice put up her arms to Grandfather, and drew down
his white head beside her own golden locks.

"Grandfather," whispered she, "I want to kiss good
Mr. Eliot!"

And, doubtless, good Mr. Eliot would gladly receive
the kiss of so sweet a child as little Alice, and would
think it a portion of his reward in heaven.

Grandfather now observed, that Dr. Francis had
written a very beautiful life of Eliot, which he advised
Laurence to peruse.   He then spoke of King Philip's
war, which began in 1675, and terminated with the
death of King Philip, in the following year.   Philip
was a proud, fierce Indian, whom Mr. Eliot had vainly
endeavored to convert to the Christian faith.

"It must have been a great anguish to the apostle,"
continued Grandfather, "to hear of mutual slaughter
and outrage between his own countrymen and those for
whom he felt the affection of a father.   A few of the
praying Indians joined the followers of King Philip.
A greater number fought on the side of the English.
In the course of the war, the little community of red
people whom Mr. Eliot had begun to civilize, was scattered, and probably never was restored to a flourishing
condition.   But his zeal did not grow cold; and only
about five years before his death he took great pains in
preparing a new edition of the Indian Bible."

"I do wish, Grandfather," cried Charley, "you would
tell us all about the battles in King Philip's war."

"Oh, no!" exclaimed Clara.   "Who wants to hear
about tomahawks and scalping knives!"

"No, Charley," replied Grandfather, "I have no time
to spare in talking about battles.   You must be content

with knowing that it was the bloodiest war that the Indians had ever waged against the white men ; and that, at its close, the English set King Philip's head upon a pole."

"Who was the captain of the English?" asked Charley.

"Their most noted captain was Benjamin Church, — a very famous warrior," said Grandfather. "But I assure you, Charley, that neither Captain Church, nor any of the officers and soldiers who fought in King Philip's war, did anything a thousandth part so glorious as Mr. Eliot did, when he translated the Bible for the Indians."

"Let Laurence be the apostle," said Charley to himself, "and I will be the captain."

CHAPTER IX

THE children were now accustomed to assemble round Grandfather's chair, at all their unoccupied moments; and often it was a striking picture to behold the white-headed old sire, with this flowery wreath of young people around him. When he talked to them, it was the past speaking to the present, or rather to the future, — for the children were of a generation which had not become actual. Their part in life, thus far, was only to be happy, and to draw knowledge from a thousand sources. As yet, it was not their time to do.

Sometimes, as Grandfather gazed at their fair, unworldly countenances, a mist of tears bedimmed his spectacles. He almost regretted that it was necessary for them to know anything of the past, or to provide aught for the future. He could have wished that they might be always the happy, youthful creatures, who had hitherto sported around his chair, without inquiring whether it had a history. It grieved him to think that his little Alice, who was a flower-bud fresh from paradise, must open her leaves to the rough breezes of the world, or ever open them in any clime. So sweet a child she was, that it seemed fit her infancy should be immortal!

But such repinings were merely flitting shadows across the old man's heart. He had faith enough to believe, and wisdom enough to know, that the bloom of the flower would be even holier and happier than its bud. Even within himself, — though Grandfather was now at that period of life when the veil of mortality is apt to hang heavily over the soul, — still, in his inmost being, he was conscious of something that he would not have exchanged for the best happiness of childhood. It was a bliss to which every sort of earthly experience, — all that he had enjoyed or suffered, or seen, or heard,

or acted, with the broodings of his soul upon the whole,
— had contributed somewhat.   In the same manner
must a bliss, of which now they could have no conception, grow up within these children, and form a part of
their sustenance for immortality.

So Grandfather, with renewed cheerfulness, continued
his history of the chair, trusting that a profounder wisdom than his own would extract, from these flowers and
weeds of Time, a fragrance that might last beyond all
time.

At this period of the story, Grandfather threw a glance
backward, as far as the year 1660.   He spoke of the
ill-concealed reluctance with which the Puritans in
America had acknowledged the sway of Charles the
Second, on his restoration to his father's throne.   When
death had stricken Oliver Cromwell, that mighty protector had no sincerer mourners than in New England.
The new king had been more than a year upon the
throne before his accession was proclaimed in Boston,
although the neglect to perform the ceremony might
have subjected the rulers to the charge of treason.

During the reign of Charles the Second, however, the
American colonies had but little reason to complain of
harsh or tyrannical treatment.   But when Charles died,
in 1685, and was succeeded by his brother James, the
patriarchs of New England began to tremble.   King
James was a bigoted Roman Catholic, and was known
to be of an arbitrary temper.   It was feared by all
Protestants, and chiefly by the Puritans, that he would
assume despotic power and attempt to establish Popery
throughout his dominions.   Our forefathers felt that
they had no security either for their religion or their
liberties.

The result proved that they had reason for their
apprehensions.   King James caused the charters of all
the American colonies to be taken away.   The old
charter of Massachusetts, which the people regarded
as a holy thing, and as the foundation of all their
liberties, was declared void.   The colonists were now no
longer freemen; they were entirely dependent on the

king's pleasure. At first, in 1685, King James appointed Joseph Dudley, a native of Massachusetts, to be President of New England. But soon afterwards, Sir Edmund Andros, an officer of the English army, arrived, with a commission to be Governor-general of New England and New York.

The king had given such powers to Sir Edmund Andros, that there was now no liberty, nor scarcely any law in the colonies over which he ruled. The inhabitants were not allowed to choose representatives, and consequently had no voice whatever in the government, nor control over the measures that were adopted. The counsellors, with whom the governor consulted on matters of state, were appointed by himself. This sort of government was no better than an absolute despotism.

"The people suffered much wrong, while Sir Edmund Andros ruled over them," continued Grandfather, "and they were apprehensive of much more. He had brought some soldiers with him from England, who took possession of the old fortress on Castle Island, and of the fortification on Fort Hill. Sometimes it was rumored that a general massacre of the inhabitants was to be perpetrated by these soldiers. There were reports, too, that all the ministers were to be slain or imprisoned."

"For what?" inquired Charley.

"Because they were the leaders of the people, Charley," said Grandfather. "A minister was a more formidable man than a general, in those days. Well, while these things were going on in America, King James had so misgoverned the people of England, that they sent over to Holland for the Prince of Orange. He had married the king's daughter, and was therefore considered to have a claim to the crown. On his arrival in England, the Prince of Orange was proclaimed king, by the name of William the Third. Poor old King James made his escape to France."

Grandfather told how, at the first intelligence of the landing of the Prince of Orange in England, the people of Massachusetts rose in their strength, and overthrew the government of Sir Edmund Andros. He, with Joseph Dudley, Edmund Randolph, and his other principal adherents, were thrown into prison. Old Simon Bradstreet, who had been governor, when King James took away the charter, was called by the people to govern them again.

"Governor Bradstreet was a venerable old man, nearly ninety years of age," said Grandfather. "He came over with the first settlers, and had been the intimate companion of all those excellent and famous men who laid the foundation of our country. They were all gone before him to the grave; and Bradstreet was the last of the Puritans."

Grandfather paused a moment, and smiled, as if he had something very interesting to tell his auditors. He then proceeded: —

"And now, Laurence, — now, Clara, — now, Charley, — now, my dear little Alice, — what chair do you think had been placed in the council chamber, for old Governor Bradstreet to take his seat in? Would you believe that it was this very chair in which Grandfather now sits, and of which he is telling you the history?"

"I am glad to hear it, with all my heart!" cried Charley, after a shout of delight. "I thought Grandfather had quite forgotten the chair."

"It was a solemn and affecting sight," said Grandfather, "when this venerable patriarch, with his white beard flowing down upon his breast, took his seat in his Chair of State. Within his remembrance and even since his mature age, the site where now stood the populous town, had been a wild and forest-covered peninsula. The province, now so fertile, and spotted with thriving villages, had been a desert wilderness. He was surrounded by a shouting multitude, most of whom had been born in the country which he had helped to found. They were of one generation, and he of another. As the old man looked upon them and beheld new faces everywhere, he must have felt that it was now time for him to go, whither his brethren had gone before him."

"Were the former governors all dead and gone?" asked Laurence.

"All of them," replied Grandfather. "Winthrop had been dead forty years. Endicott died, a very old man, in 1665. Sir Henry Vane was beheaded in London, at the beginning of the reign of Charles the Second. And Haynes, Dudley, Bellingham and Leverett, who had all been governors of Massachusetts, were now likewise in their graves. Old Simon Bradstreet was the sole representative of that departed brotherhood. There was no other public man remaining to connect the ancient system of government and manners with the new system which was about to take its place. The era of the Puritans was now completed."

"I am sorry for it," observed Laurence; "for, though they were so stern, yet it seems to me that there was something warm and real about them. I think, Grandfather, that each of these old governors should have his statue set up in our State House, sculptured out of the hardest of New England granite."

"It would not be amiss, Laurence," said Grandfather; "but perhaps clay, or some other perishable material, might suffice for some of their successors. But let us go back to our chair. It was occupied by Governor Bradstreet from April, 1689, until May, 1692. Sir William Phipps then arrived in Boston, with a new charter from King William, and a commission to be governor."

CHAPTER X

"AND what became of the chair?" inquired Clara.

"The outward aspect of our chair," replied Grandfather, "was now somewhat the worse for its long and arduous services. It was considered hardly magnificent enough to be allowed to keep its place in the council chamber of Massachusetts. In fact, it was banished as an article of useless lumber. But Sir William Phipps happened to see it, and being much pleased with its construction, resolved to take the good old chair into his private mansion. Accordingly, with his own gubernatorial hands, he repaired one of its arms, which had been slightly damaged."

"Why, Grandfather, here is the very arm!" interrupted Charley, in great wonderment. "And did Sir William Phipps put in these screws with his own hands? I am sure, he did it beautifully! But how came a governor to know how to mend a chair?"

"I will tell you a story about the early life of Sir William Phipps," said Grandfather. "You will then perceive that he well knew how to use his hands."

So Grandfather related the wonderful and true tale of

THE SUNKEN TREASURE

Picture to yourselves, my dear children, a handsome, old-fashioned room, with a large, open cupboard at one end, in which is displayed a magnificent gold cup, with some other splendid articles of gold and silver plate. In another part of the room, opposite to a tall looking-glass, stands our beloved chair, newly polished, and adorned with a gorgeous cushion of crimson velvet tufted with gold.

In the chair sits a man of strong and sturdy frame,

47

whose face has been roughened by northern tempests, and blackened by the burning sun of the West Indies. He wears an immense periwig, flowing down over his shoulders. His coat has a wide embroidery of golden foliage; and his waistcoat, likewise, is all flowered over and bedizened with gold. His red, rough hands, which have done many a good day's work with the hammer and adze, are half covered by the delicate lace ruffles at his wrists. On a table lies his silver-hilted sword, and in a corner of the room stands his gold-headed cane, made of a beautifully polished West Indian wood.

Somewhat such an aspect as this did Sir William Phipps present, when he sat in Grandfather's chair, after the king had appointed him governor of Massachusetts. Truly, there was need that the old chair should be varnished, and decorated with a crimson cushion, in order to make it suitable for such a magnificent-looking personage.

But Sir William Phipps had not always worn a gold-embroidered coat, nor always sat so much at his ease as he did in Grandfather's chair. He was a poor man's son, and was born in the Province of Maine, where he used to tend sheep upon the hills, in his boyhood and youth. Until he had grown to be a man, he did not even know how to read and write. Tired of tending sheep, he next apprenticed himself to a ship-carpenter, and spent about four years in hewing the crooked limbs of oak-trees into knees for vessels.

In 1673, when he was twenty-two years old, he came to Boston, and soon afterwards was married to a widow lady, who had property enough to set him up in business. It was not long, however, before he lost all the money that he had acquired by his marriage, and became a poor man again. Still he was not discouraged. He often told his wife that some time or other he should be very rich, and would build a "fair brick house" in the Green Lane of Boston.

Do not suppose, children, that he had been to a fortune-teller to inquire his destiny. It was his own energy and spirit of enterprise, and his resolution to lead an industrious life, that made him look forward with so much confidence to better days.

Several years passed away; and William Phipps had not yet gained the riches which he promised to himself. During this time he had begun to follow the sea for a living. In the year 1684, he happened to hear of a Spanish ship, which had been cast away near the Bahama Islands, and which was supposed to contain a great deal of gold and silver. Phipps went to the place in a small vessel, hoping that he should be able to recover some of the treasure from the wreck. He did not succeed, however, in fishing up gold and silver enough to pay the expenses of his voyage.

But, before he returned, he was told of another Spanish ship or galleon, which had been cast away near Porto de la Plata. She had now lain as much as fifty years beneath the waves. This old ship had been laden with immense wealth; and hitherto nobody had thought of the possibility of recovering any part of it from the deep sea, which was rolling and tossing it about. But though it was now an old story, and the most aged people had almost forgotten that such a vessel had been wrecked, William Phipps resolved that the sunken treasure should again be brought to light.

He went to London, and obtained admittance to King James, who had not yet been driven from his throne. He told the king of the vast wealth that was lying at the bottom of the sea. King James listened with attention, and thought this a fine opportunity to fill his treasury with Spanish gold. He appointed William Phipps to be captain of a vessel, called the Rose Algier, carrying eighteen guns and ninety-five men. So now he was Captain Phipps of the English navy.

Captain Phipps sailed from England in the Rose Algier, and cruised for nearly two years in the West Indies, endeavoring to find the wreck of the Spanish ship. But the sea is so wide and deep, that it is no easy matter to discover the exact spot where a sunken vessel lies. The prospect of success seemed very small; and most people would have thought that Captain Phipps was as far from having money enough to build a "fair brick house," as he was while he tended sheep.

The seamen of the Rose Algier became discouraged, and gave up all hope of making their fortunes by discovering the Spanish wreck. They wanted to compel Captain Phipps to turn pirate. There was a much better prospect, they thought, of growing rich by plundering vessels, which still sailed in the sea, than by seeking for a ship that had lain beneath the waves full half a century. They broke out in open mutiny, but were finally mastered by Phipps, and compelled to obey his orders. It would have been dangerous, however, to continue much longer at sea with such a crew of mutinous sailors; and, besides, the Rose Algier was leaky and unseaworthy. So Captain Phipps judged it best to return to England.

Before leaving the West Indies, he met with a Spaniard, an old man, who remembered the wreck of the Spanish ship, and gave him directions how to find the very spot. It was on a reef of rocks a few leagues from Porto de la Plata.

On his arrival in England, therefore, Captain Phipps solicited the king to let him have another vessel, and send him back again to the West Indies. But King James, who had probably expected that the Rose Algier would return laden with gold, refused to have anything more to do with the affair. Phipps might never have been able to renew the search, if the Duke of Albemarle, and some other noblemen, had not lent their assistance. They fitted out a ship and gave the command to Captain Phipps. He sailed from England, and arrived safely at Porto de la Plata, where he took an adze and assisted his men to build a large boat.

The boat was intended for the purpose of going closer to the reef of rocks than a large vessel could safely venture. When it was finished, the Captain sent several men in it, to examine the spot where the Spanish ship was said to have been wrecked. They were accompanied by some Indians, who were skilful divers, and could go down a great way into the depths of the sea.

The boat's crew proceeded to the reef of rocks, and rowed round and round it a great many times. They gazed down into the water, which was so transparent that it seemed as if they could have seen the gold and silver at the bottom, had there been any of those precious metals there. Nothing, however, could they see; nothing more valuable than a curious sea-shrub, which was growing beneath the water, in a crevice of the reef of rocks. It flaunted to and fro with the swell and reflux of the waves, and looked as bright and beautiful as if its leaves were gold.

"We won't go back empty-handed," cried an English sailor; and then he spoke to one of the Indian divers: "Dive down and bring me that pretty sea-shrub there. That's the only treasure we shall find!"

Down plunged the diver, and soon rose dripping from the water, holding the sea-shrub in his hand. But he had learnt some news at the bottom of the sea.

"There are some ship's guns," said he, the moment he had drawn breath, "some great cannon among the rocks, near where the shrub was growing."

No sooner had he spoken, than the English sailors knew that they had found the very spot where the Spanish galleon had been wrecked so many years before. The other Indian divers immediately plunged over the boat's side, and swam headlong down, groping among the rocks and sunken cannon. In a few moments one of them rose above the water, with a heavy lump of silver in his arms. That single lump was worth more than a thousand dollars. The sailors took it into the boat, and then rowed back as speedily as they could, being in haste to inform Captain Phipps of their good luck.

But, confidently as the Captain had hoped to find the Spanish wreck, yet now that it was really found, the news seemed too good to be true. He could not believe it till the sailors showed him the lump of silver.

"Thanks be to God!" then cries Captain Phipps. "We shall every man of us make our fortunes!"

Hereupon the Captain and all the crew set to work,

with iron rakes and great hooks and lines, fishing for gold and silver at the bottom of the sea. Up came the treasure in abundance. Now they beheld a table of solid silver, once the property of an old Spanish grandee. Now they found a sacramental vessel, which had been destined as a gift to some Catholic church. Now they drew up a golden cup, fit for the king of Spain to drink his wine out of. Perhaps the bony hand of its former owner had been grasping the precious cup, and was drawn up along with it. Now their rakes or fishing lines were loaded with masses of silver bullion. There were also precious stones among the treasure, glittering and sparkling, so that it is a wonder how their radiance could have been concealed.

There is something sad and terrible in the idea of snatching all this wealth from the devouring ocean, which had possessed it for such a length of years. It seems as if men had no right to make themselves rich with it. It ought to have been left with the skeletons of the ancient Spaniards, who had been drowned when the ship was wrecked, and whose bones were now scattered among the gold and silver.

But Captain Phipps and his crew were troubled with no such thoughts as these. After a day or two they lighted on another part of the wreck, where they found a great many bags of silver dollars. But nobody could have guessed that these were money-bags. By remaining so long in the salt water, they had become covered over with a crust which had the appearance of stone, so that it was necessary to break them in pieces with hammers and axes. When this was done, a stream of silver dollars gushed out upon the deck of the vessel.

The whole value of the recovered treasure, plate, bullion, precious stones, and all, was estimated at more than two millions of dollars. It was dangerous even to look at such a vast amount of wealth. A sea-captain, who had assisted Phipps in the enterprise, utterly lost his reason at the sight of it. He died two years afterwards, still raving about the treasures that lie at the bottom of the sea. It would have been better for this man, if he had left the skeletons of the shipwrecked Spaniards in quiet possession of their wealth.

Captain Phipps and his men continued to fish up plate, bullion, and dollars, as plentifully as ever, till their provisions grew short. Then, as they could not feed upon gold and silver any more than old King Midas could, they found it necessary to go in search of better sustenance. Phipps resolved to return to England. He arrived there in 1687, and was received with great joy by the Duke of Albemarle and other English lords, who had fitted out the vessel. Well they might rejoice; for they took by far the greater part of the treasure to themselves.

The Captain's share, however, was enough to make him comfortable for the rest of his days. It also enabled him to fulfil his promise to his wife, by building a "fair brick house," in the Green Lane of Boston. The Duke of Albemarle sent Mrs. Phipps a magnificent gold cup, worth at least five thousand dollars. Before Captain Phipps left London, King James made him a knight; so that, instead of the obscure ship-carpenter who had formerly dwelt among them, the inhabitants of Boston welcomed him on his return as the rich and famous Sir William Phipps.

CHAPTER XI

"SIR WILLIAM PHIPPS," continued Grandfather, "was too active and adventurous a man to sit still in the quiet enjoyment of his good fortune. In the year 1690, he went on a military expedition against the French colonies in America, conquered the whole province of Acadie, and returned to Boston with a great deal of plunder."

"Why, Grandfather, he was the greatest man that ever sat in the chair!" cried Charley.

"Ask Laurence what he thinks," replied Grandfather, with a smile. "Well, in the same year, Sir William took command of an expedition against Quebec, but did not succeed in capturing the city. In 1692, being then in London, King William the Third appointed him governor of Massachusetts. And now, my dear children, having followed Sir William Phipps through all his adventures and hardships, till we find him comfortably seated in Grandfather's chair, we will here bid him farewell. May he be as happy in ruling a people, as he was while he tended sheep!"

Charley, whose fancy had been greatly taken by the adventurous disposition of Sir William Phipps, was eager to know how he had acted, and what happened to him while he held the office of governor. But Grandfather had made up his mind to tell no more stories for the present.

"Possibly, one of these days, I may go on with the adventures of the chair," said he. "But its history becomes very obscure just at this point; and I must search into some old books and manuscripts, before proceeding further. Besides, it is now a good time to pause in our narrative; because the new charter, which Sir William Phipps brought over from England, formed a very important epoch in the history of the province."

"Really, Grandfather," observed Laurence, "this seems to be the most remarkable chair in the world. Its history cannot be told without intertwining it with the lives of distinguished men, and the great events that have befallen the country."

"True, Laurence," replied Grandfather, smiling, "we must write a book with some such title as this, — MEMOIRS OF MY OWN TIMES, BY GRANDFATHER'S CHAIR."

"That would be beautiful!" exclaimed Laurence, clapping his hands.

"But, after all," continued Grandfather, "any other old chair, if it possessed memory, and a hand to write its recollections, could record stranger stories than any that I have told you. From generation to generation, a chair sits familiarly in the midst of human interests, and is witness to the most secret and confidential intercourse that mortal man can hold with his fellow. The human heart may best be read in the fireside chair. And as to external events, Grief and Joy keep a continual vicissitude around it and within it. Now we see the glad face and glowing form of Joy, sitting merrily in the old chair, and throwing a warm firelight radiance over all the household. Now, while we thought not of it, the dark-clad mourner, Grief, has stolen into the place of Joy, but not to retain it long. The imagination can hardly grasp so wide a subject, as is embraced in the experience of a family chair."

"It makes my breath flutter, — my heart thrill, — to think of it," said Laurence. "Yes; a family chair must have a deeper history than a Chair of State."

"Oh, yes!" cried Clara, expressing a woman's feeling on the point in question, "the history of a country is not nearly so interesting as that of a single family would be."

"But the history of a country is more easily told," said Grandfather. "So, if we proceed with our narrative of the chair, I shall still confine myself to its connection with public events."

Good old Grandfather now rose and quitted the room, while the children remained gazing at the chair. Laurence, so vivid was his conception of past times, would hardly have deemed it strange, if its former occupants, one after another, had resumed the seat which they had each left vacant, such a dim length of years ago.

First, the gentle and lovely Lady Arbella would have been seen in the old chair, almost sinking out of its arms, for very weakness; then Roger Williams, in his cloak and band, earnest, energetic, and benevolent; then the figure of Anne Hutchinson, with the like gesture as when she presided at the assemblages of women; then the dark, intellectual face of Vane, "young in years, but in sage counsel old." Next would have appeared the successive governors, Winthrop, Dudley, Bellingham, and Endicott, who sat in the chair, while it was a Chair of State. Then its ample seat would have been pressed by the comfortable, rotund corporation of the honest mint-master. Then the half-frenzied shape of Mary Dyer, the persecuted Quaker woman, clad in sackcloth and ashes, would have rested in it for a moment. Then the holy apostolic form of Eliot would have sanctified it. Then would have arisen, like the shade of departed Puritanism, the venerable dignity of the white-bearded Governor Bradstreet. Lastly, on the gorgeous crimson cushion of Grandfather's chair, would have shown the purple and golden magnificence of Sir William Phipps.

But all these, with the other historic personages, in the midst of whom the chair had so often stood, had passed, both in substance and shadow, from the scene of ages. Yet here stood the chair, with the old Lincoln coat of arms, and the oaken flowers and foliage, and the fierce lion's head at the summit, the whole, apparently, in as perfect preservation as when it had first been placed in the Earl of Lincoln's hall. And what vast changes of society and of nations had been wrought by sudden convulsions or by slow degrees, since that era!

"This chair had stood firm when the thrones of kings were overturned!" thought Laurence. "Its oaken frame has proved stronger than many frames of government!"

More the thoughtful and imaginative boy might have mused; but now a large yellow cat, a great favorite with all the children, leaped in at the open window. Perceiving that Grandfather's chair was empty, and having often before experienced its comforts, puss laid herself quietly down upon the cushion. Laurence, Clara, Charley, and little Alice, all laughed at the idea of such a successor to the worthies of old times.

"Pussy," said little Alice, putting out her hand, into which the cat laid a velvet paw, "you look very wise. Do tell us a story about GRANDFATHER'S CHAIR!"

PART II

CHAPTER I

"OH, Grandfather, dear Grandfather," cried little Alice, "pray tell us some more stories about your chair!"

How long a time had fled, since the children had felt any curiosity to hear the sequel of this venerable chair's adventures! Summer was now past and gone, and the better part of Autumn likewise. Dreary, chill November was howling, out of doors, and vexing the atmosphere with sudden showers of wintry rain, or sometimes with gusts of snow, that rattled like small pebbles against the windows.

When the weather began to grow cool, Grandfather's chair had been removed from the summer parlor into a smaller and snugger room. It now stood by the side of a bright blazing wood-fire. Grandfather loved a wood-fire, far better than a grate of glowing anthracite, or than the dull heat of an invisible furnace, which seems to think that it has done its duty in merely warming the house. But the wood-fire is a kindly, cheerful, sociable spirit, sympathizing with mankind, and knowing that to create warmth is but one of the good offices which are expected from it. Therefore it dances on the hearth, and laughs broadly through the room, and plays a thousand antics, and throws a joyous glow over all the faces that encircle it.

In the twilight of the evening, the fire grew brighter and more cheerful. And thus, perhaps, there was something in Grandfather's heart, that cheered him most with its warmth and comfort in the gathering twilight of old age. He had been gazing at the red embers, as intently as if his past life were all pictured

58

there, or as if it were a prospect of the future world, when little Alice's voice aroused him.

"Dear Grandfather," repeated the little girl, more earnestly, "do talk to us again about your chair."

Laurence, and Clara, and Charley, and little Alice, had been attracted to other objects, for two or three months past. They had sported in the gladsome sunshine of the present, and so had forgotten the shadowy region of the past, in the midst of which stood Grandfather's chair. But now, in the autumnal twilight, illuminated by the flickering blaze of the wood-fire, they looked at the old chair, and thought that it had never before worn such an interesting aspect. There it stood, in the venerable majesty of more than two hundred years. The light from the hearth quivered upon the flowers and foliage, that were wrought into its open back ; and the lion's head at the summit seemed almost to move its jaws and shake its mane.

"Does little Alice speak for all of you ?" asked Grandfather. "Do you wish me to go on with the adventures of the chair ?"

"Oh, yes, yes, Grandfather !" cried Clara. "The dear old chair ! How strange that we should have forgotten it so long ! "

"Oh, pray begin, Grandfather," said Laurence ; "for I think, when we talk about old times, it should be in the early evening before the candles are lighted. The shapes of the famous persons, who once sat in the chair, will be more apt to come back, and be seen among us, in this glimmer and pleasant gloom, than they would in the vulgar daylight. And, besides, we can make pictures of all that you tell us, among the glowing embers and white ashes."

Our friend Charley, too, thought the evening the best time to hear Grandfather's stories, because he could not then be playing out of doors. So, finding his young auditors unanimous in their petition, the good old gentleman took up the narrative of the historic chair at the point where he had dropt it.

CHAPTER II

"YOU recollect, my dear children," said Grandfather, "that we took leave of the chair in 1692, while it was occupied by Sir William Phipps. This fortunate treasure-seeker, you will remember, had come over from England, with King William's commission to be Governor of Massachusetts. Within the limits of this province were now included the old colony of Plymouth, and the territories of Maine and Nova Scotia. Sir William Phipps had likewise brought a new charter from the king, which served instead of a constitution, and set forth the method in which the province was to be governed."

"Did the new charter allow the people all their former liberties?" inquired Laurence.

"No," replied Grandfather. "Under the first charter, the people had been the source of all power. Winthrop, Endicott, Bradstreet, and the rest of them, had been governors by the choice of the people, without any interference of the king. But henceforth the governor was to hold his station solely by the king's appointment, and during his pleasure; and the same was the case with the lieutenant-governor, and some other high officers. The people, however, were still allowed to choose representatives; and the governor's council was chosen by the general court."

"Would the inhabitants have elected Sir William Phipps," asked Laurence, "if the choice of governor had been left to them?"

"He might probably have been a successful candidate," answered Grandfather; "for his adventures and military enterprises had gained him a sort of renown, which always goes a great way with the people. And he had many popular characteristics, being a kind, warm-hearted man, not ashamed of his low origin, nor

60

haughty in his present elevation.   Soon after his arrival, he proved that he did not blush to recognize his former associates."

"How was that?" inquired Charley.

"He made a grand festival at his new brick house," said Grandfather, "and invited all the ship-carpenters of Boston to be his guests.   At the head of the table, in our great chair, sat Sir William Phipps himself, treating these hard-handed men as his brethren, cracking jokes with them, and talking familiarly about old times.   I know not whether he wore his embroidered dress, but I rather choose to imagine that he had on a suit of rough clothes, such as he used to labor in while he was Phipps the ship-carpenter."

"An aristocrat need not be ashamed of the trade," observed Laurence; "for the Czar Peter the Great once served an apprenticeship to it."

"Did Sir William Phipps make as good a governor as he was a ship-carpenter?" asked Charley.

"History says but little about his merits as a ship-carpenter," answered Grandfather; "but, as a governor, a great deal of fault was found with him.   Almost as soon as he assumed the government, he became engaged in a very frightful business, which might have perplexed a wiser and better-cultivated head than his.   This was the witchcraft delusion."

And here Grandfather gave his auditors such details of this melancholy affair as he thought it fit for them to know.   They shuddered to hear that a frenzy, which led to the death of many innocent persons, had originated in the wicked arts of a few children.   They belonged to the Rev. Mr. Parris, minister of Salem. These children complained of being pinched, and pricked with pins, and otherwise tormented by the shapes of men and women, who were supposed to have power to haunt them invisibly, both in darkness and daylight.   Often in the midst of their family and friends, the children would pretend to be seized with strange convulsions, and would cry out that the witches were afflicting them.

These stories spread abroad, and caused great tumult and alarm. From the foundation of New England, it had been the custom of the inhabitants, in all matters of doubt and difficulty, to look to their ministers for counsel. So they did now; but, unfortunately, the ministers and wise men were more deluded than the illiterate people. Cotton Mather, a very learned and eminent clergyman, believed that the whole country was full of witches and wizards, who had given up their hopes of heaven, and signed a covenant with the Evil One.

Nobody could be certain that his nearest neighbor, or most intimate friend, was not guilty of this imaginary crime. The number of those who pretended to be afflicted by witchcraft, grew daily more numerous; and they bore testimony against many of the best and worthiest people. A minister, named George Burroughs, was among the accused. In the months of August and September, 1692, he and nineteen other innocent men and women were put to death. The place of execution was a high hill, on the outskirts of Salem; so that many of the sufferers, as they stood beneath the gallows, could discern their own habitations in the town.

The martyrdom of these guiltless persons seemed only to increase the madness. The afflicted now grew bolder in their accusations. Many people of rank and wealth were either thrown into prison, or compelled to flee for their lives. Among these were two sons of old Simon Bradstreet, the last of the Puritan governors. Mr. Willard, a pious minister of Boston, was cried out upon as a wizard, in open court. Mrs. Hale, the wife of the minister of Beverly, was likewise accused. Philip English, a rich merchant of Salem, found it necessary to take flight, leaving his property and business in confusion. But a short time afterwards, the Salem people were glad to invite him back.

"The boldest thing that the accusers did," continued Grandfather, "was to cry out against the governor's own beloved wife. Yes; the lady of Sir William

Phipps was accused of being a witch, and of flying through the air to attend witch meetings. When the governor heard this, he probably trembled, so that our great chair shook beneath him."

"Dear Grandfather," cried little Alice, clinging closer to his knee, "is it true that witches ever come in the night-time to frighten little children?"

"No, no, dear little Alice," replied Grandfather. "Even if there were any witches, they would flee away from the presence of a pure-hearted child. But there are none; and our forefathers soon became convinced that they had been led into a terrible delusion. All the prisoners on account of witchcraft were set free. But the innocent dead could not be restored to life; and the hill where they were executed will always remind people of the saddest and most humiliating passage in our history."

Grandfather then said, that the next remarkable event, while Sir William Phipps remained in the chair, was the arrival at Boston of an English fleet, in 1693. It brought an army, which was intended for the conquest of Canada. But a malignant disease, more fatal than the small-pox, broke out among the soldiers and sailors, and destroyed the greater part of them. The infection spread into the town of Boston, and made much havoc there. This dreadful sickness caused the governor, and Sir Francis Wheeler, who was commander of the British forces, to give up all thoughts of attacking Canada.

"Soon after this," said Grandfather, "Sir William Phipps quarrelled with the captain of an English frigate, and also with the Collector of Boston. Being a man of violent temper, he gave each of them a sound beating with his cane."

"He was a bold fellow," observed Charley, who was himself somewhat addicted to a similar mode of settling disputes.

"More bold than wise," replied Grandfather; "for complaints were carried to the king, and Sir William Phipps was summoned to England, to make the best answer he could. Accordingly he went to London, where, in 1695, he was seized with a malignant fever, of which he died. Had he lived longer, he would probably have gone again in search of sunken treasure. He had heard of a Spanish ship, which was cast away in 1502, during the lifetime of Columbus. Bovadilla, Roldan, and many other Spaniards, were lost in her, together with the immense wealth of which they had robbed the South American kings."

"Why, Grandfather," exclaimed Laurence, "what magnificent ideas the governor had! Only think of recovering all that old treasure, which had lain almost two centuries under the sea! Methinks Sir William Phipps ought to have been buried in the ocean, when he died; so that he might have gone down among the sunken ships, and cargoes of treasure, which he was always dreaming about in his lifetime."

"He was buried in one of the crowded cemeteries of London," said Grandfather. "As he left no children, his estate was inherited by his nephew, from whom is descended the present Marquis of Normanby. The noble Marquis is not aware, perhaps, that the prosperity of his family originated in the successful enterprise of a New England ship-carpenter."

CHAPTER III

" **A** T the death of Sir William Phipps," proceeded Grandfather, "our chair was bequeathed to Mr. Ezekiel Cheever, a famous school-master in Boston. This old gentleman came from London in 1637, and had been teaching school ever since; so that there were now aged men, grandfathers like myself, to whom Master Cheever had taught their alphabet. He was a person of venerable aspect, and wore a long white beard."

"Was the chair placed in his school?" asked Charley.

"Yes, in his school," answered Grandfather; "and we may safely say that it had never before been regarded with such awful reverence — no, not even when the old governors of Massachusetts sat in it. Even you, Charley, my boy, would have felt some respect for the chair, if you had seen it occupied by this famous school-master."

And here Grandfather endeavored to give his auditors an idea how matters were managed in schools above a hundred years ago. As this will probably be an interesting subject to our readers, we shall make a separate sketch of it, and call it

THE OLD FASHIONED SCHOOL

Now imagine yourselves, my children, in Master Ezekiel Cheever's school-room. It is a large, dingy room, with a sanded floor, and is lighted by windows that turn on hinges, and have little diamond-shaped panes of glass. The scholars sit on long benches, with desks before them. At one end of the room is a great fire-place, so very spacious, that there is room enough for three or four boys to stand in each of the chimney-corners. This was the good old fashion of fire-places, when there was wood enough in the forests to keep people warm, without their digging into the bowels of the earth for coal.

65

It is a winter's day when we take our peep into the school-room. See what great logs of wood have been rolled into the fire-place, and what a broad, bright blaze goes leaping up the chimney! And every few moments, a vast cloud of smoke is puffed into the room, which sails slowly over the heads of the scholars, until it gradually settles upon the walls and ceiling. They are blackened with the smoke of many years already.

Next, look at our old historic chair! It is placed, you perceive, in the most comfortable part of the room, where the generous glow of the fire is sufficiently felt without being too intensely hot. How stately the old chair looks, as if it remembered its many famous occupants, but yet were conscious that a greater man is sitting in it now! Do you see the venerable school-master, severe in aspect, with a black skull-cap on his head, like an ancient Puritan, and the snow of his white beard drifting down to his very girdle? What boy would dare to play, or whisper, or even glance aside from his book, while Master Cheever is on the lookout, behind his spectacles! For such offenders, if any such there be, a rod of birch is hanging over the fire-place, and a heavy ferule lies on the master's desk.

And now school is begun. What a murmur of multitudinous tongues, like the whispering leaves of a windstirred oak, as the scholars con over their various tasks! Buz, buz, buz! Amid just such a murmur has Master Cheever spent above sixty years; and long habit has made it as pleasant to him as the hum of a bee-hive, when the insects are busy in the sunshine.

Now a class in Latin is called to recite. Forth steps a row of queer-looking little fellows, wearing squareskirted coats, and smallclothes, with buttons at the knee. They look like so many grandfathers in their second childhood. These lads are to be sent to Cambridge, and educated for the learned professions. Old Master Cheever has lived so long, and seen so many generations of school-boys grow up to be men, that now he can almost prophesy what sort of a man each boy will be. One urchin shall hereafter be a doctor, and ad-

C. Copeland 98

"The Old Chair is now a Judgment-seat."

minister pills and potions, and stalk gravely through life, perfumed with assafœtida. Another shall wrangle at the bar, and fight his way to wealth and honors, and in his declining age, shall be a worshipful member of his Majesty's council. A third — and he is the master's favorite — shall be a worthy successor to the old Puritan ministers, now in their graves; he shall preach with great unction and effect, and leave volumes of sermons, in print and manuscript, for the benefit of future generations.

But, as they are merely school-boys now, their business is to construe Virgil. Poor Virgil, whose verses, which he took so much pains to polish, have been mis-scanned, mis-parsed, and mis-interpreted, by so many generations of idle school-boys! There, sit down, ye Latinists. Two or three of you, I fear, are doomed to feel the master's ferule.

Next comes a class in Arithmetic. These boys are to be the merchants, shop-keepers, and mechanics, of a future period. Hitherto, they have traded only in marbles and apples. Hereafter, some will send vessels to England for broadcloths and all sorts of manufactured wares, and to the West Indies for sugar, and rum, and coffee. Others will stand behind counters, and measure tape, and ribbon, and cambric, by the yard. Others will upheave the blacksmith's hammer, or drive the plane over the carpenter's bench, or take the lapstone and the awl, and learn the trade of shoe-making. Many will follow the sea, and become bold, rough sea-captains.

This class of boys, in short, must supply the world with those active, skilful hands, and clear, sagacious heads, without which the affairs of life would be thrown into confusion, by the theories of studious and visionary men. Wherefore, teach them their multiplication table, good Master Cheever, and whip them well, when they deserve it; for much of the country's welfare depends on these boys!

But, alas! while we have been thinking of other matters, Master Cheever's watchful eye has caught two boys at play. Now we shall see awful times! The two male-

factors are summoned before the master's chair, wherein
he sits, with the terror of a judge upon his brow.   Our
old chair is now a judgment-seat.   Ah, Master Cheever
has taken down that terrible birch-rod!   Short is the
trial — the sentence quickly passed — and now the judge
prepares to execute it in person.   Thwack! thwack!
thwack!   In these good old times, a school-master's
blows were well laid on.

See! the birch-rod has lost several of its twigs, and
will hardly serve for another execution.   Mercy on us,
what a bellowing the urchins make!   My ears are
almost deafened, though the clamor comes through the
far length of a hundred and fifty years.   There, go to
your seats, poor boys! and do not cry, sweet little
Alice! for they have ceased to feel the pain a long
time since.

And thus the forenoon passes away.   Now it is
twelve o'clock.   The master looks at his great silver
watch, and then, with tiresome deliberation, puts the
ferule into his desk.   The little multitude await the
word of dismissal, with almost irrepressible impatience.

"You are dismissed," says Master Cheever.

The boys retire, treading softly until they have passed
the threshold ; but, fairly out of the school-room, lo, what
a joyous shout! — what a scampering and trampling of
feet! — what a sense of recovered freedom, expressed
in the merry uproar of all their voices!   What care they
for the ferule and birch-rod now?   Were boys created
merely to study Latin and Arithmetic?   No ; the better
purposes of their being are to sport, to leap, to run, to
shout, to slide upon the ice, to snow-ball!

Happy boys!   Enjoy your play-time now, and come
again to study, and to feel the birch-rod and the ferule,
to-morrow ; not till to-morrow, for to-day is Thursday-
lecture ; and ever since the settlement of Massachusetts, there has been no school on Thursday afternoons.
Therefore, sport, boys, while you may ; for the morrow
cometh, with the birch-rod and the ferule ; and after
that, another morrow, with troubles of its own.

Now the master has set everything to rights, and is

ready to go home to dinner. Yet he goes reluctantly. The old man has spent so much of his life in the smoky, noisy, buzzing school-room, that, when he has a holiday, he feels as if his place were lost, and himself a stranger in the world. But, forth he goes; and there stands our old chair, vacant and solitary, till good Master Cheever resumes his seat in it to-morrow morning.

"Grandfather," said Charley, "I wonder whether the boys did not use to upset the old chair, when the school-master was out."

"There is a tradition," replied Grandfather, "that one of its arms was dislocated, in some such manner. But I cannot believe that any school-boy would behave so naughtily."

As it was now later than little Alice's usual bed-time, Grandfather broke off his narrative, promising to talk more about Master Cheever and his scholars, some other evening.

CHAPTER IV

ACCORDINGLY, the next evening, Grandfather resumed the history of his beloved chair.

"Master Ezekiel Cheever," said he, "died in 1707, after having taught school about seventy years. It would require a pretty good scholar in arithmetic to tell how many stripes he had inflicted, and how many birch-rods he had worn out, during all that time, in his fatherly tenderness for his pupils. Almost all the great men of that period, and for many years back, had been whipt into eminence by Master Cheever. Moreover, he had written a Latin Accidence, which was used in schools more than half a century after his death; so that the good old man, even in his grave, was still the cause of trouble and stripes to idle school-boys."

Grandfather proceeded to say, that, when Master Cheever died, he bequeathed the chair to the most learned man that was educated at his school, or that had ever been born in America. This was the renowned Cotton Mather, minister of the Old North Church in Boston.

"And author of the 'Magnalia,' Grandfather, which we sometimes see you reading," said Laurence.

"Yes, Laurence," replied Grandfather. "The 'Magnalia' is a strange, pedantic history, in which true events and real personages move before the reader, with the dreamy aspect which they wore in Cotton Mather's singular mind. This huge volume, however, was written and published before our chair came into his possession. But, as he was the author of more books than there are days in the year, we may conclude that he wrote a great deal, while sitting in this chair."

"I am tired of these school-masters and learned men," said Charley. "I wish some stirring man, that knew how to do something in the world, like Sir William Phipps, would sit in the chair."

"Such men seldom have leisure to sit quietly in a chair," said Grandfather. "We must make the best of such people as we have."

As Cotton Mather was a very distinguished man, Grandfather took some pains to give the children a lively conception of his character. Over the door of his library were painted these words — BE SHORT — as a warning to visitors that they must not do the world so much harm, as needlessly to interrupt this great man's wonderful labors. On entering the room you would probably behold it crowded, and piled, and heaped with books. There were huge, ponderous folios and quartos, and little duodecimos, in English, Latin, Greek, Hebrew, Chaldaic, and all other languages, that either originated at the confusion of Babel, or have since come into use.

All these books, no doubt, were tossed about in confusion, thus forming a visible emblem of the manner in which their contents were crowded into Cotton Mather's brain. And in the middle of the room stood a table, on which, besides printed volumes, were strown manuscript sermons, historical tracts, and political pamphlets, all written in such a queer, blind, crabbed, fantastical hand, that a writing-master would have gone raving mad at the sight of them. By this table stood Grandfather's chair, which seemed already to have contracted an air of deep erudition, as if its cushion were stuffed with Latin, Greek, and Hebrew, and other hard matters.

In this chair, from one year's end to another, sat that prodigious bookworm, Cotton Mather, sometimes devouring a great book, and sometimes scribbling one as big. In Grandfather's younger days, there used to be a wax figure of him in one of the Boston museums, representing a solemn, dark-visaged person, in a minister's black gown, and with a black-letter volume before him.

"It is difficult, my children," observed Grandfather, "to make you understand such a character as Cotton Mather's, in whom there was so much good, and yet so many failings and frailties. Undoubtedly, he was a pious

man. Often he kept fasts; and once, for three whole
days, he allowed himself not a morsel of food, but spent
the time in prayer and religious meditation.   Many
a livelong night did he watch and pray.   These fasts
and vigils made him meagre and haggard, and probably
caused him to appear as if he hardly belonged to the
world."

"Was not the witchcraft delusion partly caused by
Cotton Mather?" inquired Laurence.

"He was the chief agent of the mischief," answered
Grandfather; "but we will not suppose that he acted
otherwise than conscientiously.   He believed that there
were evil spirits all about the world.   Doubtless he imagined that they were hidden in the corners and crevices
of his library, and that they peeped out from among the
leaves of many of his books, as he turned them over,
at midnight.   He supposed that these unlovely demons
were everywhere, in the sunshine as well as in the darkness, and that they were hidden in men's hearts, and
stole into their most secret thoughts."

Here Grandfather was interrupted by little Alice, who
hid her face in his lap, and murmured a wish that he
would not talk any more about Cotton Mather and the
evil spirits.   Grandfather kissed her, and told her that
angels were the only spirits whom she had anything to
do with.   He then spoke of the public affairs of the
period.

A new war between France and England had broken
out in 1702, and had been raging ever since.   In the
course of it, New England suffered much injury from
the French and Indians, who often came through the
woods from Canada, and assaulted the frontier towns.
Villages were sometimes burnt, and the inhabitants
slaughtered, within a day's ride of Boston.   The people of New England had a bitter hatred against the
French, not only for the mischief which they did with
their own hands, but because they incited the Indians
to hostility.

The New Englanders knew that they could never
dwell in security, until the provinces of France should

be subdued and brought under the English government. They frequently, in time of war, undertook military expeditions against Acadia and Canada, and sometimes besieged the fortresses, by which those territories were defended. But the most earnest wish of their hearts was to take Quebec, and so get possession of the whole province of Canada. Sir William Phipps had once attempted it, but without success.

Fleets and soldiers were often sent from England, to assist the colonists in their warlike undertakings. In 1710, Port Royal, a fortress of Acadia, was taken by the English. The next year, in the month of June, a fleet, commanded by Admiral Sir Hovenden Walker, arrived in Boston harbor. On board of this fleet was the English General Hill, with seven regiments of soldiers, who had been fighting under the Duke of Marlborough, in Flanders. The government of Massachusetts was called upon to find provisions for the army and fleet, and to raise more men to assist in taking Canada.

What with recruiting and drilling of soldiers, there was now nothing but warlike bustle in the streets of Boston. The drum and fife, the rattle of arms, and the shouts of boys, were heard from morning till night. In about a month, the fleet set sail, carrying four regiments from New England and New York, besides the English soldiers. The whole army amounted to at least seven thousand men. They steered for the mouth of the river St. Lawrence.

"Cotton Mather prayed most fervently for their success," continued Grandfather, " both in his pulpit, and when he kneeled down in the solitude of his library, resting his face on our old chair. But Providence ordered the result otherwise. In a few weeks, tidings were received that eight or nine of the vessels had been wrecked in the St. Lawrence, and that above a thousand drowned soldiers had been washed ashore, on the banks of that mighty river. After this misfortune, Sir Hovenden Walker set sail for England; and many pious people began to think it a sin, even to wish for the conquest of Canada."

" I would never give it up so," cried Charley.

" Nor did they, as we shall see," replied Grandfather. " However, no more attempts were made during this war, which came to a close in 1713. The people of New England were probably glad of some repose, for their young men had been made soldiers, till many of them were fit for nothing else. And those who remained at home had been heavily taxed to pay for the arms, ammunition, fortifications, and all the other endless expenses of a war. There was great need of the prayers of Cotton Mather, and of all pious men, not only on account of the sufferings of the people, but because the old moral and religious character of New England was in danger of being utterly lost."

" How glorious it would have been," remarked Laurence, " if our forefathers could have kept the country unspotted with blood."

" Yes," said Grandfather ; " but there was a stern warlike spirit in them, from the beginning. They seem never to have thought of questioning either the morality or piety of war."

The next event, which Grandfather spoke of, was one that Cotton Mather, as well as most of the other inhabitants of New England, heartily rejoiced at. This was the accession of the Elector of Hanover to the throne of England, in 1714, on the death of Queen Anne. Hitherto, the people had been in continual dread that the male line of the Stuarts, who were descended from the beheaded King Charles and the banished King James, would be restored to the throne. In that case, as the Stuart family were Roman Catholics, it was supposed that they would attempt to establish their own religion throughout the British dominions. But the Elector of Hanover, and all his race, were Protestants ; so that now the descendants of the old Puritans were relieved from many fears and disquietudes.

" The importance of this event," observed Grandfather, " was a thousand times greater than that of a Presidential Election, in our own days. If the people dislike their president, they may get rid of him in four years; whereas, a dynasty of kings may wear the crown for an unlimited period."

The German elector was proclaimed king from the balcony of the town-house, in Boston, by the title of George the First, while the trumpets sounded, and the people cried Amen. That night the town was illuminated; and Cotton Mather threw aside book and pen, and left Grandfather's chair vacant, while he walked hither and thither to witness the rejoicings.

CHAPTER V

"COTTON MATHER," continued Grandfather, "was a bitter enemy to Governor Dudley; and nobody exulted more than he, when that crafty politician was removed from the government, and succeeded by Colonel Shute. This took place in 1716. The new governor had been an officer in the renowned Duke of Marlborough's army, and had fought in some of the great battles in Flanders."

"Now I hope," said Charley, "we shall hear of his doing great things."

"I am afraid you will be disappointed, Charley," answered Grandfather. "It is true, that Colonel Shute had probably never led so unquiet a life while fighting the French, as he did now, while governing this province of Massachusetts Bay. But his troubles consisted almost entirely of dissensions with the legislature. The king had ordered him to lay claim to a fixed salary; but the representatives of the people insisted upon paying him only such sums, from year to year, as they saw fit."

Grandfather here explained some of the circumstances, that made the situation of a colonial governor so difficult and irksome. There was not the same feeling towards the chief magistrate, now, that had existed while he was chosen by the free suffrages of the people. It was felt, that as the king appointed the governor, and as he held his office during the king's pleasure, it would be his great object to please the king. But the people thought, that a governor ought to have nothing in view, but the best interests of those whom he governed.

"The governor," remarked Grandfather, "had two masters to serve — the king, who appointed him, and the people, on whom he depended for his pay. Few men, in this position, would have ingenuity enough to satisfy either party. Colonel Shute, though a good-natured, well-meaning man, succeeded so ill with the people, that in 1722, he suddenly went away to England, and made complaint to King George. In the mean time, Lieutenant-Governor Dummer directed the affairs of the province, and carried on a long and bloody war with the Indians."

"But where was our chair, all this time?" asked Clara.

"It still remained in Cotton Mather's library," replied Grandfather; "and I must not omit to tell you an incident, which is very much to the honor of this celebrated man. It is the more proper, too, that you should hear it, because it will show you what a terrible calamity the small-pox was to our forefathers. The history of the province, (and, of course, the history of our chair,) would be incomplete, without particular mention of it."

Accordingly, Grandfather told the children a story, to which, for want of a better title, we shall give that of

THE REJECTED BLESSING

One day, in 1721, Doctor Cotton Mather sat in his library, reading a book that had been published by the Royal Society of London. But, every few moments, he laid the book upon the table, and leaned back in Grandfather's chair, with an aspect of deep care and disquietude. There were certain things which troubled him exceedingly, so that he could hardly fix his thoughts upon what he read.

It was now a gloomy time in Boston. That terrible disease, the small-pox, had recently made its appearance in the town. Ever since the first settlement of the country, this awful pestilence had come, at intervals, and swept away multitudes of the inhabitants. Whenever it commenced its ravages, nothing seemed to stay its progress, until there were no more victims for it to seize upon. Oftentimes, hundreds of people, at once, lay groaning with its agony; and when it departed, its deep footsteps were always to be traced in many graves.

The people never felt secure from this calamity. Sometimes, perhaps, it was brought into the country by a poor sailor, who had caught the infection in foreign parts, and came hither to die, and to be the cause of many deaths. Sometimes, no doubt, it followed in the train of the pompous governors, when they came over from England. Sometimes, the disease lay hidden in the cargoes of ships, among silks and brocades, and other costly merchandise, which was imported for the rich people to wear. And, sometimes, it started up, seemingly of its own accord; and nobody could tell whence it came. The physician, being called to attend the sick person, would look at him, and say, — "It is the small-pox! let the patient be carried to the hospital."

And now, this dreadful sickness had shown itself again in Boston. Cotton Mather was greatly afflicted, for the sake of the whole province. He had children, too, who were exposed to the danger. At that very moment, he heard the voice of his youngest son, for whom his heart was moved with apprehension.

"Alas! I fear for that poor child," said Cotton Mather to himself. "What shall I do for my son Samuel?"

Again, he attempted to drive away these thoughts, by taking up the book which he had been reading. And now, all of a sudden, his attention became fixed. The book contained a printed letter that an Italian physician had written upon the very subject, about which Cotton Mather was so anxiously meditating. He ran his eye eagerly over the pages; and, behold! a method was disclosed to him, by which the small-pox might be robbed of its worst terrors. Such a method was known in Greece. The physicians of Turkey, too, those long-bearded Eastern sages, had been acquainted with it for many years. The negroes of Africa, ignorant as they were, had likewise practised it, and thus had shown themselves wiser than the white men.

"Of a truth," ejaculated Cotton Mather, clasping his

hands, and looking up to Heaven, "it was a merciful Providence that brought this book under mine eye! I will procure a consultation of physicians, and will see whether this wondrous Inoculation may not stay the progress of the Destroyer."

So he arose from Grandfather's chair, and went out of the library. Near the door he met his son Samuel, who seemed downcast and out of spirits. The boy had heard, probably, that some of his playmates were taken ill with the small-pox. But, as his father looked cheerfully at him, Samuel took courage, trusting that either the wisdom of so learned a minister would find some remedy for the danger, or else that his prayers would secure protection from on high.

Meanwhile, Cotton Mather took his staff and three-cornered hat, and walked about the streets, calling at the houses of all the physicians in Boston. They were a very wise fraternity; and their huge wigs, and black dresses, and solemn visages, made their wisdom appear even profounder than it was. One after another, he acquainted them with the discovery which he had hit upon.

But these grave and sagacious personages would scarcely listen to him. The oldest doctor in town contented himself with remarking, that no such thing as inoculation was mentioned by Galen or Hippocrates, and it was impossible that modern physicians should be wiser than those old sages. A second held up his hands in dumb astonishment and horror, at the madness of what Cotton Mather proposed to do. A third told him, in pretty plain terms, that he knew not what he was talking about. A fourth requested, in the name of the whole medical fraternity, that Cotton Mather would confine his attention to people's souls, and leave the physicians to take care of their bodies.

In short, there was but a single doctor among them all, who would grant the poor minister so much as a patient hearing. This was Doctor Zabdiel Boylston. He looked into the matter like a man of sense, and finding, beyond a doubt, that inoculation had rescued many from death, he resolved to try the experiment in his own family.

And so he did. And when the other physicians heard of it, they arose in great fury, and began a war of words, written, printed, and spoken, against Cotton Mather and Doctor Boylston. To hear them talk, you would have supposed that these two harmless and benevolent men had plotted the ruin of the country.

The people also took the alarm. Many, who thought themselves more pious than their neighbors, contended, that, if Providence had ordained them to die of the small-pox, it was sinful to aim at preventing it. The strangest reports were in circulation. Some said that Doctor Boylston had contrived a method for conveying the gout, rheumatism, sick headache, asthma, and all other diseases, from one person to another, and diffusing them through the whole community. Others flatly affirmed that the Evil One had got possession of Cotton Mather, and was at the bottom of the whole business.

You must observe, children, that Cotton Mather's fellow-citizens were generally inclined to doubt the wisdom of any measure, which he might propose to them. They recollected how he had led them astray in the old witchcraft delusion; and now, if he thought and acted ever so wisely, it was difficult for him to get the credit of it.

The people's wrath grew so hot at his attempt to guard them from the small-pox, that he could not walk the streets in peace. Whenever the venerable form of the old minister, meagre and haggard with fasts and vigils, was seen approaching, hisses were heard, and shouts of derision, and scornful and bitter laughter. The women snatched away their children from his path, lest he should do them a mischief. Still, however, bending his head meekly, and perhaps stretching out his hands to bless those who reviled him, he pursued his way. But the tears came into his eyes to think how blindly the people rejected the means of safety, that were offered them.

Indeed, there were melancholy sights enough in the

streets of Boston, to draw forth the tears of a compassionate man. Over the door of almost every dwelling, a red flag was fluttering in the air. This was a signal that the small-pox had entered the house, and attacked some member of the family; or perhaps the whole family, old and young, were struggling at once with the pestilence. Friends and relatives, when they met one another in the streets, would hurry onward without a grasp of the hand, or scarcely a word of greeting, lest they should catch or communicate the contagion; and often a coffin was borne hastily along.

"Alas, alas!" said Cotton Mather to himself. "What shall be done for this poor, misguided people? O that Providence would open their eyes, and enable them to discern good from evil!"

So furious, however, were the people, that they threatened vengeance against any person who should dare to practise inoculation, though it were only in his own family. This was a hard case for Cotton Mather, who saw no other way to rescue his poor child Samuel from the disease. But he resolved to save him, even if his house should be burnt over his head.

"I will not be turned aside," said he. "My townsmen shall see that I have faith in this thing, when I make the experiment on my beloved son, whose life is dearer to me than my own. And when I have saved Samuel, peradventure they will be persuaded to save themselves."

Accordingly, Samuel was inoculated; and so was Mr. Walter, a son-in-law of Cotton Mather. Doctor Boylston, likewise, inoculated many persons; and while hundreds died, who had caught the contagion from the garments of the sick, almost all were preserved, who followed the wise physician's advice.

But the people were not yet convinced of their mistake. One night, a destructive little instrument, called a hand-grenade, was thrown into Cotton Mather's window, and rolled under Grandfather's chair. It was supposed to be filled with gunpowder, the explosion of which would have blown the poor minister to atoms.

But the best-informed historians are of opinion, that the grenade contained only brimstone and assafœtida, and was meant to plague Cotton Mather with a very evil perfume.

This is no strange thing in human experience. Men, who attempt to do the world more good, than the world is able entirely to comprehend, are almost invariably held in bad odor. But yet, if the wise and good man can wait awhile, either the present generation or posterity will do him justice. So it proved, in the case which we have been speaking of. In after years, when inoculation was universally practised, and thousands were saved from death by it, the people remembered old Cotton Mather, then sleeping in his grave. They acknowledged that the very thing for which they had so reviled and persecuted him, was the best and wisest thing he ever did.

" Grandfather, this is not an agreeable story," observed Clara.

" No, Clara," replied Grandfather. " But it is right that you should know what a dark shadow this disease threw over the times of our forefathers. And now, if you wish to learn more about Cotton Mather, you must read his biography, written by Mr. Peabody, of Springfield. You will find it very entertaining and instructive; but perhaps the writer is somewhat too harsh in his judgment of this singular man. He estimates him fairly, indeed, and understands him well; but he unriddles his character rather by acuteness than by sympathy. Now, his life should have been written by one, who, knowing all his faults, would nevertheless love him."

So Grandfather made an end of Cotton Mather, telling his auditors that he died in 1728, at the age of sixty-five, and bequeathed the chair to Elisha Cooke. This gentleman was a famous advocate of the people's rights.

The same year, William Burnet, a son of the celebrated Bishop Burnet, arrived in Boston, with the commission of governor. He was the first that had been appointed since the departure of Colonel Shute. Governor Burnet took up his residence with Mr. Cooke, while the Province House was undergoing repairs. During this period, he was always complimented with a seat in Grandfather's chair; and so comfortable did he find it, that on removing to the Province House, he could not bear to leave it behind him. Mr. Cooke, therefore, requested his acceptance of it.

"I should think," said Laurence, "that the people would have petitioned the king always to appoint a native-born New Englander, to govern them."

"Undoubtedly it was a grievance," answered Grandfather, "to see men placed in this station, who perhaps had neither talents nor virtues to fit them for it, and who certainly could have no natural affection for the country. The king generally bestowed the governorships of the American colonies upon needy noblemen, or hangers-on at court, or disbanded officers. The people knew that such persons would be very likely to make the good of the country subservient to the wishes of the king. The legislature, therefore, endeavored to keep as much power as possible in their own hands, by refusing to settle a fixed salary upon the governors. It was thought better to pay them according to their deserts."

"Did Governor Burnet work well for his money?" asked Charley.

Grandfather could not help smiling at the simplicity of Charley's question. Nevertheless, it put the matter in a very plain point of view.

He then described the character of Governor Burnet, representing him as a good scholar, possessed of much ability, and likewise of unspotted integrity. His story affords a striking example, how unfortunate it is for a man, who is placed as ruler over a country, to be compelled to aim at anything but the good of the people. Governor Burnet was so chained down by his instructions from the king, that he could not act as he might otherwise have wished. Consequently, his whole term of office was wasted in quarrels with the legislature.

"I am afraid, children," said Grandfather, "that
Governor Burnet found but little rest or comfort in our
old chair. Here he used to sit, dressed in a coat which
was made of rough, shaggy cloth outside, but of smooth
velvet within. It was said that his own character resembled that coat, for his outward manner was rough, but
his inward disposition soft and kind. It is a pity that
such a man could not have been kept free from trouble.
But so harassing were his disputes with the representatives of the people, that he fell into a fever, of which
he died, in 1729. The legislature had refused him a
salary, while alive ; but they appropriated money enough
to give him a splendid and pompous funeral."

And now Grandfather perceived that little Alice had
fallen fast asleep, with her head upon his footstool. Indeed, as Clara observed, she had been sleeping from the
time of Sir Hovenden Walker's expedition against Quebec,
until the death of Governor Burnet — a period of about
eighteen years. And yet, after so long a nap, sweet
little Alice was a golden-haired child, of scarcely five
years old.

"It puts me in mind," said Laurence, "of the story
of the Enchanted Princess, who slept many a hundred
years, and awoke as young and beautiful as ever."

CHAPTER VI

A FEW evenings afterwards, cousin Clara happened to inquire of Grandfather, whether the old chair had never been present at a ball. At the same time, little Alice brought forward a doll, with whom she had been holding a long conversation.

"See, Grandfather," cried she. " Did such a pretty lady as this ever sit in your great chair?"

These questions led Grandfather to talk about the fashions and manners, which now began to be introduced from England into the provinces. The simplicity of the good old Puritan times was fast disappearing. This was partly owing to the increasing number and wealth of the inhabitants, and to the additions which they continually received, by the arrival and settlement of people from beyond the sea.

Another cause of a pompous and artificial mode of life, among those who could afford it, was, that the example was set by the royal governors. Under the old charter, the governors were the representatives of the people, and therefore their way of living had probably been marked by a popular simplicity. But now, as they represented the person of the king, they thought it necessary to preserve the dignity of their station, by the practice of high and gorgeous ceremonials. And, besides, the profitable offices under the government were filled by men who had lived in London, and had there contracted fashionable and luxurious habits of living. which they would not now lay aside. The wealthy people of the province imitated them ; and thus began a general change in social life.

"So, my dear Clara," said Grandfather, "after our chair had entered the Province House, it must often have been present at balls and festivals, though I cannot give you a description of any particular one. But I doubt not that they were very magnificent; and slaves in gorgeous liveries waited on the guests, and offered them wine in goblets of massive silver."

"Were there slaves in those days?" exclaimed Clara.

"Yes, black slaves and white," replied Grandfather. "Our ancestors not only bought negroes from Africa, but Indians from South America, and white people from Ireland. These last were sold, not for life, but for a certain number of years, in order to pay the expenses of their voyage across the Atlantic. Nothing was more common than to see a lot of likely Irish girls, advertised for sale in the newspapers. As for the little negro babies, they were offered to be given away, like young kittens."

"Perhaps Alice would have liked one to play with, instead of her doll," said Charley, laughing.

But little Alice clasped the waxen doll closer to her bosom.

"Now, as for this pretty doll, my little Alice," said Grandfather, "I wish you could have seen what splendid dresses the ladies wore in those times. They had silks, and satins, and damasks, and brocades, and high head-dresses, and all sorts of fine things. And they used to wear hooped petticoats, of such enormous size that it was quite a journey to walk round them."

"And how did the gentlemen dress?" asked Charley.

"With full as much magnificence as the ladies," answered Grandfather. "For their holiday suits, they had coats of figured velvet, crimson, green, blue, and all other gay colors, embroidered with gold or silver lace. Their waistcoats, which were five times as large as modern ones, were very splendid. Sometimes, the whole waistcoat, which came down almost to the knees, was made of gold brocade."

"Why, the wearer must have shone like a golden image!" said Clara.

"And, then," continued Grandfather, "they wore various sorts of periwigs, such as the Tie, the Spencer, the Brigadier, the Major, the Albemarle, the Ramilies, the Feather-top, and the Full-bottom! Their three-cornered hats were laced with gold or silver. They had shining buckles at the knees of their smallclothes, and buckles likewise in their shoes. They wore swords with beautiful hilts, either of silver, or sometimes of polished steel, inlaid with gold."

"Oh, I should like to wear a sword!" cried Charley.

"And an embroidered crimson velvet coat," said Clara, laughing, "and a gold brocade waistcoat down to your knees!"

"And knee-buckles and shoe-buckles," said Laurence, laughing also.

"And a periwig," added little Alice, soberly, not knowing what was the article of dress which she recommended to our friend Charley.

Grandfather smiled at the idea of Charley's sturdy little figure in such a grotesque caparison. He then went on with the history of the chair, and told the children, that, in 1730, King George the Second appointed Jonathan Belcher to be Governor of Massachusetts, in place of the deceased Governor Burnet. Mr. Belcher was a native of the province, but had spent much of his life in Europe.

The new governor found Grandfather's chair in the Province House. He was struck with its noble and stately aspect, but was of opinion, that age and hard services had made it scarcely so fit for courtly company, as when it stood in the Earl of Lincoln's hall. Wherefore, as Governor Belcher was fond of splendor, he employed a skilful artist to beautify the chair. This was done by polishing and varnishing it, and by gilding the carved work of the elbows, and likewise the oaken flowers of the back. The lion's head now shone like a veritable lump of gold. Finally, Governor Belcher gave the chair a cushion of blue damask, with a rich golden fringe.

"Our good old chair being thus glorified," proceeded Grandfather, "it glittered with a great deal more splendor than it had exhibited just a century before, when the Lady Arbella brought it over from England. Most people mistook it for a chair of the latest London fashion. And this may serve for an example, that there is almost always an old and time-worn substance under all the glittering show of new invention."

"Grandfather, I cannot see any of the gilding," remarked Charley, who had been examining the chair very minutely.

"You will not wonder that it has been rubbed off," replied Grandfather, "when you hear all the adventures that have since befallen the chair. Gilded it was; and the handsomest room in the Province House was adorned by it."

There was not much to interest the children, in what happened during the years that Governor Belcher remained in the chair. At first, like Colonel Shute and Governor Burnet, he was engaged in disputing with the legislature about his salary. But, as he found it impossible to get a fixed sum, he finally obtained the king's leave to accept whatever the legislature chose to give him. And thus the people triumphed, after this long contest for the privilege of expending their own money as they saw fit.

The remainder of Governor Belcher's term of office was principally taken up in endeavoring to settle the currency. Honest John Hull's pine-tree shillings had long ago been worn out, or lost, or melted down again, and their place was supplied by bills of paper or parchment, which were nominally valued at three pence and upwards. The value of these bills kept continually sinking, because the real hard money could not be obtained for them. They were a great deal worse than the old Indian currency of clam-shells. These disorders of the circulating medium were a source of endless plague and perplexity to the rulers and legislators, not only in Governor Belcher's days, but for many years before and afterwards.

Finally, the people suspected that Governor Belcher was secretly endeavoring to establish the Episcopal mode of worship in the provinces. There was enough of the old Puritan spirit remaining to cause most of the true sons of New England to look with horror upon such an attempt. Great exertions were made to induce the king to remove the governor. Accordingly, in 1740, he was compelled to resign his office, and Grandfather's chair into the bargain, to Mr. Shirley.

CHAPTER VII

"WILLIAM SHIRLEY," said Grandfather, "had come from England a few years before, and begun to practise law in Boston. You will think, perhaps, that, as he had been a lawyer, the new governor used to sit in our great chair, reading heavy law-books from morning to night. On the contrary, he was as stirring and active a governor as Massachusetts ever had. Even Sir William Phipps hardly equalled him. The first year or two of his administration was spent in trying to regulate the currency. But, in 1744, after a peace of more than thirty years, war broke out between France and England."

"And I suppose," said Charley, "the governor went to take Canada."

"Not exactly, Charley," said Grandfather, "though you have made a pretty shrewd conjecture. He planned, in 1745, an expedition against Louisbourg. This was a fortified city, on the Island of Cape Breton, near Nova Scotia. Its walls were of immense height and strength, and were defended by hundreds of heavy cannon. It was the strongest fortress which the French possessed in America ; and if the king of France had guessed Governor Shirley's intentions, he would have sent all the ships he could muster to protect it."

As the siege of Louisbourg was one of the most remarkable events that ever the inhabitants of New England were engaged in, Grandfather endeavored to give his auditors a lively idea of the spirit with which they set about it. We shall call his description

THE PROVINCIAL MUSTER

The expedition against Louisbourg first began to be thought of in the month of January. From that time, the governor's chair was continually surrounded by counsellors, representatives, clergymen, captains, pilots, and all manner of people, with whom he consulted about this wonderful project.

First of all, it was necessary to provide men and arms. The legislature immediately sent out a huge quantity of paper money, with which, as if by magic spell, the governor hoped to get possession of all the old cannon, powder and balls, rusty swords and muskets, and everything else that would be serviceable in killing Frenchmen. Drums were beaten in all the villages of Massachusetts to enlist soldiers for the service. Messages were sent to the other governors of New England, and to New York and Pennsylvania, entreating them to unite in this crusade against the French. All these provinces agreed to give what assistance they could.

But there was one very important thing to be decided. Who shall be the General of this great army? Peace had continued such an unusual length of time, that there was now less military experience among the colonists, than at any former period. The old Puritans had always kept their weapons bright, and were never destitute of warlike captains, who were skilful in assault or defence. But the swords of their descendants had grown rusty by disuse. There was nobody in New England that knew anything about sieges, or any other regular fighting. The only persons at all acquainted with warlike business were a few elderly men, who had hunted Indians through the underbrush of the forest, in old Governor Dummer's war.

In this dilemma, Governor Shirley fixed upon a wealthy merchant, named William Pepperell, who was pretty well known and liked among the people. As to military skill, he had no more of it than his neighbors. But as the governor urged him very pressingly, Mr. Pepperell consented to shut up his ledger, gird on a sword, and assume the title of General.

Meantime, what a hubbub was raised by this scheme! Rub-a-dub-dub! Rub-a-dub-dub! The rattle of drums, beaten out of all manner of time, was heard above every other sound.

Nothing now was so valuable as arms, of whatever style and fashion they might be. The bellows blew, and the hammer clanged continually upon the anvil, while the blacksmiths were repairing the broken weapons of other wars. Doubtless, some of the soldiers lugged out those enormous, heavy muskets, which used to be fired with rests, in the time of the early Puritans. Great horse-pistols, too, were found, which would go off with a bang like a cannon. Old cannon, with touch-holes almost as big as their muzzles, were looked upon as inestimable treasures. Pikes, which, perhaps, had been handled by Miles Standish's soldiers, now made their appearance again. Many a young man ransacked the garret, and brought forth his great-grandfather's sword, corroded with rust, and stained with the blood of King Philip's war.

Never had there been such arming as this, when a people, so long peaceful, rose to the war, with the best weapons that they could lay their hands upon. And still the drums were heard — rub-a-dub-dub! rub-a-dub-dub! — in all the towns and villages; and louder and more numerous grew the trampling footsteps of the recruits that marched behind.

And now the army began to gather into Boston. Tall, lanky, awkward fellows came in squads, and companies, and regiments, swaggering along, dressed in their brown homespun clothes and blue yarn stockings. They stooped, as if they still had hold of the plough-handles, and marched without any time or tune. Hither they came, from the corn-fields, from the clearing in the forest, from the blacksmith's forge, from the carpenter's workshop, and from the shoemaker's seat. They were an army of rough faces and sturdy frames. A trained officer of Europe would have laughed at them, till his sides had ached. But there was a spirit in their bosoms, which is more essential to soldiership than to wear red coats, and march in stately ranks to the sound of regular music.

Still was heard the beat of the drum — rub-a-dub-dub! — and now a host of three or four thousand men

"AND NOW THE ARMY BEGAN TO GATHER INTO BOSTON."

had found their way to Boston. Little quiet was there then! Forth scampered the school-boys, shouting behind the drums. The whole town — the whole land — was on fire with war.

After the arrival of the troops, they were probably reviewed upon the Common. We may imagine Governor Shirley and General Pepperell riding slowly along the line, while the drummers beat strange old tunes, like psalm-tunes, and all the officers and soldiers put on their most warlike looks. It would have been a terrible sight for the Frenchmen, could they but have witnessed it!

At length, on the twenty-fourth of March, 1745, the army gave a parting shout, and set sail from Boston in ten or twelve vessels, which had been hired by the governor. A few days afterwards, an English fleet, commanded by Commodore Peter Warren, sailed also for Louisbourg, to assist the provincial army. So, now, after all this bustle of preparation, the town and province were left in stillness and repose.

But stillness and repose, at such a time of anxious expectation, are hard to bear. The hearts of the old people and women sank within them, when they reflected what perils they had sent their sons, and husbands, and brothers, to encounter. The boys loitered heavily to school, missing the rub-a-dub-dub, and the trampling march, in the rear of which they had so lately run and shouted. All the ministers prayed earnestly, in their pulpits, for a blessing on the army of New England. In every family, when the good man lifted up his heart in domestic worship, the burthen of his petition was for the safety of those dear ones, who were fighting under the walls of Louisbourg.

Governor Shirley, all this time, was probably in an ecstasy of impatience. He could not sit still a moment. He found no quiet, not even in Grandfather's chair, but hurried to and fro, and up and down the staircase of the Province House. Now, he mounted to the cupola, and looked seaward, straining his eyes to discover if there were a sail upon the horizon. Now, he hastened down the stairs, and stood beneath the portal, on the red free-stone steps, to receive some mud-bespattered courtier, from whom he hoped to hear tidings of the army. — A few weeks after the departure of the troops, Commodore Warren sent a small vessel to Boston with two French prisoners. One of them was Monsieur Bouladrie, who had been commander of a battery, outside of the walls of Louisbourg. The other was the Marquis de la Maison Forte, captain of a French frigate, which had been taken by Commodore Warren's fleet. These prisoners assured Governor Shirley, that the fortifications of Louisbourg were far too strong ever to be stormed by the provincial army.

Day after day, and week after week, went on. The people grew almost heart-sick with anxiety; for the flower of the country was at peril in this adventurous expedition. It was now daybreak, on the morning of the third of July.

But hark! what sound is this? The hurried clang of a bell! There is the Old North, pealing suddenly out! — there, the Old South strikes in! — now, the peal comes from the church in Brattle Street! — the bells of nine or ten steeples are all flinging their iron voices, at once, upon the morning breeze! Is it joy or alarm? There goes the roar of a cannon, too! A royal salute is thundered forth. And now, we hear the loud exulting shout of a multitude, assembled in the street. Huzza, huzza! Louisbourg has surrendered! Huzza!

"Oh, Grandfather, how glad I should have been to live in those times!" cried Charley. "And what reward did the king give to General Pepperell and Governor Shirley?"

"He made Pepperell a baronet; so that he was now to be called Sir William Pepperell," replied Grandfather. "He likewise appointed both Pepperell and Shirley to be colonels in the royal army. These rewards, and higher ones, were well deserved; for this was the greatest triumph that the English met with in the whole course of that war. General Pepperell became a man of great fame. I have seen a full-length portrait of him, representing him in a splendid scarlet uniform, standing before the walls of Louisbourg, while several bombs are falling through the air."

"But did the country gain any real good by the conquest of Louisbourg?" asked Laurence. "Or was all the benefit reaped by Pepperell and Shirley?"

"The English Parliament," said Grandfather, "agreed to pay the colonists for all the expenses of the siege. Accordingly, in 1749, two hundred and fifteen chests of Spanish dollars, and one hundred casks of copper coin, were brought from England to Boston. The whole amount was about a million of dollars. Twenty-seven carts and trucks carried this money from the wharf to the provincial treasury. Was not this a pretty liberal reward?"

"The mothers of the young men, who were killed at the siege of Louisbourg, would not have thought it so," said Laurence.

"No, Laurence," rejoined Grandfather; "and every warlike achievement involves an amount of physical and moral evil, for which all the gold in the Spanish mines would not be the slightest recompense. But we are to consider that this siege was one of the occasions on which the colonists tested their ability for war, and thus were prepared for the great contest of the Revolution. In that point of view, the valor of our forefathers was its own reward."

Grandfather went on to say, that the success of the expedition against Louisbourg induced Shirley and Pepperell to form a scheme for conquering Canada. This plan, however, was not carried into execution.

In the year 1746, great terror was excited by the arrival of a formidable French fleet upon the coast. It was commanded by the Duke d'Anville, and consisted of forty ships of war, besides vessels with soldiers on board. With this force the French intended to retake Louisbourg, and afterwards to ravage the whole of New England. Many people were ready to give up the country for lost.

But the hostile fleet met with so many disasters and losses, by storm and shipwreck, that the Duke d'Anville is said to have poisoned himself in despair. The officer next in command threw himself upon his sword and perished. Thus deprived of their commanders, the remainder of the ships returned to France. This was as great a deliverance for New England as that which Old England had experienced in the days of Queen Elizabeth, when the Spanish Armada was wrecked upon her coast.

"In 1747," proceeded Grandfather, "Governor Shirley was driven from the Province House, not by a hostile fleet and army, but by a mob of the Boston people. They were so incensed at the conduct of the British Commodore Knowles, who had impressed some of their fellow-citizens, that several thousands of them surrounded the council-chamber, and threw stones and brick-bats into the windows. The governor attempted to pacify them; but, not succeeding, he thought it necessary to leave the town, and take refuge within the walls of Castle William. Quiet was not restored, until Commodore Knowles had sent back the impressed men. This affair was a flash of spirit that might have warned the English not to venture upon any oppressive measures against their colonial brethren."

Peace being declared between France and England in 1748, the governor had now an opportunity to sit at his ease in Grandfather's chair. Such repose, however, appears not to have suited his disposition; for, in the following year, he went to England, and thence was despatched to France on public business. Meanwhile, as Shirley had not resigned his office, Lieutenant-Governor Phipps acted as chief magistrate in his stead.

CHAPTER VIII

IN the early twilight of Thanksgiving eve, came Laurence, and Clara, and Charley, and little Alice, hand in hand, and stood in a semicircle round Grandfather's chair. They had been joyous, throughout that day of festivity, mingling together in all kinds of play, so that the house had echoed with their airy mirth.

Grandfather, too, had been happy, though not mirthful. He felt that this was to be set down as one of the good Thanksgivings of his life. In truth, all his former Thanksgivings had borne their part in the present one; for his years of infancy, and youth, and manhood, with their blessings and their griefs, had flitted before him, while he sat silently in the great chair. Vanished scenes had been pictured in the air. The forms of departed friends had visited him. Voices, to be heard no more on earth, had sent an echo from the infinite and the eternal. These shadows, if such they were, seemed almost as real to him, as what was actually present — as the merry shouts and laughter of the children — as their figures, dancing like sunshine before his eyes.

He felt that the past was not taken from him. The happiness of former days was a possession forever. And there was something in the mingled sorrow of his lifetime, that became akin to happiness, after being long treasured in the depths of his heart. There it underwent a change, and grew more precious than pure gold.

And now came the children, somewhat aweary with their wild play, and sought the quiet enjoyment of Grandfather's talk. The good old gentleman rubbed his eyes, and smiled round upon them all. He was glad as most aged people are, to find that he was yet of consequence, and could give pleasure to the world. After being so merry all day long, did these children desire to hear his

97

sober talk? Oh, then, old Grandfather had yet a place to fill among living men, — or at least among boys and girls!

"Begin quick, Grandfather," cried little Alice; "for Pussy wants to hear you."

And, truly, our yellow friend, the cat, lay upon the hearth-rug, basking in the warmth of the fire, pricking up her ears, and turning her head from the children to Grandfather, and from Grandfather to the children, as if she felt herself very sympathetic with them all. A loud purr, like the singing of a tea-kettle, or the hum of a spinning-wheel, testified that she was as comfortable and happy as a cat could be. For Puss had feasted, and therefore, like Grandfather and the children, had kept a good Thanksgiving.

"Does Pussy want to hear me?" said Grandfather, smiling. "Well; we must please Pussy if we can!"

And so he took up the history of the chair, from the epoch of the peace of 1748. By one of the provisions of the treaty, Louisbourg, which the New Englanders had been at so much pains to take, was restored to the king of France.

The French were afraid that, unless their colonies should be better defended than heretofore, another war might deprive them of the whole. Almost as soon as peace was declared, therefore, they began to build strong fortifications in the interior of North America. It was strange to behold these warlike castles, on the banks of solitary lakes, and far in the midst of woods. The Indian, paddling his birch-canoe on Lake Champlain, looked up at the high ramparts of Ticonderoga, stone piled on stone, bristling with cannon, and the white flag of France floating above. There were similar fortifications on Lake Ontario, and near the great Falls of Niagara, and at the sources of the Ohio River. And all around these forts and castles lay the eternal forest; and the roll of the drum died away in those deep solitudes.

The truth was, that the French intended to build forts, all the way from Canada to Louisiana. They would then have had a wall of military strength, at the back of the English settlements, so as completely to hem them in. The king of England considered the building of these forts as a sufficient cause of war, which was accordingly commenced in 1754.

"Governor Shirley," said Grandfather, "had returned to Boston in 1753. While in Paris, he had married a second wife, a young French girl, and now brought her to the Province House. But, when war was breaking out, it was impossible for such a bustling man to stay quietly at home, sitting in our old chair, with his wife and children round about him. He therefore obtained a command in the English forces."

"And what did Sir William Pepperell do?" asked Charley.

"He staid at home," said Grandfather, "and was general of the militia. The veteran regiments of the English army, which were now sent across the Atlantic, would have scorned to fight under the orders of an old American merchant. And now began what aged people call the Old French War. It would be going too far astray from the history of our chair, to tell you one half of the battles that were fought. I cannot even allow myself to describe the bloody defeat of General Braddock, near the sources of the Ohio River, in 1755. But I must not omit to mention, that when the English general was mortally wounded, and his army routed, the remains of it were preserved by the skill and valor of GEORGE WASHINGTON."

At the mention of this illustrious name, the children started, as if a sudden sunlight had gleamed upon the history of their country, now that the great Deliverer had arisen above the horizon.

Among all the events of the Old French War, Grandfather thought that there was none more interesting than the removal of the inhabitants of Acadia. From the first settlement of this ancient province of the French, in 1604, until the present time, its people could scarcely ever know what kingdom held dominion over them. They were a peaceful race, taking no delight in warfare, and caring nothing for military renown. And yet, in every war, their region was infested with iron-hearted soldiers, both French and English, who fought one another for the privilege of ill-treating these poor harmless Acadians. Sometimes the treaty of peace made them subjects of one king, sometimes of another.

At the peace of 1748, Acadia had been ceded to England. But the French still claimed a large portion of it, and built forts for its defence. In 1755, these forts were taken, and the whole of Acadia was conquered, by three thousand men from Massachusetts, under the command of General Winslow. The inhabitants were accused of supplying the French with provisions, and of doing other things that violated their neutrality.

"These accusations were probably true," observed Grandfather; "for the Acadians were descended from the French, and had the same friendly feelings towards them, that the people of Massachusetts had for the English. But their punishment was severe. The English determined to tear these poor people from their native homes and scatter them abroad."

The Acadians were about seven thousand in number. A considerable part of them were made prisoners, and transported to the English colonies. All their dwellings and churches were burnt, their cattle were killed, and the whole country was laid waste, so that none of them might find shelter or food in their old homes, after the departure of the English. One thousand of the prisoners were sent to Massachusetts; and Grandfather allowed his fancy to follow them thither, and tried to give his auditors an idea of their situation.

We shall call this passage the story of

The Acadian Exiles

A sad day it was for the poor Acadians, when the armed soldiers drove them, at the point of the bayonet, down to the seashore. Very sad were they, likewise, while tossing upon the ocean, in the crowded transport vessels. But, methinks, it must have been sadder still, when they were landed on the Long Wharf, in Boston, and left to themselves, on a foreign strand.

Then, probably, they huddled together, and looked into one another's faces for the comfort which was not there. Hitherto, they had been confined on board of separate vessels, so that they could not tell whether their relatives and friends were prisoners along with them. But, now, at least, they could tell that many had been left behind, or transported to other regions.

Now, a desolate wife might be heard calling for her husband. He, alas! had gone, she knew not whither, or perhaps had fled into the woods of Acadia, and had now returned to weep over the ashes of their dwelling.

An aged widow was crying out, in a querulous lamentable tone, for her son, whose affectionate toil had supported her for many a year. He was not in the crowd of exiles; and what could this aged widow do but sink down and die? Young men and maidens, whose hearts had been torn asunder by separation, had hoped, during the voyage, to meet their beloved ones at its close. Now, they began to feel that they were separated forever. And, perhaps, a lonesome little girl, a golden-haired child of five years old, the very picture of our little Alice, was weeping and wailing for her mother, and found not a soul to give her a kind word.

Oh, how many broken bonds of affection were here! Country lost! — friends lost! — their rural wealth of cottage, field, and herds, all lost together! Every tie between these poor exiles and the world seemed to be cut off at once. They must have regretted that they had not died before their exile; for even the English would not have been so pitiless as to deny them graves in their native soil. The dead were happy; for they were not exiles!

While they thus stood upon the wharf, the curiosity and inquisitiveness of the New England people would naturally lead them into the midst of the poor Acadians. Prying busybodies thrust their heads into the circle, wherever two or three of the exiles were conversing together. How puzzled did they look, at the outlandish sound of the French tongue! There were seen the New England women, too. They had just come out of their warm, safe homes, where everything was regular and comfortable, an l where their husbands and children would be with them at nightfall. Surely, they could pity the wretched wives and mothers of Acadia! Or, did the sign of the cross, which the Acadians continually made upon their breasts, and which was abhorred by the descendants of the Puritans — did that sign exclude all pity?

Among the spectators, too, was the noisy brood of Boston school-boys, who came running, with laughter and shouts, to gaze at this crowd of oddly-dressed foreigners. At first they danced and capered around them, full of merriment and mischief. But the despair of the Acadians soon had its effect upon these thoughtless lads, and melted them into tearful sympathy.

At a little distance from the throng, might be seen the wealthy and pompous merchants, whose warehouses stood on Long Wharf. It was difficult to touch these rich men's hearts; for they had all the comforts of the world at their command; and when they walked abroad, their feelings were seldom moved, except by the roughness of the pavement, irritating their gouty toes. Leaning upon their gold-headed canes, they watched the scene with an aspect of composure. But, let us hope, they distributed some of their superfluous coin among these hapless exiles, to purchase food and a night's lodging.

After standing a long time at the end of the wharf, gazing seaward, as if to catch a glimpse of their lost Acadia, the strangers began to stray into the town.

They went, we will suppose, in parties and groups, here a hundred, there a score, there ten, there three or four, who possessed some bond of unity among themselves. Here and there was one, who, utterly desolate, stole away by himself, seeking no companionship.

Whither did they go? I imagine them wandering about the streets, telling the town's-people, in outlandish, unintelligible words, that no earthly affliction ever equalled what had befallen them. Man's brotherhood with man was sufficient to make the New Englanders understand this language. The strangers wanted food. Some of them sought hospitality at the doors of the stately mansions, which then stood in the vicinity of Hanover Street and the North Square. Others were applicants at the humble wooden tenements, where dwelt the petty shop-keepers and mechanics. Pray Heaven, that no family in Boston turned one of these poor exiles from their door! It would be a reproach upon New England, a crime worthy of heavy retribution, if the aged women and children, or even the strong men, were allowed to feel the pinch of hunger.

Perhaps some of the Acadians, in their aimless wanderings through the town, found themselves near a large brick edifice, which was fenced in from the street by an iron railing, wrought with fantastic figures. They saw a flight of red freestone steps, ascending to a portal, above which was a balcony and balustrade. Misery and desolation give men the right of free passage everywhere. Let us suppose, then, that they mounted the flight of steps, and passed into the Province House. Making their way into one of the apartments, they beheld a richly-clad gentleman, seated in a stately chair with gilding upon the carved work of its back, and a gilded lion's head at the summit. This was Governor Shirley, meditating upon matters of war and state, in Grandfather's chair!

If such an incident did happen, Shirley, reflecting what a ruin of peaceful and humble hopes had been wrought by the cold policy of the statesman, and the iron hand of the warrior, might have drawn a deep moral from it. It should have taught him that the poor man's hearth is sacred, and that armies and nations have no right to violate it. It should have made him feel, that England's triumph, and increased dominion, could not compensate to mankind, nor atone to Heaven, for the ashes of a single Acadian cottage. But it is not thus that statesmen and warriors moralize.

" Grandfather," cried Laurence, with emotion trembling in his voice, "did iron-hearted War itself ever do so hard and cruel a thing as this before?"

"You have read in history, Laurence, of whole regions wantonly laid waste," said Grandfather. "In the removal of the Acadians, the troops were guilty of no cruelty or outrage, except what was inseparable from the measure."

Little Alice, whose eyes had, all along, been brimming full of tears, now burst forth a-sobbing; for Grandfather had touched her sympathies more than he intended.

"To think of a whole people, homeless in the world!" said Clara, with moistened eyes. "There never was anything so sad!"

"It was their own fault," cried Charley, energetically. "Why did not they fight for the country where they were born? Then if the worst had happened to them they could only have been killed and buried there. They would not have been exiles then!"

"Certainly, their lot was as hard as death," said Grandfather. "All that could be done for them, in the English provinces, was to send them to the almshouses, or bind them out to task-masters. And this was the fate of persons, who had possessed a comfortable property in their native country. Some of them found means to embark for France; but though it was the land of their forefathers, it must have been a foreign land to them. Those who remained behind always cherished a belief, that the king of France would never make peace with England, till his poor Acadians were restored their country and their homes."

"And did he?" inquired Clara.

"Alas, my dear Clara," said Grandfather, "it is improbable that the slightest whisper of the woes of Acadia ever reached the ears of Louis the Fifteenth. The exiles grew old in the British provinces, and never saw Acadia again. Their descendants remain among us, to this day. They have forgotten the language of their ancestors, and probably retain no tradition of their misfortunes. But, methinks, if I were an American poet, I would choose Acadia for the subject of my song."

Since Grandfather first spoke these words, the most famous of American poets has drawn sweet tears from all of us, by his beautiful poem of Evangeline.

And now, having thrown a gentle gloom around the Thanksgiving fireside, by a story that made the children feel the blessing of a secure and peaceful hearth, Grandfather put off the other events of the Old French War till the next evening.

CHAPTER IX

IN the twilight of the succeeding eve, when the red beams of the fire were dancing upon the wall, the children besought Grandfather to tell them what had next happened to the old chair.

"Our chair," said Grandfather, "stood all this time in the Province House. But Governor Shirley had seldom an opportunity to repose within its arms. He was leading his troops through the forest, or sailing in a flat-boat on Lake Ontario, or sleeping in his tent, while the awful cataract of Niagara sent its roar through his dreams. At one period, in the early part of the war, Shirley had the chief command of all the king's forces in America."

"Did his young wife go with him to the war?" asked Clara.

"I rather imagine," replied Grandfather, "that she remained in Boston. This lady, I suppose, had our chair all to herself, and used to sit in it, during those brief intervals when a young French woman can be quiet enough to sit in a chair. The people of Massachusetts were never fond of Governor Shirley's young French wife. They had a suspicion that she betrayed the military plans of the English to the generals of the French armies."

"And was it true?" inquired Clara.

"Probably not," said Grandfather. "But the mere suspicion did Shirley a great deal of harm. Partly, perhaps, for this reason, but much more on account of his inefficiency as a general, he was deprived of his command, in 1756, and recalled to England. He never afterwards made any figure in public life."

As Grandfather's chair had no locomotive properties, and did not even run on castors, it cannot be supposed to have marched in person to the Old French War. But Grandfather delayed its momentous history, while he touched briefly upon some of the bloody battles, sieges, and onslaughts, the tidings of which kept continually coming to the ears of the old inhabitants of Boston. The woods of the north were populous with fighting men. All the Indian tribes uplifted their tomahawks, and took part either with the French or English. The rattle of musketry and roar of cannon disturbed the ancient quiet of the forest, and actually drove the bears and other wild beasts to the more cultivated portion of the country in the vicinity of the seaports. The children felt as if they were transported back to those forgotten times, and that the couriers from the army, with the news of a battle lost or won, might even now be heard galloping through the streets. Grandfather told them about the battle of Lake George, in 1755, when the gallant Colonel Williams, a Massachusetts officer, was slain, with many of his countrymen. But General Johnson and General Lyman, with their army, drove back the enemy, and mortally wounded the French leader, who was called the Baron Dieskau. A gold watch, pilfered from the poor Baron, is still in existence, and still marks each moment of time, without complaining of weariness, although its hands have been in motion ever since the hour of battle.

In the first years of the war, there were many disasters on the English side. Among these was the loss of Fort Oswego, in 1756, and of Fort William Henry, in the following year. But the greatest misfortune that befell the English, during the whole war, was the repulse of General Abercrombie, with his army, from the ramparts of Ticonderoga in 1758. He attempted to storm the walls ; but a terrible conflict ensued, in which more than two thousand Englishmen and New Englanders were killed or wounded. The slain soldiers now lie buried around that ancient fortress. When the plough passes over the soil, it turns up here and there a mouldering bone.

Up to this period, none of the English generals had shown any military talent. Shirley, the Earl of London, and General Abercrombie, had each held the chief command, at different times; but not one of them had won a single important triumph for the British arms. This ill success was not owing to the want of means; for, in 1758, General Abercrombie had fifty thousand soldiers under his command. But the French general, the famous Marquis de Montcalm, possessed a great genius for war, and had something within him, that taught him how battles were to be won.

At length, in 1759, Sir Jeffrey Amherst was appointed commander-in-chief of all the British forces in America. He was a man of ability, and a skilful soldier. A plan was now formed for accomplishing that object, which had so long been the darling wish of the New Englanders, and which their fathers had so many times attempted. This was the conquest of Canada.

Three separate armies were to enter Canada, from different quarters. One of the three, commanded by General Prideaux, was to embark on Lake Ontario, and proceed to Montreal. The second, at the head of which was Sir Jeffrey Amherst himself, was destined to reach the River St. Lawrence, by the way of Lake Champlain, and then go down the river to meet the third army. This last, led by General Wolfe, was to enter the St. Lawrence from the sea, and ascend the river to Quebec. It is to Wolfe and his army that England owes one of the most splendid triumphs ever written in her history.

Grandfather described the siege of Quebec, and told how Wolfe led his soldiers up a rugged and lofty precipice that rose from the shore of the river to the plain on which the city stood. This bold adventure was achieved in the darkness of night. At daybreak, tidings were carried to the Marquis de Montcalm, that the English army was waiting to give him battle on the plains of Abraham. This brave French general ordered his drums to strike up, and immediately marched to encounter Wolfe.

He marched to his own death. The battle was the most fierce and terrible that had ever been fought in America. General Wolfe was at the head of his soldiers, and while encouraging them onward, received a mortal wound. He reclined against a stone, in the agonies of death; but it seemed as if his spirit could not pass away, while the fight yet raged so doubtfully. Suddenly, a shout came pealing across the battle-field — "They flee! they flee!" and for a moment, Wolfe lifted his languid head. "Who flee?" he inquired. "The French," replied an officer. "Then I die satisfied!" said Wolfe, and expired in the arms of victory.

"If ever a warrior's death were glorious, Wolfe's was so!" said Grandfather; and his eye kindled, though he was a man of peaceful thoughts, and gentle spirit. "His lifeblood streamed to baptize the soil which he had added to the dominion of Britain! His dying breath was mingled with his army's shout of victory!"

"Oh, it was a good death to die!" cried Charley, with glistening eyes. "Was it not a good death, Laurence?"

Laurence made no reply; for his heart burned within him, as the picture of Wolfe, dying on the blood-stained field of victory, arose to his imagination; and yet, he had a deep inward consciousness, that, after all, there was a truer glory than could thus be won.

"There were other battles in Canada, after Wolfe's victory," resumed Grandfather; "but we may consider the Old French War as having terminated with this great event. The treaty of peace, however, was not signed until 1763. The terms of the treaty were very disadvantageous to the French; for all Canada, and all Acadia, and the island of Cape Breton, in short, all the territories that France and England had been fighting about, for nearly a hundred years — were surrendered to the English."

"So, now, at last," said Laurence, "New England had gained her wish. Canada was taken!"

"And now there was nobody to fight with, but the Indians," said Charley.

Grandfather mentioned two other important events. The first was the great fire of Boston, in 1760, when the glare from nearly three hundred buildings, all in flames at once, shone through the windows of the Province House, and threw a fierce lustre upon the gilded foliage

and lion's head of our old chair.   The second event was
the proclamation, in the same year, of George the Third
as king of Great Britain.   The blast of the trumpet
sounded from the balcony of the Town House, and
awoke the echoes far and wide, as if to challenge all
mankind to dispute King George's title.

Seven times, as the successive monarchs of Britain
ascended the throne, the trumpet-peal of proclamation
had been heard by those who sat in our venerable chair.
But when the next king put on his father's crown, no
trumpet-peal proclaimed it to New England! Long
before that day, America had shaken off the royal
government.

CHAPTER X

NOW that Grandfather had fought through the Old French War, in which our chair made no very distinguished figure, he thought it high time to tell the children some of the more private history of that praiseworthy old piece of furniture.

"In 1757," said Grandfather, "after Shirley had been summoned to England, Thomas Pownall was appointed governor of Massachusetts. He was a gay and fashionable English gentleman, who had spent much of his life in London, but had a considerable acquaintance with America. The new governor appears to have taken no active part in the war that was going on; although, at one period, he talked of marching against the enemy, at the head of his company of cadets. But, on the whole, he probably concluded that it was more befitting a governor to remain quietly in our chair, reading the newspapers and official documents."

"Did the people like Pownall?" asked Charley.

"They found no fault with him," replied Grandfather. "It was no time to quarrel with the governor, when the utmost harmony was required, in order to defend the country against the French. But Pownall did not remain long in Massachusetts. In 1759, he was sent to be governor of South Carolina. In thus exchanging one government for another, I suppose he felt no regret, except at the necessity of leaving Grandfather's chair behind him."

"He might have taken it to South Carolina," observed Clara.

"It appears to me," said Laurence, giving the rein to his fancy, "that the fate of this ancient chair was, somehow or other, mysteriously connected with the fortunes of old Massachusetts. If Governor Pownall

had put it aboard the vessel in which he sailed for
South Carolina, she would probably have lain wind-
bound in Boston harbor. It was ordained that the
chair should not be taken away. Don't you think so,
Grandfather?"

"It was kept here for Grandfather and me to sit in
together," said little Alice, "and for Grandfather to tell
stories about."

"And Grandfather is very glad of such a companion,
and such a theme," said the old gentleman, with a smile.
"Well, Laurence, if our oaken chair, like the wooden
Palladium of Troy, was connected with the country's
fate, yet there appears to have been no supernatural
obstacle to its removal from the Province House. In
1760, Sir Francis Bernard, who had been governor of
New Jersey, was appointed to the same office in Massachusetts. He looked at the old chair, and thought
it quite too shabby to keep company with a new set of
mahogany chairs, and an aristocratic sofa, which had
just arrived from London. He therefore ordered it to
be put away in the garret."

The children were loud in their exclamations against
this irreverent conduct of Sir Francis Bernard. But
Grandfather defended him, as well as he could. He
observed, that it was then thirty years since the chair
had been beautified by Governor Belcher. Most of the
gilding was worn off by the frequent scourings which
it had undergone, beneath the hands of a black slave.
The damask cushion, once so splendid, was now
squeezed out of all shape, and absolutely in tatters,
so many were the ponderous gentlemen who had de-
posited their weight upon it, during these thirty years.

Moreover, at a council held by the Earl of London
with the governors of New England, in 1757, his lord-
ship, in a moment of passion, had kicked over the chair
with his military boot. By this unprovoked and unjustifiable act, our venerable friend had suffered a fracture
of one of its rungs.

"But," said Grandfather, "our chair, after all, was
not destined to spend the remainder of its days in the

inglorious obscurity of a garret. Thomas Hutchinson, lieutenant-governor of the province, was told of Sir Francis Bernard's design. This gentleman was more familiar with the history of New England than any other man alive. He knew all the adventures and vicissitudes through which the old chair had passed, and could have told, as accurately as your own Grandfather, who were the personages that had occupied it. Often, while visiting at the Province House, he had eyed the chair with admiration, and felt a longing desire to become the possessor of it. He now waited upon Sir Francis Bernard, and easily obtained leave to carry it home."

"And I hope," said Clara, "he had it varnished and gilded anew."

" No," answered Grandfather. "What Mr. Hutchinson desired was to restore the chair, as much as possible, to its original aspect, such as it had appeared, when it was first made out of the Earl of Lincoln's oak-tree. For this purpose he ordered it to be well scoured with soap and sand and polished with wax, and then provided it with a substantial leather cushion. When all was completed to his mind, he sat down in the old chair, and began to write his 'History of Massachusetts.'"

"Oh, that was a bright thought in Mr. Hutchinson!" exclaimed Laurence. "And, no doubt, the dim figures of the former possessors of the chair flitted around him, as he wrote, and inspired him with a knowledge of all that they had done and suffered while on earth."

"Why, my dear Laurence," replied Grandfather, smiling, "if Mr. Hutchinson was favored with any such extraordinary inspiration, he made but a poor use of it in his History; for a duller piece of composition never came from any man's pen. However, he was accurate, at least, though far from possessing the brilliancy or philosophy of Mr. Bancroft."

"But if Hutchinson knew the history of the chair," rejoined Laurence, "his heart must have been stirred by it."

"It must, indeed," said Grandfather. "It would be

entertaining and instructive at the present day, to imagine what were Mr. Hutchinson's thoughts as he looked
back upon the long vista of events with which this chair
was so remarkably connected."

And Grandfather allowed his fancy to shape out an
image of Lieutenant-Governor Hutchinson, sitting in an
evening reverie by his fireside, and meditating on the
changes that had slowly passed around the chair.

A devoted monarchist, Hutchinson would heave no
sigh for the subversion of the original republican government, the purest that the world had seen, with which
the colony began its existence. While reverencing the
grim and stern old Puritans as the founders of his native
land, he would not wish to recall them from their graves,
nor to awaken again that king-resisting spirit, which he
imagined to be laid asleep with them forever. Winthrop, Dudley, Bellingham, Endicott, Leverett, and
Bradstreet! All these had had their day. Ages might
come and go, but never again would the people's suffrages place a republican governor in their ancient Chair
of State!

Coming down to the epoch of the second charter,
Hutchinson thought of the ship-carpenter Phipps, spring-
ing from the lowest of the people, and attaining to the
loftiest station in the land. But he smiled to perceive
that this governor's example would awaken no turbulent
ambition in the lower orders, for it was a king's gracious
boon alone that made the ship-carpenter a ruler. Hutchinson rejoiced to mark the gradual growth of an aristocratic class, to whom the common people, as in duty
bound, were learning humbly to resign the honors,
emoluments, and authority of state. He saw, — or else
deceived himself, — that, throughout this epoch, the people's disposition to self-government had been growing
weaker, through long disuse, and now existed only as a
faint traditionary feeling.

The lieutenant-governor's reverie had now come down
to the period at which he himself was sitting in the historic chair. He endeavored to throw his glance forward,
over the coming years. There, probably, he saw visions

of hereditary rank, for himself and other aristocratic colonists. He saw the fertile fields of New England portioned out among a few great landholders, and descending by entail from generation to generation. He saw the people a race of tenantry, dependent on their lords. He saw stars, garters, coronets, and castles.

"But," added Grandfather, turning to Laurence, "the lieutenant-governor's castles were built nowhere but among the red embers of the fire, before which he was sitting. And, just as he had constructed a baronial residence for himself and his posterity, the fire rolled down upon the hearth, and crumbled it to ashes!"

Grandfather now looked at his watch, which hung within a beautiful little ebony Temple, supported by four Ionic columns. He then laid his hand on the golden locks of little Alice, whose head had sunk down upon the arm of our illustrious chair.

"To bed, to bed, dear child!" said he. "Grandfather has put you to sleep, already, by his stories about these FAMOUS OLD PEOPLE."

PART III

CHAPTER I

ON the evening of New Year's day, Grandfather was walking to and fro, across the carpet, listening to the rain which beat hard against the curtained windows. The riotous blast shook the casement, as if a strong man were striving to force his entrance into the comfortable room. With every puff of the wind, the fire leaped upward from the hearth, laughing and rejoicing at the shrieks of the wintry storm.

Meanwhile, Grandfather's chair stood in its customary place by the fireside. The bright blaze gleamed upon the fantastic figures of its oaken back, and shone through the open-work, so that a complete pattern was thrown upon the opposite side of the room. Sometimes, for a moment or two, the shadow remained immovable, as if it were painted on the wall. Then, all at once, it began to quiver, and leap, and dance, with a frisky motion. Anon, seeming to remember that these antics were unworthy of such a dignified and venerable chair, it suddenly stood still. But soon it began to dance anew.

"Only see how Grandfather's chair is dancing!" cried little Alice.

And she ran to the wall, and tried to catch hold of the flickering shadow; for to children of five years old, a shadow seems almost as real as a substance.

"I wish," said Clara, "Grandfather would sit down in the chair, and finish its history."

If the children had been looking at Grandfather, they would have noticed that he paused in his walk across the room, when Clara made this remark. The kind old gentleman was ready and willing to resume his stories of departed times. But he had resolved to wait till his auditors should request him to proceed, in order that they might find the instructive history of the chair a pleasure, and not a task.

"Grandfather," said Charley, "I am tired to death of this dismal rain, and of hearing the wind roar in the chimney. I have had no good time all day. It would be better to hear stories about the chair, than to sit doing nothing, and thinking of nothing."

To say the truth, our friend Charley was very much out of humor with the storm, because it had kept him all day within doors, and hindered him from making a trial of a splendid sled, which Grandfather had given him for a New Year's gift. As all sleds, nowadays, must have a name, the one in question had been honored with the title of Grandfather's Chair, which was painted in golden letters, on each of the sides. Charley greatly admired the construction of the new vehicle, and felt certain that it would outstrip any other sled that ever dashed adown the long slopes of the Common.

As for Laurence, he happened to be thinking, just at this moment, about the history of the chair. Kind old Grandfather had made him a present of a volume of engraved portraits, representing the features of eminent and famous people of all countries. Among them Laurence found several who had formerly occupied our chair, or been connected with its adventures. While Grandfather walked to and fro across the room, the imaginative boy was gazing at the historic chair. He endeavored to summon up the portraits which he had seen in his volume, and to place them, like living figures, in the empty seat.

"The old chair has begun another year of its existence, to-day," said Laurence. "We must make haste, or it will have a new history to be told before we finish the old one."

"Yes, my children," replied Grandfather, with a smile and a sigh, "another year has been added to those of the two centuries, and upward, which have passed since the Lady Arbella brought this chair over from England. It is three times as old as your Grandfather; but a year makes no impression on its oaken frame, while it bends the old man nearer and nearer to the earth; so let me go on with my stories while I may."

Accordingly, Grandfather came to the fireside, and seated himself in the venerable chair. The lion's head looked down with a grimly good-natured aspect, as the children clustered around the old gentleman's knees. It almost seemed as if a real lion were peeping over the back of the chair, and smiling at the group of auditors, with a sort of lion-like complaisance. Little Alice, whose fancy often inspired her with singular ideas, exclaimed that the lion's head was nodding at her, and that it looked as if it were going to open its wide jaws and tell a story.

But, as the lion's head appeared to be in no haste to speak, and as there was no record or tradition of its having spoken, during the whole existence of the chair, Grandfather did not consider it worth while to wait.

CHAPTER II

"CHARLEY, my boy," said Grandfather, "do you remember who was the last occupant of the chair?"

"It was Lieutenant-Governor Hutchinson," answered Charley. "Sir Francis Bernard, the new governor, had given him the chair, instead of putting it away in the garret of the Province House. And when we took leave of Hutchinson, he was sitting by his fireside, and thinking of the past adventures of the chair, and of what was to come."

"Very well," said Grandfather; "and you recollect that this was in 1763, or thereabouts, at the close of the Old French War. Now, that you may fully comprehend the remaining adventures of the chair, I must make some brief remarks on the situation and character of the New England colonies at this period."

So Grandfather spoke of the earnest loyalty of our fathers during the Old French War, and after the conquest of Canada had brought that war to a triumphant close.

The people loved and reverenced the king of England, even more than if the ocean had not rolled its waves between him and them; for, at the distance of three thousand miles, they could not discover his bad qualities and imperfections. Their love was increased by the dangers which they had encountered in order to heighten his glory and extend his dominion. Throughout the war, the American colonists had fought side by side with the soldiers of Old England; and nearly thirty thousand young men had laid down their lives for the honor of King George. And the survivors loved him the better, because they had done and suffered so much for his sake.

But, there were some circumstances, that caused America to feel more independent of England than at an earlier period.   Canada and Acadia had now become British provinces ; and our fathers were no longer afraid of the bands of French and Indians, who used to assault them in old times.   For a century and a half this had been the great terror of New England.   Now, the old French soldier was driven from the north forever.   And even had it been otherwise, the English colonies were growing so populous and powerful, that they might have felt fully able to protect themselves without any help from England.

There were thoughtful and sagacious men, who began to doubt whether a great country like America would always be content to remain under the government of an island three thousand miles away.   This was the more doubtful, because the English Parliament had long ago made laws which were intended to be very beneficial to England, at the expense of America.   By these laws, the colonists were forbidden to manufacture articles for their own use, or to carry on trade with any nation but the English.

"Now," continued Grandfather, " if King George the Third and his counsellors had considered these things wisely they would have taken another course than they did.   But, when they saw how rich and populous the colonies had grown, their first thought was, how they might make more profit out of them than heretofore. England was enormously in debt, at the close of the Old French War, and it was pretended, that this debt had been contracted for the defence of the American colonies, and that therefore a part of it ought to be paid by them."

"Why, this was nonsense," exclaimed Charley ; " did not our fathers spend their lives, and their money too, to get Canada for King George ? "

" True, they did," said Grandfather ; " and they told the English rulers so.   But the king and his ministers would not listen to good advice.   In 1765, the British Parliament passed a Stamp Act."

"What was that ? " inquired Charley.

" The Stamp Act," replied Grandfather, " was a law by which all deeds, bonds, and other papers of the same kind, were ordered to be marked with the king's stamp; and without this mark, they were declared illegal and void.   Now, in order to get a blank sheet of paper, with the king's stamp upon it, people were obliged to pay three pence more than the actual value of the paper. And this extra sum of three pence was a tax, and was to be paid into the king's treasury."

"I am sure three pence was not worth quarrelling about!" remarked Clara.

" It was not for three pence, nor for any amount of money, that America quarrelled with England," replied Grandfather; "it was for a great principle. The colonists were determined not to be taxed, except by their own representatives.   They said that neither the king and Parliament, nor any other power on earth, had a right to take their money out of their pockets, unless they freely gave it.   And, rather than pay three pence when it was unjustly demanded, they resolved to sacrifice all the wealth of the country, and their lives along with it.   They therefore made a most stubborn resistance to the Stamp Act."

"That was noble!" exclaimed Laurence.   "I understand how it was.   If they had quietly paid the tax of three pence, they would have ceased to be freemen, and would have become tributaries of England.   And so they contended about a great question of right and wrong, and put everything at stake for it."

"You are right, Laurence," said Grandfather; "and it was really amazing and terrible to see what a change came over the aspect of the people, the moment the English Parliament had passed this oppressive act. The former history of our chair, my children, has given you some idea of what a harsh, unyielding, stern set of men the old Puritans were.   For a good many years back, however, it had seemed as if these characteristics were disappearing.   But no sooner did England offer wrong to the colonies, than the descendants of the early settlers proved that they had the same kind of temper as their forefathers. The moment before, New England appeared like an humble and loyal subject of the crown; the next instant, she showed the grim, dark features of an old king-resisting Puritan."

Grandfather spoke briefly of the public measures that were taken in opposition to the Stamp Act. As this law affected all the American colonies alike, it naturally led them to think of consulting together in order to procure its repeal. For this purpose, the legislature of Massachusetts proposed that delegates from every colony should meet in Congress. Accordingly nine colonies, both northern and southern, sent delegates to the city of New York.

" And did they consult about going to war with England?" asked Charley.

" No, Charley," answered Grandfather; "a great deal of talking was yet to be done, before England and America could come to blows. The Congress stated the rights and the grievances of the colonists. They sent an humble petition to the king, and a memorial to the Parliament, beseeching that the Stamp Act might be repealed. This was all that the delegates had it in their power to do."

" They might as well have staid at home, then," said Charley.

" By no means," replied Grandfather. "It was a most important and memorable event — this first coming together of the American people, by their representatives from the north and south. If England had been wise, she would have trembled at the first word that was spoken in such an assembly!"

These remonstrances and petitions, as Grandfather observed, were the work of grave, thoughtful, and prudent men. Meantime, the young and hot-headed people went to work in their own way. It is probable that the petitions of Congress would have had little or no effect on the British statesmen, if the violent deeds of the American people had not shown how much excited the people were. LIBERTY TREE was soon heard of in England.

"What was Liberty Tree?" inquired Clara.

"It was an old elm-tree," answered Grandfather, "which stood near the corner of Essex Street, opposite the Boylston market. Under the spreading branches of this great tree, the people used to assemble, whenever they wished to express their feelings and opinions. Thus, after a while, it seemed as if the liberty of the country was connected with Liberty Tree."

"It was glorious fruit for a tree to bear," remarked Laurence.

"It bore strange fruit sometimes," said Grandfather. "One morning in August, 1765, two figures were found hanging on the sturdy branches of Liberty Tree. They were dressed in square-skirted coats and smallclothes; and, as their wigs hung down over their faces, they looked like real men. One was intended to represent the Earl of Bute, who was supposed to have advised the king to tax America. The other was meant for the effigy of Andrew Oliver, a gentleman belonging to one of the most respectable families in Massachusetts."

"What harm had he done?" inquired Charley.

"The king had appointed him to be distributer of the stamps," answered Grandfather. "Mr. Oliver would have made a great deal of money by this business. But the people frightened him so much by hanging him in effigy, and afterwards by breaking into his house, that he promised to have nothing to do with the stamps. And all the king's friends throughout America were compelled to make the same promise."

CHAPTER III

"LIEUTENANT-GOVERNOR HUTCHINSON," continued Grandfather, "now began to be unquiet in our old chair. He had formerly been much respected and beloved by the people, and had often proved himself a friend to their interests. But the time was come, when he could not be a friend to the people, without ceasing to be a friend to the king. It was pretty generally understood, that Hutchinson would act according to the king's wishes, right or wrong, like most of the other gentlemen who held offices under the crown. Besides, as he was brother-in-law of Andrew Oliver, the people now felt a particular dislike to him."

"I should think," said Laurence, "as Mr. Hutchinson had written the history of our Puritan forefathers, he would have known what the temper of the people was, and so have taken care not to wrong them."

"He trusted in the might of the king of England," replied Grandfather, "and thought himself safe under the shelter of the throne. If no dispute had arisen between the king and the people, Hutchinson would have had the character of a wise, good, and patriotic magistrate. But, from the time that he took part against the rights of his country, the people's love and respect were turned to scorn and hatred; and he never had another hour of peace."

In order to show what a fierce and dangerous spirit was now aroused among the inhabitants, Grandfather related a passage from history, which we shall call

THE HUTCHINSON MOB

On the evening of the twenty-sixth of August, 1765, a bonfire was kindled in King Street. It flamed high upward, and threw a ruddy light over the front of the

Town House, on which was displayed a carved repre-sentation of the royal arms. The gilded vane of the cupola glittered in the blaze. The kindling of this bonfire was the well-known signal for the populace of Boston to assemble in the street.

Before the tar-barrels, of which the bonfire was made, were half burnt out, a great crowd had come together. They were chiefly laborers and seafaring men, together with many young apprentices, and all those idle people about town who are ready for any kind of mischief. Doubtless some school-boys were among them.

While these rough figures stood round the blazing bonfire, you might hear them speaking bitter words against the high officers of the province. Governor Bernard, Hutchinson, Oliver, Storey, Hallowell, and other men whom King George delighted to honor, were reviled as traitors to the country. Now and then, per-haps, an officer of the crown passed along the street, wearing the gold-laced hat, white wig, and embroidered waistcoat, which were the fashion of the day. But, when the people beheld him, they set up a wild and angry howl, and their faces had an evil aspect, which was made more terrible by the flickering blaze of the bonfire.

"I should like to throw the traitor right into that blaze!" perhaps one fierce rioter would say.

"Yes, and all his brethren, too!" another might reply; "and the governor and old Tommy Hutchinson in the hottest of it!"

"And the Earl of Bute along with them," muttered a third; "and burn the whole pack of them under King George's nose! No matter if it singed him!"

Some such expressions as these, either shouted aloud, or muttered under the breath, were doubtless heard in King Street. The mob, meanwhile, were growing fiercer and fiercer, and seemed ready even to set the town on fire, for the sake of burning the king's friends out of house and home. And yet, angry as they were, they sometimes broke into a loud roar of laughter, as if mischief and destruction were their sport.

But we must now leave the rioters for a time, and take a peep into the lieutenant-governor's splendid mansion. It was a large brick house, decorated with Ionic pilasters, and stood in Garden Court Street, near the North Square.

While the angry mob in King Street were shouting his name, Lieutenant-Governor Hutchinson sat quietly in Grandfather's chair, unsuspicious of the evil that was about to fall upon his head. His beloved family were in the room with him. He had thrown off his embroidered coat and powdered wig, and had on a loose flowing gown and purple velvet cap. He had likewise laid aside the cares of state, and all the thoughts that had wearied and perplexed him throughout the day.

Perhaps, in the enjoyment of his home, he had forgotten all about the Stamp Act, and scarcely remembered that there was a king, across the ocean, who had resolved to make tributaries of the New Englanders. Possibly, too, he had forgotten his own ambition, and would not have exchanged his situation, at that moment, to be governor, or even a lord.

The wax candles were now lighted, and showed a handsome room, well provided with rich furniture. On the walls hung the pictures of Hutchinson's ancestors, who had been eminent men in their day, and were honorably remembered in the history of the country. Every object served to mark the residence of a rich, aristocratic gentleman, who held himself high above the common people, and could have nothing to fear from them. In a corner of the room, thrown carelessly upon a chair, were the scarlet robes of the chief justice. This high office, as well as those of lieutenant-governor, counsellor, and judge of probate, was filled by Hutchinson.

Who or what could disturb the domestic quiet of such a great and powerful personage as now sat in Grandfather's chair?

The lieutenant-governor's favorite daughter sat by his side. She leaned on the arm of our great chair, and looked up affectionately into her father's face, rejoicing to

perceive that a quiet smile was on his lips.   But suddenly
a shade came across her countenance.   She seemed to
listen attentively, as if to catch a distant sound.

"What is the matter, my child?" inquired Hutchinson.   "Father, do you not hear a tumult in the street?"
said she.

The lieutenant-governor listened.   But his ears were
duller than those of his daughter; he could hear nothing
more terrible than the sound of a summer breeze, sigh-
ing among the tops of the elm-trees.

"No, foolish child!" he replied, playfully patting her
cheek.   "There is no tumult.   Our Boston mobs are
satisfied with what mischief they have already done.
The king's friends need not tremble."

So Hutchinson resumed his pleasant and peaceful
meditations, and again forgot that there were any
troubles in the world.   But his family were alarmed,
and could not help straining their ears to catch the
slightest sound.   More and more distinctly they heard
shouts, and then the trampling of many feet.   While
they were listening, one of the neighbors rushed breath-
less into the room.

"A mob!—a terrible mob!" cried he; "they have
broken into Mr. Storey's house, and into Mr. Hallowell's,
and have made themselves drunk with the liquors in his
cellar, and now they are coming hither, as wild as so
many tigers.   Flee, lieutenant-governor, for your life!
for your life!"

"Father, dear father, make haste," shrieked his
children.

But Hutchinson would not hearken to them.   He was
an old lawyer; and he could not realize that the people
would do anything so utterly lawless as to assault him
in his peaceful home.   He was one of King George's
chief officers; and it would be an insult and outrage
upon the king himself, if the lieutenant-governor should
suffer any wrong.

"Have no fears on my account," said he; "I am perfectly safe.   The king's name shall be my protection."

Yet he bade his family retire into one of the neighboring houses.   His daughter would have remained, but he forced her away.

The huzzas and riotous uproar of the mob were now heard, close at hand.   The sound was terrible, and struck Hutchinson with the same sort of dread as if an enraged wild beast had broken loose, and were roaring for its prey.   He crept softly to the window.   There he beheld an immense concourse of people, filling all the street, and rolling onward to his house.   It was like a tempestuous flood, that had swelled beyond its bounds, and would sweep everything before it.   Hutchinson trembled; he felt at that moment, that the wrath of the people was a thousand-fold more terrible than the wrath of a king.

That was a moment when a loyalist and an aristocrat, like Hutchinson, might have learned how powerless are kings, nobles, and great men, when the low and humble range themselves against them.   King George could do nothing for his servant now.   Had King George been there, he could have done nothing for himself.   If Hutchinson had understood this lesson, and remembered it, he need not, in after years, have been an exile from his native country, or finally have laid his bones in a distant land.

There was now a rush against the doors of the house. The people sent up a hoarse cry.   At this instant, the lieutenant-governor's daughter, whom he had supposed to be in a place of safety, ran into the room, and threw her arms around him.   She had returned by a private entrance.

"Father, are you mad!" cried she.   "Will the king's name protect you now?   Come with me, or they will have your life."

"True," muttered Hutchinson to himself; "what care these roarers for the name of king?   I must flee or they will trample me down, on the door of my own dwelling!"

Hurrying away, he and his daughter made their escape by the private passage, at the moment when the rioters broke into the house.   The foremost of them rushed up the staircase, and entered the room which Hutchinson had just quitted.   There they beheld our good old chair, facing them with quiet dignity, while the lion's head seemed to move its jaws in the unsteady light of their torches. Perhaps the stately aspect of our venerable friend, which had stood firm through a century and a half of trouble, arrested them for an instant.   But they were thrust forward by those behind, and the chair lay overthrown.

Then began the work of destruction.   The carved and polished mahogany tables were shattered with heavy clubs, and hewn to splinters with axes.   The marble hearths and mantel-pieces were broken.   The volumes of Hutchinson's library, so precious to a studious man, were torn out of their covers, and the leaves sent flying out of the windows.   Manuscripts, containing secrets of our country's history, which are now lost forever, were scattered to the winds.

The old ancestral portraits, whose fixed countenances looked down on the wild scene, were rent from the walls. The mob triumphed in their downfall and destruction, as if these pictures of Hutchinson's forefathers had committed the same offences as their descendant.   A tall looking-glass, which had hitherto presented a reflection of the enraged and drunken multitude, was now smashed into a thousand fragments.   We gladly dismiss the scene from the mirror of our fancy.

Before morning dawned, the walls of the house were all that remained.   The interior was a dismal scene of ruin.   A shower pattered in at the broken windows, and when Hutchinson and his family returned, they stood shivering in the same room, where the last evening had seen them so peaceful and happy.

"Grandfather," said Laurence, indignantly, "if the people acted in this manner, they were not worthy of even so much liberty as the king of England was willing to allow them."

"It was a most unjustifiable act, like many other popular movements at that time," replied Grandfather. "But we must not decide against the justice of the people's cause, merely because an excited mob was guilty

of outrageous violence.   Besides, all these things were
done in the first fury of resentment.   Afterwards, the
people grew more calm, and were more influenced by
the counsel of those wise and good men who conducted
them safely and gloriously through the Revolution."

Little Alice, with tears in her blue eyes, said that she
hoped the neighbors had not let Lieutenant-Governor
Hutchinson and his family be homeless in the street,
but had taken them into their houses, and been kind to
them.   Cousin Clara, recollecting the perilous situation
of our beloved chair, inquired what had become of it.

" Nothing was heard of our chair for some time afterwards," answered Grandfather.   "One day in September, the same Andrew Oliver, of whom I before told
you, was summoned to appear at high noon, under Liberty Tree.   This was the strangest summons that had
ever been heard of ; for it was issued in the name of
the whole people, who thus took upon themselves the
authority of a sovereign power.   Mr. Oliver dared not
disobey.   Accordingly, at the appointed hour, he went,
much against his will, to Liberty Tree."

Here Charley interposed a remark that poor Mr. Oliver found but little liberty under Liberty Tree.   Grandfather assented.

" It was a stormy day," continued he.   "The equi-
noctial gale blew violently, and scattered the yellow
leaves of Liberty Tree all along the street.   Mr. Oliver's
wig was dripping with water-drops, and he probably
looked haggard, disconsolate, and humbled to the earth.
Beneath the tree, in Grandfather's chair, — our own venerable chair, — sat Mr. Richard Dana, a justice of the
peace.   He administered an oath to Mr. Oliver, that he
would never have anything to do with distributing the
stamps.   A vast concourse of people heard the oath,
and shouted when it was taken."

" There is something grand in this," said Laurence.
" I like it, because the people seem to have acted with
thoughtfulness and dignity ; and this proud gentleman,
one of his Majesty's high officers, was made to feel that
King George could not protect him in doing wrong."

"He crept softly to the Window."

"But it was a sad day for poor Mr. Oliver," observed Grandfather. "From his youth upward, it had probably been the great principle of his life, to be faithful and obedient to the king. And now, in his old age, it must have puzzled and distracted him, to find the sovereign people setting up a claim to his faith and obedience."

Grandfather closed the evening's conversation by saying that the discontent of America was so great, that, in 1766, the British Parliament was compelled to repeal the Stamp Act. The people made great rejoicings, but took care to keep Liberty Tree well pruned, and free from caterpillars and canker worms. They foresaw, that there might yet be occasion for them to assemble under its far-projecting shadow.

CHAPTER IV

THE next evening, Clara, who remembered that our chair had been left standing in the rain, under Liberty Tree, earnestly besought Grandfather to tell when and where it had next found shelter. Perhaps she was afraid that the venerable chair, by being exposed to the inclemency of a September gale, might get the rheumatism in its aged joints.

"The chair," said Grandfather, "after the ceremony of Mr. Oliver's oath, appears to have been quite forgotten by the multitude. Indeed, being much bruised and rather rickety, owing to the violent treatment it had suffered from the Hutchinson mob, most people would have thought that its days of usefulness were over. Nevertheless, it was conveyed away, under cover of the night, and committed to the care of a skilful joiner. He doctored our old friend so successfully, that, in the course of a few days, it made its appearance in the public room of the British Coffee House in King Street."

"But why did not Mr. Hutchinson get possession of it again?" inquired Charley.

"I know not," answered Grandfather, "unless he considered it a dishonor and disgrace to the chair to have stood under Liberty Tree. At all events, he suffered it to remain at the British Coffee House, which was the principal hotel in Boston. It could not possibly have found a situation, where it would be more in the midst of business and bustle, or would witness more important events, or be occupied by a greater variety of persons."

Grandfather went on to tell the proceedings of the despotic king and ministry of England, after the repeal of the Stamp Act. They could not bear to think, that their right to tax America should be disputed by the people. In the year 1767, therefore, they caused Parliament to pass an act for laying a duty on tea, and some

132

other articles that were in general use. Nobody could now buy a pound of tea, without paying a tax to King George. This scheme was pretty craftily contrived; for the women of America were very fond of tea, and did not like to give up the use of it.

But the people were as much opposed to this new act of Parliament, as they had been to the Stamp Act. England, however, was determined that they should submit. In order to compel their obedience, two regiments, consisting of more than seven hundred British soldiers, were sent to Boston. They arrived in September, 1768, and were landed on Long Wharf. Thence they marched to the Common, with loaded muskets, fixed bayonets, and great pomp and parade. So now, at last, the free town of Boston was guarded and overawed by redcoats, as it had been in the days of old Sir Edmund Andros.

In the month of November, more regiments arrived. There were now four thousand troops in Boston. The Common was whitened with their tents. Some of the soldiers were lodged in Faneuil Hall, which the inhabitants looked upon as a consecrated place, because it had been the scene of a great many meetings in favor of liberty. One regiment was placed in the Town House, which we now call the Old State House. The lower floor of this edifice had hitherto been used by the merchants as an exchange. In the upper stories were the chambers of the judges, the representatives, and the governor's council. The venerable counsellors could not assemble to consult about the welfare of the province, without being challenged by sentinels, and passing among the bayonets of the British soldiers.

Sentinels likewise were posted at the lodgings of the officers, in many parts of the town. When the inhabitants approached, they were greeted by the sharp question — " Who goes there?" while the rattle of the soldier's musket was heard, as he presented it against their breasts. There was no quiet, even on the Sabbath day. The pious descendants of the Puritans were shocked by the uproar of military music, the drum, fife,

and bugle drowning the holy organ peal and the voices
of the singers.   It would appear as if the British took
every method to insult the feelings of the people.

"Grandfather," cried Charley, impatiently, "the
people did not go to fighting half soon enough! These
British red-coats ought to have been driven back to their
vessels, the very moment they landed on Long Wharf."

"Many a hot-headed young man said the same as you
do, Charley," answered Grandfather.   "But the elder
and wiser people saw that the time was not yet come.
Meanwhile, let us take another peep at our old chair."

"Ah, it drooped its head I know," said Charley,
"when it saw how the province was disgraced.   Its old
Puritan friends never would have borne such doings."

"The chair," proceeded Grandfather, "was now continually occupied by some of the high tories, as the king's
friends were called, who frequented the British Coffee
House.   Officers of the custom-house, too, which stood
on the opposite side of King Street, often sat in the
chair, wagging their tongues against John Hancock."

"Why against him?" asked Charley.

"Because he was a great merchant, and contended
against paying duties to the king," said Grandfather.

"Well, frequently, no doubt, the officers of the British
regiments, when not on duty, used to fling themselves
into the arms of our venerable chair.   Fancy one of
them, a red-nosed captain, in his scarlet uniform, playing with the hilt of his sword, and making a circle of his
brother officers merry with ridiculous jokes at the expense of the poor Yankees.   And perhaps he would call
for a bottle of wine or a steaming bowl of punch, and
drink confusion to all rebels."

"Our grave old chair must have been scandalized at
such scenes," observed Laurence.   "The chair that had
been the Lady Arbella's, and which the holy Apostle
Eliot had consecrated."

"It certainly was little less than sacrilege," replied
Grandfather; "but the time was coming, when even the
churches, where hallowed pastors had long preached the
word of God, were to be torn down or desecrated by

the British troops. Some years passed, however, before such things were done."

Grandfather now told his auditors that, in 1769, Sir Francis Bernard went to England, after having been governor of Massachusetts ten years. He was a gentleman of many good qualities, an excellent scholar, and a friend to learning. But he was naturally of an arbitrary disposition; and he had been bred at the University of Oxford, where young men were taught that the divine right of kings was the only thing to be regarded in matters of government. Such ideas were ill adapted to please the people of Massachusetts. They rejoiced to get rid of Sir Francis Bernard, but liked his successor, Lieutenant-Governor Hutchinson, no better than himself.

About this period the people were much incensed at an act, committed by a person who held an office in the custom-house. Some lads, or young men, were snowballing his windows. He fired a musket at them and killed a poor German boy, only eleven years old. This event made a great noise in town and country, and much increased the resentment that was already felt against the servants of the crown.

"Now, children," said Grandfather, "I wish to make you comprehend the position of the British troops in King Street. This is the same which we now call State Street. On the south side of the Town House, or Old State House, was what military men call a court of guard, defended by two brass cannons, which pointed directly at one of the doors of the above edifice. A large party of soldiers were always stationed in the court of guard. The custom-house stood at a little distance down King Street, nearly where the Suffolk Bank now stands; and a sentinel was continually pacing before its front."

"I shall remember this, to-morrow," said Charley; "and I will go to State Street, so as to see exactly where the British troops were stationed."

"And, before long," observed Grandfather, "I shall have to relate an event, which made King Street sadly famous on both sides of the Atlantic. The history of our chair will soon bring us to this melancholy business."

Here Grandfather described the state of things, which arose from the ill-will that existed between the inhabitants and the red-coats. The old and sober part of the town's-people were very angry at the government for sending soldiers to overawe them. But those gray-headed men were cautious, and kept their thoughts and feelings in their own breasts, without putting themselves in the way of the British bayonets.

The younger people, however, could hardly be kept within such prudent limits. They reddened with wrath at the very sight of a soldier, and would have been willing to come to blows with them, at any moment. For it was their opinion, that every tap of a British drum within the peninsula of Boston, was an insult to the brave old town.

"It was sometimes the case," continued Grandfather, "that affrays happened between such wild young men as these, and small parties of the soldiers. No weapons had hitherto been used, except fists or cudgels. But, when men have loaded muskets in their hands, it is easy to foretell that they will soon be turned against the bosoms of those who provoke their anger."

"Grandfather," said little Alice, looking fearfully into his face, "your voice sounds as though you were going to tell us something awful!"

CHAPTER V

LITTLE Alice, by her last remark, proved herself a good judge of what was expressed by the tones of Grandfather's voice. He had given the above description of the enmity between the town's-people and the soldiers, in order to prepare the minds of his auditors for a very terrible event. It was one that did more to heighten the quarrel between England and America, than anything that had yet occurred.

Without further preface, Grandfather began the story of

THE BOSTON MASSACRE

It was now the 3d of March, 1770. The sunset music of the British regiments was heard, as usual, throughout the town. The shrill fife and rattling drum awoke the echoes in King Street, while the last ray of sunshine was lingering on the cupola of the Town House. And now, all the sentinels were posted. One of them marched up and down before the custom-house, treading a short path through the snow, and longing for the time when he would be dismissed to the warm fireside of the guard-room. Meanwhile, Captain Preston was perhaps sitting in our great chair, before the hearth of the British Coffee House. In the course of the evening, there were two or three slight commotions, which seemed to indicate that trouble was at hand. Small parties of young men stood at the corners of the streets, or walked along the narrow pavements. Squads of soldiers, who were dismissed from duty, passed by them, shoulder to shoulder, with the regular step which they had learned at the drill. Whenever these encounters took place, it appeared to be the object of the young men to treat the soldiers with as much incivility as possible.

"Turn out, you lobster-backs!" one would say. "Crowd them off the side-walks!" another would cry. "A red-coat has no right in Boston streets."

"Oh, you rebel rascals!" perhaps the soldiers would reply, glaring fiercely at the young men. "Some day or other, we'll make our way through Boston streets, at the point of the bayonet!"

Once or twice, such disputes as these brought on a scuffle; which passed off, however, without attracting much notice. About eight o'clock, for some unknown cause, an alarm bell rang loudly and hurriedly.

At the sound, many people ran out of their houses, supposing it to be an alarm of fire. But there were no flames to be seen; nor was there any smell of smoke in the clear frosty air; so that most of the townsmen went back to their own firesides, and sat talking with their wives and children about the calamities of the times. Others, who were younger and less prudent, remained in the streets; for there seems to have been a presentiment that some strange event was on the eve of taking place.

Later in the evening, not far from nine o'clock, several young men passed by the Town House and walked down King Street. The sentinel was still on his post, in front of the custom-house, pacing to and fro, while, as he turned, a gleam of light, from some neighboring window, glittered on the barrel of his musket. At no great distance were the barracks and the guard-house, where his comrades were probably telling stories of battle and bloodshed.

Down towards the custom-house, as I told you, came a party of wild young men. When they drew near the sentinel, he halted on his post, and took his musket from his shoulder, ready to present the bayonet at their breasts.

"Who goes there?" he cried, in the gruff, peremptory tones of a soldier's challenge.

The young men, being Boston boys, felt as if they had a right to walk their own streets, without being accountable to a British red-coat, even though he challenged them in King George's name. They made some rude answer to the sentinel. There was a dispute, or perhaps a scuffle. Other soldiers heard the noise, and ran hastily from the barracks, to assist their comrade. At the same time, many of the town's-people rushed into King Street, by various avenues, and gathered in a crowd round about the custom-house. It seemed wonderful how such a multitude had started up, all of a sudden.

The wrongs and insults, which the people had been suffering for many months, now kindled them into a rage. They threw snow-balls and lumps of ice at the soldiers. As the tumult grew louder, it reached the ears of Captain Preston, the officer of the day. He immediately ordered eight soldiers of the main guard to take their muskets and follow him. They marched across the street, forcing their way roughly through the crowd, and pricking the town's-people with their bayonets.

A gentleman (it was Henry Knox, afterwards general of the American artillery) caught Captain Preston's arm.

"For Heaven's sake, sir," exclaimed he, "take heed what you do, or here will be bloodshed."

"Stand aside!" answered Captain Preston, haughtily. "Do not interfere, sir. Leave me to manage the affair."

Arriving at the sentinel's post, Captain Preston drew up his men in a semicircle, with their faces to the crowd and their rear to the custom-house. When the people saw the officer, and beheld the threatening attitude with which the soldiers fronted them, their rage became almost uncontrollable.

"Fire, you lobster-backs!" bellowed some.

"You dare not fire, you cowardly red-coats," cried others.

"Rush upon them!" shouted many voices. "Drive the rascals to their barracks! Down with them! Down with them! Let them fire, if they dare!"

Amid the uproar, the soldiers stood glaring at the people, with the fierceness of men whose trade was to shed blood.

Oh, what a crisis had now arrived! Up to this very moment the angry feelings between England and America might have been pacified. England had but to stretch out the hand of reconciliation, and acknowledge that she had hitherto mistaken her rights but would do so no more. Then, the ancient bonds of brotherhood would again have been knit together, as firmly as in old times. The habit of loyalty, which had grown as strong as instinct, was not utterly overcome. The perils shared, the victories won, in the Old French War, when the soldiers of the colonies fought side by side with their comrades from beyond the sea, were unforgotten yet. England was still that beloved country which the colonists called their home. King George, though he had frowned on America, was still reverenced as a father.

But, should the king's soldiers shed one drop of American blood, then it was a quarrel to the death. Never — never would America rest satisfied, until she had torn down the royal authority and trampled it in the dust.

" Fire, if you dare, villains! " hoarsely shouted the people, while the muzzles of the muskets were turned upon them ; "you dare not fire! "

They appeared ready to rush upon the levelled bayonets. Captain Preston waved his sword, and uttered a command which could not be distinctly heard, amid the uproar of shouts that issued from a hundred throats. But his soldiers deemed that he had spoken the fatal mandate — " Fire! " The flash of their muskets lighted up the street, and the report rang loudly between the edifices. It was said, too, that the figure of a man with a cloth hanging down over his face, was seen to step into the balcony of the custom-house, and discharge a musket at the crowd.

A gush of smoke had overspread the scene. It rose heavily, as if it were loath to reveal the dreadful spectacle beneath it. Eleven of the sons of New England lay stretched upon the street. Some, sorely wounded, were struggling to rise again. Others stirred not, nor groaned, for they were past all pain. Blood was streaming upon the snow; and that purple stain, in the midst of King Street, though it melted away in the next day's sun, was never forgotten nor forgiven by the people.

Grandfather was interrupted by the violent sobs of little Alice. In his earnestness, he had neglected to soften down the narrative, so that it might not terrify the heart of this unworldly infant. Since Grandfather began the history of our chair, little Alice had listened to many tales of war. But, probably, the idea had never really impressed itself upon her mind, that men have shed the blood of their fellow-creatures. And now that this idea was forcibly presented to her, it affected the sweet child with bewilderment and horror.

"I ought to have remembered our dear little Alice," said Grandfather reproachfully to himself. "Oh, what a pity! Her heavenly nature has now received its first impression of earthly sin and violence. Well, Clara, take her to bed, and comfort her. Heaven grant that she may dream away the recollection of the Boston Massacre!"

"Grandfather," said Charley, when Clara and little Alice had retired, "did not the people rush upon the soldiers, and take revenge?"

"The town drums beat to arms," replied Grandfather, "the alarm bells rang, and an immense multitude rushed into King Street. Many of them had weapons in their hands. The British prepared to defend themselves. A whole regiment was drawn up in the street, expecting an attack; for the townsmen appeared ready to throw themselves upon the bayonets."

"And how did it end?" asked Charley.

"Governor Hutchinson hurried to the spot," said Grandfather, "and besought the people to have patience, promising that strict justice should be done. A day or two afterward, the British troops were withdrawn from town, and stationed at Castle William. Captain Preston and the eight soldiers were tried for murder. But none of them were found guilty. The judges told

the jury that the insults and violence which had been offered to the soldiers justified them in firing at the mob."

"The Revolution," observed Laurence, who had said
but little during the evening, "was not such a calm,
majestic movement as I supposed.   I do not love to
hear of mobs and broils in the street.   These things
were unworthy of the people, when they had such a
great object to accomplish."

"Nevertheless, the world has seen no grander movement than that of our Revolution, from first to last,"
said Grandfather.   "The people, to a man, were full of
a great and noble sentiment.   True, there may be much
fault to find with their mode of expressing this sentiment ; but they knew no better — the necessity was
upon them to act out their feelings, in the best manner
they could.   We must forgive what was wrong in their
actions, and look into their hearts and minds for the
honorable motives that impelled them."

"And I suppose," said Laurence, "there were men
who knew how to act worthily of what they felt."

"There were many such," replied Grandfather, "and
we will speak of some of them, hereafter."

Grandfather here made a pause.   That night, Charley
had a dream about the Boston Massacre, and thought
that he himself was in the crowd, and struck down Captain Preston with a great club.   Laurence dreamed that
he was sitting in our great chair, at the window of the
British Coffee House, and beheld the whole scene which
Grandfather had described.   It seemed to him, in his
dream, that if the town's-people and the soldiers would
but have heard him speak a single word, all the slaughter
might have been averted.   But there was such an uproar
that it drowned his voice.

The next morning, the two boys went together to State
Street, and stood on the very spot where the first blood
of the Revolution had been shed.   The Old State House
was still there, presenting almost the same aspect that it
had worn on that memorable evening, one-and-seventy
years ago.   It is the sole remaining witness of the Boston
Massacre.

CHAPTER VI

THE next evening the astral lamp was lighted earlier than usual, because Laurence was very much engaged in looking over the collection of portraits which had been his New Year's gift from Grandfather.

Among them he found the features of more than one famous personage who had been connected with the adventures of our old chair. Grandfather bade him draw the table nearer to the fireside; and they looked over the portraits together, while Clara and Charley likewise lent their attention. As for little Alice, she sat in Grandfather's lap, and seemed to see the very men alive, whose faces were there represented.

Turning over the volume, Laurence came to the portrait of a stern, grim-looking man, in plain attire of much more modern fashion than that of the old Puritans. But the face might well have befitted one of those iron-hearted men. Beneath the portrait was the name of Samuel Adams.

"He was a man of great note in all the doings that brought about the Revolution," said Grandfather. "His character was such, that it seemed as if one of the ancient Puritans had been sent back to earth, to animate the people's hearts with the same abhorrence of tyranny, that had distinguished the earliest settlers. He was as religious as they, as stern and inflexible, and as deeply imbued with democratic principles. He, better than any one else, may be taken as a representative of the people of New England, and of the spirit with which they engaged in the revolutionary struggle. He was a poor man, and earned his bread by an humble occupation; but with his tongue and pen, he made the king of England tremble on his throne. Remember him, my children, as one of the strong men of our country."

"Here is one whose looks show a very different character," observed Laurence, turning to the portrait of John Hancock. "I should think, by his splendid dress and courtly aspect, that he was one of the king's friends."

"There never was a greater contrast than between Samuel Adams and John Hancock," said Grandfather. "Yet they were of the same side in politics, and had an equal agency in the Revolution. Hancock was born to the inheritance of the largest fortune in New England. His tastes and habits were aristocratic. He loved gorgeous attire, a splendid mansion, magnificent furniture, stately festivals, and all that was glittering and pompous in external things. His manners were so polished, that there stood not a nobleman at the footstool of King George's throne, who was a more skilful courtier than John Hancock might have been. Nevertheless, he, in his embroidered clothes, and Samuel Adams, in his threadbare coat, wrought together in the cause of liberty. Adams acted from pure and rigid principle. Hancock, though he loved his country, yet thought quite as much of his own popularity as he did of the people's rights. It is remarkable, that these two men, so very different as I describe them, were the only two exempted from pardon by the king's proclamation."

On the next leaf of the book was the portrait of General Joseph Warren. Charley recognized the name, and said that here was a greater man than either Hancock or Adams.

"Warren was an eloquent and able patriot," replied Grandfather. "He deserves a lasting memory for his zealous efforts in behalf of liberty. No man's voice was more powerful in Faneuil Hall than Joseph Warren's. If his death had not happened so early in the contest, he would probably have gained a high name as a soldier."

The next portrait was a venerable man who held his thumb under his chin, and, through his spectacles, appeared to be attentively reading a manuscript.

"Here we see the most illustrious Boston boy that ever lived," said Grandfather. "This is Benjamin

Franklin! But I will not try to compress, into a few sentences, the character of the sage who, as a Frenchman expressed it, snatched the lightning from the sky, and the sceptre from the tyrant. Mr. Sparks must help you to the knowledge of Franklin."

The book likewise contained portraits of James Otis and Josiah Quincy. Both of them, Grandfather observed, were men of wonderful talents and true patriotism. Their voices were like the stirring tones of a trumpet, arousing the country to defend its freedom. Heaven seemed to have provided a greater number of eloquent men than had appeared at any other period, in order that the people might be fully instructed as to their wrongs, and the method of resistance.

"It is marvellous," said Grandfather, "to see how many powerful writers, orators, and soldiers started up, just at the time when they were wanted. There was a man for every kind of work. It is equally wonderful, that men of such different characters were all made to unite in the one object of establishing the freedom and independence of America. There was an overruling Providence above them."

"Here was another great man," remarked Laurence, pointing to the portrait of John Adams.

"Yes; an earnest, warm-tempered, honest, and most able man," said Grandfather. "At the period of which we are now speaking, he was a lawyer in Boston. He was destined, in after years, to be ruler over the whole American people, whom he contributed so much to form into a nation."

Grandfather here remarked, that many a New Englander, who had passed his boyhood and youth in obscurity, afterward attained to a fortune, which he never could have foreseen, even in his most ambitious dreams. John Adams, the second president of the United States, and the equal of crowned kings, was once a schoolmaster and country lawyer. Hancock, the first signer of the Declaration of Independence, served his apprenticeship with a merchant. Samuel Adams, afterwards governor of Massachusetts, was a small tradesman and a tax-gatherer. General Warren was a physician, General Lincoln a farmer, and General Knox a bookbinder. General Nathaniel Greene, the best soldier, except Washington, in the revolutionary army, was a Quaker and a blacksmith. All these became illustrious men, and can never be forgotten in American history.

"And any boy, who is born in America, may look forward to the same things," said our ambitious friend Charley.

After these observations, Grandfather drew the book of portraits towards him, and showed the children several British peers and members of Parliament, who had exerted themselves either for or against the rights of America. There were the Earl of Bute, Mr. Grenville, and Lord North. These were looked upon as deadly enemies to our country.

Among the friends of America was Mr. Pitt, afterward Earl of Chatham, who spent so much of his wondrous eloquence in endeavoring to warn England of the consequences of her injustice. He fell down on the floor of the House of Lords, after uttering almost his dying words in defence of our privileges as freemen. There was Edmund Burke, one of the wisest men and greatest orators that ever the world produced. There was Colonel Barré, who had been among our fathers, and knew that they had courage enough to die for their rights. There was Charles James Fox, who never rested until he had silenced our enemies in the House of Commons.

"It is very remarkable to observe how many of the ablest orators in the British Parliament were favorable to America," said Grandfather. "We ought to remember these great Englishmen with gratitude; for their speeches encouraged our fathers, almost as much as those of our own orators in Faneuil Hall and under Liberty Tree. Opinions which might have been received with doubt, if expressed only by a native American, were set down as true, beyond dispute, when they came from the lips of Chatham, Burke, Barré, or Fox."

"But, Grandfather," asked Laurence, " were there no

able and eloquent men in this country who took the
part of King George?"

"There were many men of talent, who said what
they could in defence of the king's tyrannical proceedings," replied Grandfather. "But they had the worst
side of the argument and therefore seldom said anything
worth remembering. Moreover their hearts were faint
and feeble; for they felt that the people scorned and
detested them. They had no friends, no defence, except
in the bayonets of the British troops. A blight fell
upon all their faculties, because they were contending
against the rights of their own native land."

"What were the names of some of them?" inquired
Charley.

"Governor Hutchinson, Chief Justice Oliver, Judge
Auchmuty, the Reverend Mather Byles and several
other clergymen were among the most noted loyalists,"
answered Grandfather.

"I wish the people had tarred and feathered every
man of them!" cried Charley.

"That wish is very wrong, Charley," said Grandfather. "You must not think that there was no integrity and honor, except among those who stood up for
the freedom of America. For aught I know, there was
quite as much of these qualities on one side as on the
other. Do you see nothing admirable in a faithful ad-
herence to an unpopular cause? Can you not respect
that principle of loyalty, which made the royalists give
up country, friends, fortune, everything, rather than be
false to their king? It was a mistaken principle; but
many of them cherished it honorably, and were martyrs
to it."

"Oh, I was wrong!" said Charley, ingenuously. "And
I would risk my life, rather than one of those good old
royalists should be tarred and feathered."

"The time is now come when we may judge fairly of
them," continued Grandfather. "Be the good and true
men among them honored; for they were as much our
countrymen as the patriots were. And, thank Heaven!
our country need not be ashamed of her sons — of most

of them, at least — whatever side they took in the revolutionary contest."

Among the portraits was one of King George the Third. Little Alice clapped her hands, and seemed pleased with the bluff good-nature of his physiognomy.. But Laurence thought it strange that a man with such a face, indicating hardly a common share of intellect, should have had influence enough on human affairs, to convulse the world with war. Grandfather observed that this poor king had always appeared to him one of the most unfortunate persons that ever lived. He was so honest and conscientious, that if he had been only a private man, his life would probably have been blameless and happy. But his was that worst of fortunes, to be placed in a station far beyond his abilities.

"And so," said Grandfather, "his life, while he retained what intellect Heaven had gifted him with, was one long mortification. At last, he grew crazed with care and trouble. For nearly twenty years, the monarch of England was confined as a madman. In his old age, too, God took away his eyesight; so that his royal palace was nothing to him but a dark, lonesome prison-house."

CHAPTER VII

"OUR old chair," resumed Grandfather, "did not now stand in the midst of a gay circle of British officers. The troops, as I told you, had been removed to Castle William, immediately after the Boston Massacre. Still, however, there were many tories, customhouse officers, and Englishmen, who used to assemble in the British Coffee House, and talk over the affairs of the period. Matters grew worse and worse; and in 1773, the people did a deed, which incensed the king and ministry more than any of their former doings."

Grandfather here described the affair, which is known by the name of the Boston Tea Party. The Americans, for some time past, had left off importing tea, on account of the oppressive tax. The East India Company, in London, had a large stock of tea on hand, which they had expected to sell to the Americans, but could find no market for it. But, after a while, the government persuaded this company of merchants to send the tea to America.

"How odd it is," observed Clara, "that the liberties of America should have had anything to do with a cup of tea!"

Grandfather smiled, and proceeded with his narrative. When the people of Boston heard that several cargoes of tea were coming across the Atlantic, they held a great many meetings at Faneuil Hall, in the Old South Church, and under Liberty Tree. In the midst of their debates, three ships arrived in the harbor with the tea on board. The people spent more than a fortnight in consulting what should be done. At last, on the 16th of December, 1773, they demanded of Governor Hutchinson that he should immediately send the ships back to England.

149

The governor replied that the ships must not leave the harbor, until the custom-house duties upon the tea should be paid. Now, the payment of these duties was the very thing against which the people had set their faces, because it was a tax unjustly imposed upon America by the English government. Therefore, in the dusk of the evening, as soon as Governor Hutchinson's reply was received, an immense crowd hastened to Griffin's Wharf, where the tea-ships lay. The place is now called Liverpool Wharf.

"When the crowd reached the wharf," said Grandfather, "they saw that a set of wild-looking figures were already on board of the ships. You would have imagined that the Indian warriors, of old times, had come back again; for they wore the Indian dress, and had their faces covered with red and black paint, like the Indians, when they go to war. These grim figures hoisted the tea chests on the decks of the vessels, broke them open, and threw all the contents into the harbor."

"Grandfather," said little Alice, "I suppose Indians don't love tea; else they would never waste it so."

"They were not real Indians, my child," answered Grandfather. "They were white men in disguise; because a heavy punishment would have been inflicted on them, if the King's officers had found who they were. But it was never known. From that day to this, though the matter has been talked of by all the world, nobody can tell the names of those Indian figures. Some people say that there were very famous men among them, who afterwards became governors and generals. Whether this be true I cannot tell."

When tidings of this bold deed were carried to England, King George was greatly enraged. Parliament immediately passed an act, by which all vessels were forbidden to take in or discharge their cargoes at the port of Boston. In this way, they expected to ruin all the merchants, and starve the poor people by depriving them of employment. At the same time, another act was passed, taking away many rights and privileges which had been granted in the charter of Massachusetts.

Governor Hutchinson, soon afterward, was summoned to England, in order that he might give his advice about the management of American affairs. General Gage, an officer of the Old French War, and since commander-in-chief of the British forces in America, was appointed governor in his stead. One of his first acts was to make Salem, instead of Boston, the metropolis of Massachusetts, by summoning the General Court to meet there.

According to Grandfather's description, this was the most gloomy time that Massachusetts had ever seen. The people groaned under as heavy a tyranny as in the days of Sir Edmund Andros. Boston looked as if it were afflicted with some dreadful pestilence, — so sad were the inhabitants, and so desolate the streets. There was no cheerful hum of business. The merchants shut up their warehouses, and the laboring men stood idle about the wharves. But all America felt interested in the good town of Boston; and contributions were raised, in many places, for the relief of the poor inhabitants.

"Our dear old chair!" exclaimed Clara. "How dismal it must have been now!"

"Oh," replied Grandfather, "a gay throng of officers had now come back to the British Coffee House; so that the old chair had no lack of mirthful company. Soon after General Gage became governor, a great many troops had arrived, and were encamped upon the Common. Boston was now a garrisoned and fortified town; for the general had built a battery across the neck, on the road to Roxbury, and placed guards for its defence. Everything looked as if a civil war were close at hand."

"Did the people make ready to fight?" asked Charley.

"A continental Congress assembled at Philadelphia," said Grandfather, "and proposed such measures as they thought most conducive to the public good. A

provincial Congress was likewise chosen in Massachusetts.   They exhorted the people to arm and discipline
themselves.   A great number of minute men were
enrolled.   The Americans called them minute men,
because they engaged to be ready to fight at a minute's
warning.   The English officers laughed, and said that
the name was a very proper one, because the minute
men would run away the minute they saw the enemy.
Whether they would fight or run, was soon to be
proved."

Grandfather told the children, that the first open
resistance offered to the British troops, in the province
of Massachusetts, was at Salem.   Colonel Timothy
Pickering, with thirty or forty militia men, prevented
the English colonel, Leslie, with four times as many
regular soldiers, from taking possession of some military
stores.   No blood was shed on this occasion; but, soon
afterward, it began to flow.   General Gage sent eight
hundred soldiers to Concord, about eighteen miles
from Boston, to destroy some ammunition and provisions which the colonists had collected there.   They
set out on their march in the evening of the 18th of
April, 1775.   The next morning, the general sent Lord
Percy, with nine hundred men, to strengthen the troops
that had gone before.   All that day the inhabitants of
Boston heard various rumors.   Some said that the
British were making great slaughter among our countrymen.   Others affirmed that every man had turned
out with his musket, and that not a single soldier would
ever get back to Boston.

"It was after sunset," continued Grandfather, "when
the troops, who had marched forth so proudly, were
seen entering Charlestown.   They were covered with
dust, and so hot and weary that their tongues hung
out of their mouths.   Many of them were faint with
wounds.   They had not all returned.   Nearly three
hundred were strown, dead or dying, along the road
from Concord.   The yeomanry had risen upon the
invaders, and driven them back."

"Was this the battle of Lexington?" asked Charley.

"Yes," replied Grandfather; "it was so called, because the British, without provocation, had fired upon a party of minute men, near Lexington meeting-house, and killed eight of them. That fatal volley, which was fired by order of Major Pitcairn, began the war of the Revolution."

About this time, if Grandfather had been correctly informed, our chair disappeared from the British Coffee House. The manner of its departure cannot be satisfactorily ascertained. Perhaps the keeper of the Coffee House turned it out of doors, on account of its old-fashioned aspect. Perhaps he sold it as a curiosity. Perhaps it was taken, without leave, by some person who regarded it as public property, because it had once figured under Liberty Tree. Or, perhaps, the old chair, being of a peaceable disposition, had made use of its four oaken legs, and run away from the seat of war.

"It would have made a terrible clattering over the pavement," said Charley, laughing.

"Meanwhile," continued Grandfather, "during the mysterious non-appearance of our chair, an army of twenty thousand men had started up, and come to the siege of Boston. General Gage and his troops were cooped up within the narrow precincts of the peninsula. On the 17th of June, 1775, the famous battle of Bunker Hill was fought. Here General Warren fell. The British got the victory, indeed, but with the loss of more than a thousand officers and men."

"Oh, Grandfather," cried Charley, "you must tell us about that famous battle."

"No, Charley," said Grandfather, "I am not like other historians. Battles shall not hold a prominent place in the history of our quiet and comfortable old chair. But, to-morrow evening, Laurence, Clara, and yourself, and dear little Alice too, shall visit the Diorama of Bunker Hill. There you shall see the whole business, the burning of Charlestown and all, with your own eyes, and hear the cannon and musketry with your own ears."

CHAPTER VIII

THE next evening but one, when the children had given Grandfather a full account of the Diorama of Bunker Hill, they entreated him not to keep them any longer in suspense about the fate of his chair. The reader will recollect, that at the last accounts, it had trotted away upon its poor old legs, nobody knew whither. But, before gratifying their curiosity, Grandfather found it necessary to say something about public events.

The continental Congress, which was assembled at Philadelphia, was composed of delegates from all the colonies. They had now appointed George Washington, of Virginia, to be commander-in-chief of all the American armies. He was, at that time, a member of Congress, but immediately left Philadelphia, and began his journey to Massachusetts. On the 3d of July, 1775, he arrived at Cambridge, and took command of the troops which were besieging General Gage.

"Oh, Grandfather," exclaimed Laurence, "it makes my heart throb to think what is coming now. We are to see General Washington himself."

The children crowded around Grandfather, and looked earnestly into his face. Even little Alice opened her sweet blue eyes, with her lips apart, and almost held her breath to listen; so instinctive is the reverence of childhood for the father of his country. Grandfather paused a moment; for he felt as if it might be irreverent to introduce the hallowed shade of Washington into a history, where an ancient elbow chair occupied the most prominent place. However, he determined to proceed with his narrative, and speak of the hero when it was needful, but with an unambitious simplicity.

So Grandfather told his auditors, that, on General

Washington's arrival at Cambridge, his first care was to reconnoitre the British troops with his spy-glass, and to examine the condition of his own army. He found that the American troops amounted to about fourteen thousand men. They were extended all round the peninsula of Boston, a space of twelve miles, from the high grounds of Roxbury on the right, to Mystic River on the left. Some were living in tents of sail-cloth, some in shanties, rudely constructed of boards, some in huts of stone or turf, with curious windows and doors of basket-work.

In order to be near the centre, and oversee the whole of this wide-stretched army, the commander-in-chief made his headquarters at Cambridge, about half a mile from the colleges. A mansion-house, which perhaps had been the country-seat of some tory gentleman, was provided for his residence.

"When General Washington first entered this mansion," said Grandfather, "he was ushered up the staircase, and shown into a handsome apartment. He sat down in a large chair, which was the most conspicuous object in the room. The noble figure of Washington would have done honor to a throne. As he sat there, with his hand resting on the hilt of his sheathed sword, which was placed between his knees, his whole aspect well befitted the chosen man on whom his country leaned for the defence of her dearest rights. America seemed safe, under his protection. His face was grander than any sculptor had ever wrought in marble; none could behold him without awe and reverence. Never before had the lion's head, at the summit of the chair, looked down upon such a face and form as Washington's!"

"Why! Grandfather," cried Clara, clasping her hands in amazement, "was it really so? Did General Washington sit in our great chair?"

"I knew how it would be," said Laurence; "I foresaw it, the moment Grandfather began to speak."

Grandfather smiled. But, turning from the personal and domestic life of the illustrious leader, he spoke of

the methods which Washington adopted to win back
the metropolis of New England from the British.

The army, when he took command of it, was without
any discipline or order.   The privates considered themselves as good as their officers, and seldom thought it
necessary to obey their commands, unless they understood the why and wherefore.   Moreover, they were
enlisted for so short a period, that, as soon as they
began to be respectable soldiers, it was time to discharge them.   Then came new recruits, who had to be
taught their duty, before they could be of any service.
Such was the army with which Washington had to
contend against more than twenty veteran British regiments.

Some of the men had no muskets, and almost all were
without bayonets.   Heavy cannon, for battering the
British fortifications, were much wanted.   There was
but a small quantity of powder and ball, few tools to
build intrenchments with, and a great deficiency of
provisions and clothes for the soldiers.   Yet, in spite
of these perplexing difficulties, the eyes of the whole
people were fixed on General Washington, expecting
him to undertake some great enterprise against the
hostile army.

The first thing that he found necessary, was to bring
his own men into better order and discipline.   It is
wonderful how soon he transformed this rough mob of
country people into the semblance of a regular army.
One of Washington's most invaluable characteristics
was the faculty of bringing order out of confusion.   All
business, with which he had any concern, seemed to
regulate itself, as if by magic.   The influence of his
mind was like light, gleaming through an unshaped
world.   It was this faculty, more than any other, that
made him so fit to ride upon the storm of the Revolution, when everything was unfixed and drifting about in
a troubled sea.

"Washington had not been long at the head of the
army," proceeded Grandfather, "before his soldiers
thought as highly of him as if he had led them to a

hundred victories.   They knew that he was the very man whom the country needed, and the only one who could bring them safely through the great contest against the might of England.   They put entire confidence in his courage, wisdom, and integrity."

"And were they not eager to follow him against the British?" asked Charley.

"Doubtless they would have gone whithersoever his sword pointed the way," answered Grandfather; "and Washington was anxious to make a decisive assault upon the enemy.   But, as the enterprise was very hazardous, he called a council of all the generals in the army.   Accordingly, they came from their different posts, and were ushered into the reception room.   The commander-in-chief arose from our great chair to greet them."

"What were their names?" asked Charley.

"There was General Artemas Ward," replied Grandfather, "a lawyer by profession.   He had commanded the troops before Washington's arrival.   Another was General Charles Lee, who had been a colonel in the English army, and was thought to possess vast military science.   He came to the council, followed by two or three dogs, who were always at his heels.   There was General Putnam, too, who was known all over New England by the name of Old Put."

"Was it he who killed the wolf?" inquired Charley.

"The same," said Grandfather; "and he had done good service in the Old French War.   His occupation was that of a farmer; but he left his plough in the furrow, at the news of Lexington battle.   Then there was General Gates, who afterward gained great renown at Saratoga, and lost it again at Camden.   General Greene, of Rhode Island, was likewise at the council.   Washington soon discovered him to be one of the best officers in the army."

When the generals were all assembled, Washington consulted them about a plan for storming the English batteries.   But it was their unanimous opinion that so perilous an enterprise ought not to be attempted.   The army, therefore, continued to besiege Boston, preventing the enemy from obtaining supplies of provisions, but without taking any immediate measures to get possession of the town. In this manner the summer, autumn, and winter passed away.

"Many a night, doubtless," said Grandfather, "after Washington had been all day on horseback, galloping from one post of the army to another, he used to sit in our great chair, wrapt in earnest thought. Had you seen him, you might have supposed that his whole mind was fixed on the blue china tiles, which adorned the old-fashioned fire-place. But, in reality, he was meditating how to capture the British army, or drive it out of Boston. Once when there was a hard frost, he formed a scheme to cross the Charles River on the ice. But the other generals could not be persuaded that there was any prospect of success."

"What were the British doing all this time?" inquired Charley.

"They lay idle in the town," replied Grandfather. "General Gage had been recalled to England, and was succeeded by Sir William Howe. The British army, and the inhabitants of Boston, were now in great distress. Being shut up in the town so long, they had consumed almost all their provisions, and burnt up all their fuel. The soldiers tore down the Old North Church, and used its rotten boards and timbers for firewood. To heighten their distress the small-pox broke out. They probably lost far more men by cold, hunger, and sickness, than had been slain at Lexington and Bunker Hill."

"What a dismal time for the poor women and children!" exclaimed Clara.

"At length," continued Grandfather, "in March, 1776, General Washington, who had now a good supply of powder, began a terrible cannonade and bombardment from Dorchester heights. One of the cannon balls which he fired into the town struck the tower of the Brattle Street Church, where it may still be seen. Sir William Howe made preparations to cross over in boats, and drive the Americans from their batteries, but was prevented by a violent gale and storm. General Washington next erected a battery on Nook's Hill, so near the enemy, that it was impossible for them to remain in Boston any longer."

"Hurra! Hurra!" cried Charley, clapping his hands triumphantly. "I wish I had been there, to see how sheepish the Englishmen looked."

And, as Grandfather thought that Boston had never witnessed a more interesting period than this, when the royal power was in its death agony, he determined to take a peep into the town, and imagine the feelings of those who were quitting it forever.

CHAPTER IX

" ALAS for the poor tories!" said Grandfather. "Until the very last morning after Washington's troops had shown themselves on Nook's Hill, these unfortunate persons could not believe that the audacious rebels, as they called the Americans, would ever prevail against King George's army. But, when they saw the British soldiers preparing to embark on board of the ships of war, then they knew that they had lost their country. Could the patriots have known how bitter were their regrets, they would have forgiven them all their evil deeds, and sent a blessing after them as they sailed away from their native shore."

In order to make the children sensible of the pitiable condition of these men, Grandfather singled out Peter Oliver, chief justice of Massachusetts under the crown, and imagined him walking through the streets of Boston, on the morning before he left it forever.

This effort of Grandfather's fancy may be called —

THE TORY'S FAREWELL

Old Chief Justice Oliver threw on his red cloak, and placed his three-cornered hat on the top of his white wig. In this garb he intended to go forth and take a parting look at objects that had been familiar to him from his youth. Accordingly, he began his walk in the north part of the town, and soon came to Faneuil Hall. This edifice, the cradle of liberty, had been used by the British officers as a play-house.

"Would that I could see its walls crumble to dust!" thought the chief justice; and, in the bitterness of his heart, he shook his fist at the famous hall. "There began the mischief which now threatens to render asunder the British empire. The seditious harangues of demagogues in Faneuil Hall have made rebels of a loyal people, and deprived me of my country."

He then passed through a narrow avenue, and found himself in King Street, almost in the very spot which, six years before, had been reddened by the blood of the Boston Massacre. The chief justice stepped cautiously, and shuddered, as if he were afraid, that, even now, the gore of his slaughtered countrymen might stain his feet.

Before him rose the Town House, on the front of which were still displayed the royal arms. Within that edifice he had dispensed justice to the people, in the days when his name was never mentioned without honor. There, too, was the balcony whence the trumpet had been sounded, and the proclamation read to an assembled multitude, whenever a new king of England ascended the throne.

"I remember — I remember," said Chief Justice Oliver to himself, " when his present most sacred Majesty was proclaimed. Then how the people shouted. Each man would have poured out his life-blood to keep a hair of King George's head from harm. But now, there is scarcely a tongue in all New England that does not imprecate curses on his name. It is ruin and disgrace to love him. Can it be possible that a few fleeting years have wrought such a change!"

It did not occur to the chief justice, that nothing but the most grievous tyranny could so soon have changed the people's hearts. Hurrying from the spot, he entered Cornhill, as the lower part of Washington Street was then called. Opposite to the Town House was the waste foundation of the Old North Church. The sacrilegious hands of the British soldiers had torn it down, and kindled their barrack fires with the fragments.

Further on, he passed beneath the tower of the Old South. The threshold of this sacred edifice was worn by the iron tramp of horses' feet, for the interior had been used as a riding-school and rendezvous for a regiment of dragoons. As the chief justice lingered an instant at the door, a trumpet sounded within, and the regiment came clattering forth, and galloped down the street. They were proceeding to the place of embarkation.

"Let them go!" thought the chief justice, with somewhat of an old Puritan feeling in his breast. "No good can come of men who desecrate the house of God."

He went on a few steps further, and paused before the Province House. No range of brick stores had then sprung up to hide the mansion of the royal governors from public view. It had a spacious courtyard, bordered with trees, and inclosed with a wrought-iron fence. On the cupola, that surmounted the edifice, was the gilded figure of an Indian chief, ready to let fly an arrow from his bow. Over the wide front door was a balcony, in which the chief justice had often stood, when the governor and high officers of the province showed themselves to the people.

While Chief Justice Oliver gazed sadly at the Province House, before which a sentinel was pacing, the double leaves of the door were thrown open, and Sir William Howe made his appearance. Behind him came a throng of officers, whose steel scabbards clattered against the stones, as they hastened down the courtyard. Sir William Howe was a dark-complexioned man, stern and haughty in his deportment. He stepped as proudly, in that hour of defeat, as if he were going to receive the submission of the rebel general.

The chief justice bowed and accosted him.

"This is a grievous hour for both of us, Sir William," said he.

"Forward! gentlemen," said Sir William Howe to the officers who attended him; "we have no time to hear lamentations now!"

And, coldly bowing, he departed. Thus the chief justice had a foretaste of the mortifications which the exiled New Englanders afterwards suffered from the haughty Britons. They were despised even by that country which they had served more faithfully than their own.

A still heavier trial awaited Chief Justice Oliver, as he passed onward from the Province House. He was recognized by the people in the street. They had long known him as the descendant of an ancient and honorable family. They had seen him sitting, in his scarlet robes, upon the judgment seat. All his life long, either for the sake of his ancestors, or on account of his own dignified station and unspotted character, he had been held in high respect. The old gentry of the province were looked upon almost as noblemen, while Massachusetts was under royal government.

But now, all hereditary reverence for birth and rank was gone. The inhabitants shouted in derision, when they saw the venerable form of the old chief justice. They laid the wrongs of the country, and their own sufferings during the siege, — their hunger, cold, and sickness, — partly to his charge, and to that of his brother Andrew, and his kinsman Hutchinson. It was by their advice that the king had acted, in all the colonial troubles. But the day of recompense was come.

"See the old tory!" cried the people, with bitter laughter. "He is taking his last look at us. Let him show his white wig among us an hour hence, and we'll give him a coat of tar and feathers!"

The chief justice, however, knew that he need fear no violence, so long as the British troops were in possession of the town. But alas! it was a bitter thought, that he should leave no loving memory behind him. His forefathers, long after their spirits left the earth, had been honored in the affectionate remembrance of the people. But he, who would henceforth be dead to his native land, would have no epitaph save scornful vindictive words. The old man wept.

"They curse me — they invoke all kinds of evil on my head!" thought he, in the midst of his tears. "But, if they could read my heart, they would know that I love New England well. Heaven bless her, and bring her again under the rule of our gracious king! A blessing, too, on these poor misguided people!"

The chief justice flung out his hands with a gesture, as if he were bestowing a parting benediction on his countrymen. He had now reached the southern portion

of the town, and was far within the range of cannon
shot from the American batteries.   Close beside him
was the broad stump of a tree, which appeared to have
been recently cut down.   Being weary and heavy at
heart he was about to sit down upon the stump.

Suddenly, it flashed upon his recollection, that this
was the stump of Liberty Tree !   The British soldiers
had cut it down, vainly boasting that they could as easily
overthrow the liberties of America.   Under its shadowy
branches, ten years before, the brother of Chief Justice
Oliver had been compelled to acknowledge the suprem-
acy of the people, by taking the oath which they pre-
scribed.   This tree was connected with all the events
that had severed America from England.

" Accursed tree ! " cried the chief justice, gnashing
his teeth, for anger overcame his sorrow.   " Would that
thou hadst been left standing, till Hancock, Adams, and
every other traitor were hanged upon thy branches !
Then fitly mightest thou have been hewn down, and
cast into the flames."

He turned back, hurried to Long Wharf without looking behind him, embarked with the British troops for
Halifax, and never saw his country more.   Throughout
the remainder of his days, Chief Justice Oliver was agitated with those same conflicting emotions, that had
tortured him, while taking his farewell walk through the
streets of Boston.   Deep love and fierce resentment
burned in one flame within his breast.   Anathemas
struggled with benedictions.   He felt as if one breath
of his native air would renew his life, yet would have
died, rather than breathe the same air with rebels.

And such, likewise, were the feelings of the other
exiles, a thousand in number, who departed with the
British army.   Were they not the most unfortunate of
men ?

" The misfortunes of these exiled tories," observed
Laurence, " must have made them think of the poor
exiles of Acadia."

" They had a sad time of it, I suppose," said Charley.

"But I choose to rejoice with the patriots, rather than be sorrowful with the tories. Grandfather, what did General Washington do now?"

"As the rear of the British army embarked from the wharf," replied Grandfather, "General Washington's troops marched over the neck, through the fortification gates, and entered Boston in triumph. And now, for the first time since the pilgrims landed, Massachusetts was free from the dominion of England. May she never again be subjected to foreign rule — never again feel the rod of oppression!"

"Dear Grandfather," asked little Alice, "did General Washington bring our chair back to Boston?"

"I know not how long the chair remained at Cambridge," said Grandfather. "Had it staid there till this time, it could not have found a better or more appropriate shelter. The mansion which General Washington occupied is still standing; and his apartments have since been tenanted by several eminent men. Governor Everett, while a professor in the university, resided there. So, at an after period, did Mr. Sparks, whose invaluable labors have connected his name with the immortality of Washington. And, at this very time, a venerable friend and contemporary of your Grandfather, after long pilgrimages beyond the sea, has set up his staff of rest at Washington's headquarters."

"You mean Professor Longfellow, Grandfather," said Laurence. "Oh, how I should love to see the author of those beautiful VOICES OF THE NIGHT!"

"We will visit him next summer," answered Grandfather, "and take Clara and little Alice with us — and Charley, too, if he will be quiet."

CHAPTER X

WHEN Grandfather resumed his narrative, the next evening, he told the children that he had some difficulty in tracing the movements of the chair, during a short period after General Washington's departure from Cambridge.

Within a few months, however, it made its appearance at a shop in Boston, before the door of which was seen a striped pole. In the interior was displayed a stuffed alligator, a rattle-snake's skin, a bundle of Indian arrows, an old-fashioned match-lock gun, a walking-stick of Governor Winthrop's, a wig of old Cotton Mather's, and a colored print of the Boston Massacre. In short, it was a barber's shop, kept by a Mr. Pierce, who prided himself on having shaved General Washington, Old Put, and many other famous persons.

"This was not a very dignified situation for our venerable chair," continued Grandfather; "but, you know, there is no better place for news, than a barber's shop. All the events of the revolutionary war were heard of there, sooner than anywhere else. People used to sit in the chair, reading the newspaper or talking, and waiting to be shaved, while Mr. Pierce, with his scissors and razor, was at work upon the heads or chins of his other customers."

"I am sorry the chair could not betake itself to some more suitable place of refuge," said Laurence. "It was old now, and must have longed for quiet. Besides, after it had held Washington in its arms, it ought not to have been compelled to receive all the world. It should have been put into the pulpit of the Old South Church, or some other consecrated place."

"Perhaps so," answered Grandfather. "But the chair, in the course of its varied existence, had grown so accustomed to general intercourse with society, that

I doubt whether it would have contented itself in the pulpit of the Old South. There it would have stood solitary, or with no livelier companion than the silent organ, in the opposite gallery, six days out of seven. I incline to think, that it had seldom been situated more to its mind, than on the sanded floor of the snug little barber's shop."

Then Grandfather amused his children and himself, with fancying all the different sorts of people who had occupied our chair, while they awaited the leisure of the barber.

There was the old clergyman, such as Dr. Chauncey, wearing a white wig, which the barber took from his head, and placed upon a wig-block. Half an hour, perhaps, was spent in combing and powdering this reverend appendage to a clerical skull. There, too, were officers of the continental army, who required their hair to be pomatumed and plastered, so as to give them a bold and martial aspect. There, once in a while, was seen the thin, care-worn, melancholy visage of an old tory, with a wig that, in times long past, had perhaps figured at a Province House ball. And there, not unfrequently, sat the rough captain of a privateer, just returned from a successful cruise, in which he had captured half a dozen richly-laden vessels, belonging to King George's subjects. And, sometimes, a rosy little school-boy climbed into our chair, and sat staring, with wide-open eyes, at the alligator, the rattle-snake, and the other curiosities of the barber's shop. His mother had sent him, with sixpence in his hand, to get his glossy curls cropped off. The incidents of the Revolution plentifully supplied the barber's customers with topics of conversation. They talked sorrowfully of the death of General Montgomery, and the failure of our troops to take Quebec; for the New Englanders were now as anxious to get Canada from the English, as they had formerly been to conquer it from the French.

"But, very soon," said Grandfather, "came news from Philadelphia, the most important that America had ever heard of. On the 4th of July, 1776, Congress

had signed the Declaration of Independence. The thirteen colonies were now free and independent states.
Dark as our prospects were, the inhabitants welcomed
these glorious tidings, and resolved to perish, rather
than again bear the yoke of England!"

"And I would perish too!" cried Charley.

"It was a great day — a glorious deed!" said Laurence, coloring high with enthusiasm. "And, Grandfather, I love to think that the sages in Congress showed
themselves as bold and true as the soldiers in the field.
For it must have required more courage to sign the
Declaration of Independence, than to fight the enemy
in battle."

Grandfather acquiesced in Laurence's view of the
matter. He then touched briefly and hastily upon the
prominent events of the Revolution. The thunder-
storm of war had now rolled southward, and did not
again burst upon Massachusetts, where its first fury
had been felt. But she contributed her full share to
the success of the contest. Wherever a battle was
fought — whether at Long Island, White Plains, Tren-
ton, Princeton, Brandywine, or Germantown — some of
her brave sons were found slain upon the field.

In October, 1777, General Burgoyne surrendered his
army, at Saratoga, to the American general, Gates.
The captured troops were sent to Massachusetts. Not
long afterwards, Doctor Franklin and other American
commissioners made a treaty at Paris by which France
bound herself to assist our countrymen. The gallant
Lafayette was already fighting for our freedom, by the
side of Washington. In 1778, a French fleet, commanded by Count d'Estaing, spent a considerable time
in Boston Harbor. It marks the vicissitudes of human
affairs, that the French, our ancient enemies, should
come hither as comrades and brethren, and that kindred
England should be our foe.

"While the war was raging in the Middle and Southern States," proceeded Grandfather, "Massachusetts
had leisure to settle a new constitution of government,
instead of the royal charter. This was done in 1780.

In the same year, John Hancock, who had been president of Congress, was chosen governor of the state. He was the first whom the people had elected, since the days of old Simon Bradstreet."

"But, Grandfather, who had been governor since the British were driven away?" inquired Laurence. "General Gage and Sir William Howe were the last whom you have told us of."

"There had been no governor for the last four years," replied Grandfather. "Massachusetts had been ruled by the legislature, to whom the people paid obedience of their own accord. It is one of the most remarkable circumstances in our history, that, when the charter government was overthrown by the war, no anarchy, nor the slightest confusion ensued. This was a great honor to the people. But, now, Hancock was proclaimed governor by sound of trumpet; and there was again a settled government."

Grandfather again adverted to the progress of the war. In 1781, General Greene drove the British from the Southern States. In October, of the same year, General Washington compelled Lord Cornwallis to surrender his army, at Yorktown, in Virginia. This was the last great event of the revolutionary contest. King George and his ministers perceived that all the might of England could not compel America to renew her allegiance to the crown. After a great deal of discussion a treaty of peace was signed, in September, 1783.

"Now, at last," said Grandfather, "after weary years of war, the regiments of Massachusetts returned in peace to their families. Now, the stately and dignified leaders such as General Lincoln and General Knox, with their powdered hair and their uniforms of blue and buff, were seen moving about the streets."

"And little boys ran after them, I suppose," remarked Charley; "and the grown people bowed respectfully."

"They deserved respect, for they were good men, as well as brave," answered Grandfather. "Now, too, the inferior officers and privates came home to seek some peaceful occupation. Their friends remembered them as slender and smooth-cheeked young men; but they returned with the erect and rigid mien of disciplined soldiers. Some hobbled on crutches and wooden legs; others had received wounds, which were still rankling in their breasts. Many, alas! had fallen in battle and perhaps were left unburied on the bloody field."

"The country must have been sick of war," observed Laurence.

"One would have thought so," said Grandfather. "Yet only two or three years elapsed, before the folly of some misguided men caused another mustering of soldiers. This affair was called Shays' War, because a Captain Shays was the chief leader of the insurgents."

"Oh, Grandfather, don't let there be another war!" cried little Alice, piteously.

Grandfather comforted his dear little girl by assuring her that there was no great mischief done. Shays' War happened in the latter part of 1786, and the beginning of the following year. Its principal cause was the badness of the times. The State of Massachusetts, in its public capacity, was very much in debt. So, likewise, were many of the people. An insurrection took place, the object of which seems to have been to interrupt the course of law, and get rid of debts and taxes."

James Bowdoin, a good and able man, was now governor of Massachusetts. He sent General Lincoln, at the head of four thousand men, to put down the insurrection. This general, who had fought through several hard campaigns in the Revolution, managed matters like an old soldier, and totally defeated the rebels, at the expense of very little blood.

"There is but one more public event to be recorded in the history of our chair," proceeded Grandfather. "In the year 1794, Samuel Adams was elected governor of Massachusetts. I have told you what a distinguished patriot he was, and how much he resembled the stern old Puritans. Could the ancient freemen of Massachusetts, who lived in the days of the first charter, have arisen from their graves, they would probably have voted for Samuel Adams to be governor."

"Well, Grandfather, I hope he sat in our chair!" said Clara.

"He did," replied Grandfather. "He had long been in the habit of visiting the barber's shop, where our venerable chair, philosophically forgetful of its former dignities, had now spent nearly eighteen not uncomfortable years. Such a remarkable piece of furniture, so evidently a relic of long-departed times, could not escape the notice of Samuel Adams. He made minute researches into its history, and ascertained what a succession of excellent and famous people had occupied it."

"How did he find it out?" asked Charley. "For I suppose the chair could not tell its own history."

"There used to be a vast collection of ancient letters and other documents in the tower of the Old South Church," answered Grandfather. "Perhaps the history of our chair was contained among these. At all events Samuel Adams appears to have been well acquainted with it. When he became governor, he felt that he could have no more honorable seat, than that which had been the ancient Chair of State. He therefore purchased it for a trifle, and filled it worthily for three years as governor of Massachusetts."

"And what next?" asked Charley.

"That is all," said Grandfather, heaving a sigh; for he could not help being a little sad, at the thought that his stories must close here. "Samuel Adams died in 1803, at the age of above threescore and ten. He was a great patriot, but a poor man. At his death, he left scarcely property enough to pay the expenses of his funeral. This precious chair, among his other effects, was sold at auction; and your Grandfather, who was then in the strength of his years, became the purchaser."

Laurence, with a mind full of thoughts, that struggled for expression, but could find none, looked steadfastly at the chair.

He had now learned all its history, yet was not satisfied.

"Oh, how I wish that the chair could speak!" cried he. "After its long intercourse with mankind — after looking upon the world for ages — what lessons of golden wisdom it might utter! It might teach a private person how to lead a good and happy life — or a statesman how to make his country prosperous!"

CHAPTER XI

GRANDFATHER was struck by Laurence's idea, that the historic chair should utter a voice, and thus pour forth the collected wisdom of two centuries. The old gentleman had once possessed no inconsiderable share of fancy; and, even now, its fading sunshine occasionally glimmered among his more sombre reflections.

As the history of the chair had exhausted all his facts, Grandfather determined to have recourse to fable. So, after warning the children that they must not mistake this story for a true one, he related what we shall call

GRANDFATHER'S DREAM

Laurence and Clara, where were you last night? Where were you, Charley, and dear little Alice? You had all gone to rest, and left old Grandfather to meditate alone in his great chair. The lamp had grown so dim, that its light hardly illuminated the alabaster shade. The wood-fire had crumbled into heavy embers, among which the little flames danced, and quivered, and sported about, like fairies.

And here sat Grandfather, all by himself. He knew that it was bedtime; yet he could not help longing to hear your merry voices, or to hold a comfortable chat with some old friend ; because then his pillow would be visited by pleasant dreams. But, as neither children nor friends were at hand, Grandfather leaned back in the great chair, and closed his eyes, for the sake of meditating more profoundly.

And, when Grandfather's meditations had grown very profound indeed, he fancied that he heard a sound over his head, as if somebody were preparing to speak.

"Hem!" it said, in a dry, husky tone. "H-e-m! Hem!"

As Grandfather did not know that any person was in the room, he started up in great surprise, and peeped hither and thither, behind the chair, and into the recess by the fireside, and at the dark nook yonder, near the bookcase. Nobody could he see.

"Pooh!" said Grandfather to himself, "I must have been dreaming."

But, just as he was going to resume his seat, Grandfather happened to look at the great chair. The rays of fire-light were flickering upon it in such a manner that it really seemed as if its oaken frame were all alive. What! Did it not move its elbow? There, too! It certainly lifted one of its ponderous fore-legs, as if it had a notion of drawing itself a little nearer to the fire. Meanwhile, the lion's head nodded at Grandfather, with as polite and sociable a look as a lion's visage, carved in oak, could possibly be expected to assume. Well, this is strange!

"Good evening, my old friend," said the dry and husky voice, now a little clearer than before. "We have been intimately acquainted so long, that I think it high time we have a chat together."

Grandfather was looking straight at the lion's head, and could not be mistaken in supposing that it moved its lips. So here the mystery was all explained.

"I was not aware," said Grandfather, with a civil salutation to his oaken companion, "that you possessed the faculty of speech. Otherwise, I should often have been glad to converse with such a solid, useful, and substantial, if not brilliant member of society."

"Oh!" replied the ancient chair, in a quiet and easy tone, for it had now cleared its throat of the dust of ages. "I am naturally a silent and incommunicative sort of character. Once or twice, in the course of a century, I unclose my lips. When the gentle Lady Arbella departed this life, I uttered a groan. When the honest mint-master weighed his plump daughter against the pine-tree shillings, I chuckled audibly at the joke. When old Simon Bradstreet took the place of the tyrant Andros, I joined in the general huzza, and capered upon my wooden legs for joy. To be sure, the bystanders were so fully occupied with their own feelings, that my sympathy was quite unnoticed."

"And have you often held a private chat with your friends ? " asked Grandfather.

"Not often," answered the chair. " I once talked with Sir William Phipps, and communicated my ideas about the witchcraft delusion. Cotton Mather had several conversations with me, and derived great benefit from my historical reminiscences. In the days of the Stamp Act, I whispered in the ear of Hutchinson, bidding him to remember what stock his countrymen were descended of, and to think whether the spirit of their forefathers had utterly departed from them. The last man whom I favored with a colloquy, was that stout old republican, Samuel Adams."

" And how happens it," inquired Grandfather, "that there is no record nor tradition of your conversational abilities ? It is an uncommon thing to meet with a chair that can talk."

"Why, to tell you the truth," said the chair, giving itself a hitch nearer to the hearth, " I am not apt to choose the most suitable moments for unclosing my lips. Sometimes I have inconsiderately begun to speak when my occupant, lolling back in my arms, was inclined to take an after-dinner nap. Or, perhaps, the impulse to talk may be felt at midnight, when the lamp burns dim, and the fire crumbles into decay, and the studious or thoughtful man finds that his brain is in a mist. Oftenest, I have unwisely uttered my wisdom in the ears of sick persons, when the inquietude of fever made them toss about upon my cushion. And so it happens, that, though my words make a pretty strong impression at the moment, yet my auditors invariably remember them only as a dream. I should not wonder if you, my excellent friend, were to do the same, to-morrow morning."

"Nor I either," thought Grandfather to himself. However, he thanked this respectable old chair for beginning the conversation, and begged to know whether it had anything particular to communicate.

"I have been listening attentively to your narrative of my adventures," replied the chair, "and it must be owned, that your correctness entitles you to be held up as a pattern to biographers. Nevertheless, there are a few omissions, which I should be glad to see supplied. For instance, you make no mention of the good knight, Sir Richard Saltonstall, nor of the famous Hugh Peters, nor of those old regicide judges, Whalley, Goffe, and Dixwell. Yet I have borne the weight of all these distinguished characters, at one time or another."

Grandfather promised amendment, if ever he should have an opportunity to repeat his narrative. The good old chair, which still seemed to retain a due regard for outward appearance, then reminded him how long a time had passed since it had been provided with a new cushion. It likewise expressed the opinion, that the oaken figures on its back would show to much better advantage by the aid of a little varnish.

"And I have had a complaint in this joint," continued the chair, endeavoring to lift one of its legs, "ever since Charley trundled his wheelbarrow against me."

"It shall be attended to," said Grandfather. "And now, venerable chair, I have a favor to solicit. During an existence of more than two centuries, you have had a familiar intercourse with men who were esteemed the wisest of their day. Doubtless, with your capacious understanding, you have treasured up many an invaluable lesson of wisdom. You certainly have had time enough to guess the riddle of life. Tell us poor mortals, then, how we may be happy!"

The lion's head fixed its eyes thoughtfully upon the fire, and the whole chair assumed an aspect of deep meditation. Finally, it beckoned to Grandfather with its elbow, and made a step sideways towards him, as if it had a very important secret to communicate.

"As long as I have stood in the midst of human affairs," said the chair, with a very oracular enunciation, "I have constantly observed that JUSTICE, TRUTH, and LOVE are the chief ingredients of every happy life."

"Justice, Truth, and Love!" exclaimed Grandfather.

"We need not exist two centuries to find out that these qualities are essential to our happiness. This is no secret. Every human being is born with the instinctive knowledge of it."

"Ah!" cried the chair, drawing back in surprise. "From what I have observed of the dealings of man with man, and nation with nation, I never should have suspected that they knew this all-important secret. And, with this eternal lesson written in your soul, do you ask me to sift new wisdom for you, out of my petty existence of two or three centuries?"

"But, my dear chair —" said Grandfather.

"Not a word more," interrupted the chair; "here I close my lips for the next hundred years. At the end of that period, if I shall have discovered any new precepts of happiness, better than what Heaven has already taught you, they shall assuredly be given to the world."

In the energy of its utterance, the oaken chair seemed to stamp its foot, and trod (we hope unintentionally) upon Grandfather's toe. The old gentleman started, and found that he had been asleep in the great chair, and that his heavy walking-stick had fallen down across his foot.

"Grandfather," cried little Alice, clapping her hands, "you must dream a new dream, every night, about our chair!"

Laurence, and Clara, and Charley said the same. But the good old gentleman shook his head, and declared that here ended the history, real or fabulous of GRANDFATHER'S CHAIR.

BIOGRAPHICAL STORIES

BENJAMIN WEST,
SIR ISAAC NEWTON,
SAMUEL JOHNSON,

OLIVER CROMWELL,
BENJAMIN FRANKLIN,
QUEEN CHRISTINA.

This small volume, and others of a similar character, from the same hand, have not been composed without a deep sense of responsibility. The author regards children as sacred, and would not, for the world, cast anything into the fountain of a young heart, that might embitter and pollute its waters. And, even in point of the reputation to be aimed at, juvenile literature is as well worth cultivating as any other. The writer, if he succeed in pleasing his little readers, may hope to be remembered by them till their own old age — a far longer period of literary existence than is generally attained, by those who seek immortality from the judgments of full-grown men.

BIOGRAPHICAL STORIES

CHAPTER I

WHEN Edward Temple was about eight or nine years old, he was afflicted with a disorder of the eyes. It was so severe, and his sight was naturally so delicate, that the surgeon felt some apprehensions lest the boy should become totally blind. He therefore gave strict directions to keep him in a darkened chamber, with a bandage over his eyes. Not a ray of the blessed light of Heaven could be suffered to visit the poor lad.

This was a sad thing for Edward! It was just the same as if there were to be no more sunshine, nor moonlight, nor glow of the cheerful fire, nor light of lamps. A night had begun which was to continue perhaps for months, — a longer and drearier night than that which voyagers are compelled to endure, when their ship is icebound, throughout the winter, in the Arctic Ocean. His dear father and mother, his brother George, and the sweet face of little Emily Robinson, must all vanish, and leave him in utter darkness and solitude. Their voices and footsteps, it is true, would be heard around him; he would feel his mother's embrace, and the kind pressure of all their hands; but still it would seem as if they were a thousand miles away.

And then his studies! They were to be entirely given up. This was another grievous trial; for Edward's memory hardly went back to the period when he had not known how to read. Many and many a holiday had he spent at his book, poring over its pages until the deepening twilight confused the print, and made all the letters run into long words. Then would he press his hands across his eyes, and wonder why they pained him so, and, when the candles were lighted, what was the reason that they burned so dimly, like the moon in a foggy night? Poor little fellow! So far as his eyes were concerned, he was already an old man, and needed a pair of spectacles almost as much as his own grandfather did.

And now, alas! the time was come, when even grandfather's spectacles could not have assisted Edward to read. After a few bitter tears, which only pained his eyes the more, the poor boy submitted to the surgeon's orders. His eyes were bandaged, and, with his mother on one side, and his little friend Emily on the other, he was led into a darkened chamber.

"Mother, I shall be very miserable," said Edward, sobbing.

"Oh, no, my dear child!" replied his mother, cheerfully. "Your eyesight was a precious gift of Heaven, it is true; but you would do wrong to be miserable for its loss, even if there were no hope of regaining it. There are other enjoyments, besides what come to us through our eyes."

"None that are worth having," said Edward.

"Ah! but you will not think so long," rejoined Mrs. Temple, with tenderness. "All of us — your father, and myself, and George, and our sweet Emily — will try to find occupation and amusement for you. We will use all our eyes to make you happy. Will they not be better than a single pair?"

"I will sit by you all day long," said Emily, in her low, sweet voice, putting her hand into that of Edward.

"And so will I, Ned," said George, his elder brother, — "school-time and all, if my father will permit me."

Edward's brother George was three or four years older than himself, a fine, hardy lad, of a bold and ardent temper. He was the leader of his comrades in all their enterprises and amusements. As to his proficiency at study, there was not much to be said. He had sense and ability enough to have made himself a scholar, but found so many pleasanter things to do, that he seldom took hold of a book with his whole heart.

So fond was George of boisterous sports and exercises, that it was really a great token of affection and sympathy, when he offered to sit all day long in a dark chamber, with his poor brother Edward.

As for little Emily Robinson, she was the daughter of one of Mr. Temple's dearest friends. Ever since her mother went to Heaven, (which was soon after Emily's birth,) the little girl had dwelt in the household where we now find her. Mr. and Mrs. Temple seemed to love her as well as their own children; for they had no daughter except Emily; nor would the boys have known the blessing of a sister, had not this gentle stranger come to teach them what it was. If I could show you Emily's face, with her dark hair smoothed away from her forehead, you would be pleased with her look of simplicity and loving-kindness, but might think that she was somewhat too grave for a child of seven years old. But you would not love her the less for that.

So brother George, and this loving little girl, were to be Edward's companions and playmates, while he should be kept prisoner in the dark chamber. When the first bitterness of his grief was over, he began to feel that there might be some comforts and enjoyments in life, even for a boy whose eyes were covered with a bandage.

"I thank you, dear mother," said he, with only a few sobs, "and you, Emily; and you too, George. You will all be very kind to me, I know. And my father — will not he come and see me, every day?"

"Yes, my dear boy," said Mr. Temple; for, though invisible to Edward, he was standing close beside him. "I will spend some hours of every day with you. And as I have often amused you by relating stories and adventures, while you had the use of your eyes, I can do the same, now that you are unable to read. Will that please you, Edward?"

"Oh, very much!" replied Edward.

"Well, then," said his father, "this evening we will begin the series of Biographical Stories, which I promised you some time ago."

CHAPTER II

WHEN evening came, Mr. Temple found Edward considerably revived in spirits, and disposed to be resigned to his misfortune. Indeed, the figure of the boy, as it was dimly seen by the firelight, reclining in a well-stuffed easy-chair, looked so very comfortable that many people might have envied him. When a man's eyes have grown old with gazing at the ways of the world, it does not seem such a terrible misfortune to have them bandaged.

Little Emily Robinson sat by Edward's side, with the air of an accomplished nurse. As well as the duskiness of the chamber would permit, she watched all his motions, and each varying expression of his face, and tried to anticipate her patient's wishes, before his tongue could utter them. Yet it was noticeable, that the child manifested an indescribable awe and disquietude, whenever she fixed her eyes on the bandage; for to her simple and affectionate heart, it seemed as if her dear friend Edward was separated from her, because she could not see his eyes. A friend's eyes tell us many things, which could never be spoken by the tongue.

George, likewise, looked awkward and confused, as stout and healthy boys are accustomed to do, in the society of the sick or afflicted. Never having felt pain or sorrow, they are abashed, from not knowing how to sympathize with the sufferings of others.

"Well, my dear Edward," inquired Mrs. Temple, "is your chair quite comfortable? and has your little nurse provided for all your wants? If so, your father is ready to begin his stories."

"Oh, I am very well now," answered Edward, with a faint smile. "And my ears have not forsaken me, though my eyes are good for nothing. So, pray, dear father, begin!"

It was Mr. Temple's design to tell the children a series of true stories, the incidents of which should be taken from the childhood and early life of eminent people. Thus he hoped to bring George, and Edward, and Emily, into closer acquaintance with the famous persons who have lived in other times, by showing that they also had been children once. Although Mr. Temple was scrupulous to relate nothing but what was founded on fact, yet he felt himself at liberty to clothe the incidents of his narrative in a new coloring, so that his auditors might understand them the better.

"My first story," said he, "shall be about a painter of pictures."

"Dear me!" cried Edward, with a sigh. "I am afraid I shall never look at pictures any more."

"We will hope for the best," answered his father. "In the meantime, you must try to see things within your own mind."

Mr. Temple then began the following story : —

BENJAMIN WEST

Born 1738. Died 1820

In the year 1738, there came into the world, in the town of Springfield, Pennsylvania, a Quaker infant, from whom his parents and neighbors looked for wonderful things. A famous preacher of the Society of Friends had prophesied about little Ben, and foretold that he would be one of the most remarkable characters that had appeared on the earth since the days of William Penn. On this account the eyes of many people were fixed upon the boy. Some of his ancestors had won great renown in the old wars of England and France; but it was probably expected that Ben would become a preacher, and would convert multitudes to the peaceful doctrines of the Quakers. Friend West and his wife were thought to be very fortunate in having such a son.

Little Ben lived to the ripe age of six years, without doing anything that was worthy to be told in history. But, one summer afternoon, in his seventh year, his mother put a fan into his hand, and bade him keep the flies away from the face of a little babe, who lay fast asleep in the cradle. She then left the room.

The boy waved the fan to and fro, and drove away the buzzing flies whenever they had the impertinence to come near the baby's face. When they had all flown out of the window, or into distant parts of the room, he bent over the cradle, and delighted himself with gazing at the sleeping infant. It was, indeed, a very pretty sight. The little personage in the cradle slumbered peacefully, with its waxen hands under its chin, looking as full of blissful quiet as if angels were singing lullabies in its ear. Indeed, it must have been dreaming about Heaven; for, while Ben stooped over the cradle, the little baby smiled.

"How beautiful she looks!" said Ben to himself. "What a pity it is, that such a pretty smile should not last forever!"

Now Ben, at this period of his life, had never heard of that wonderful art, by which a look, that appears and vanishes in a moment, may be made to last for hundreds of years. But though nobody had told him of such an art, he may be said to have invented it for himself. On a table, near at hand, there were pens and paper, and ink of two colors, black and red. The boy seized a pen and sheet of paper, and kneeling down beside the cradle, began to draw a likeness of the infant. While he was busied in this manner, he heard his mother's step approaching, and hastily tried to conceal the paper.

"Benjamin, my son, what hast thou been doing?" inquired his mother, observing marks of confusion in his face.

At first, Ben was unwilling to tell; for he felt as if there might be something wrong in stealing the baby's face, and putting it upon a sheet of paper. However, as his mother insisted, he finally put the sketch into her hand, and then hung his head, expecting to be well scolded. But when the good lady saw what was on the paper, in lines of red and black ink, she uttered a scream of surprise and joy.

"Bless me!" cried she. "It is a picture of little Sally!"

And then she threw her arms round our friend Benjamin, and kissed him so tenderly, that he never afterwards was afraid to show his performances to his mother.

As Ben grew older, he was observed to take vast delight in looking at the hues and forms of nature. For instance, he was greatly pleased with the blue violets of spring, the wild roses of summer, and the scarlet cardinal-flowers of early autumn. In the decline of the year, when the woods were variegated with all the colors of the rainbow, Ben seemed to desire nothing better than to gaze at them from morn till night. The purple and golden clouds of sunset were a joy to him. And he was continually endeavoring to draw the figures of trees, men, mountains, houses, cattle, geese, ducks, and turkeys, with a piece of chalk, on barn-doors, or on the floor.

In these old times, the Mohawk Indians were still numerous in Pennsylvania. Every year a party of them used to pay a visit to Springfield, because the wigwams of their ancestors had formerly stood there. These wild men grew fond of little Ben, and made him very happy by giving him some of the red and yellow paint with which they were accustomed to adorn their faces. His mother, too, presented him with a piece of indigo. Thus he now had three colors, — red, blue, and yellow — and could manufacture green, by mixing the yellow with the blue. Our friend Ben was overjoyed, and doubtless showed his gratitude to the Indians by taking their likenesses, in the strange dresses which they wore, with feathers, tomahawks, and bows and arrows.

But, all this time, the young artist had no paint-brushes, nor were there any to be bought, unless he had sent to Philadelphia on purpose. However, he was a very ingenious boy, and resolved to manufacture paint-brushes for himself. With this design, he laid hold upon — what do you think? why, upon a respectable old black cat, who was sleeping quietly by the fireside.

"Puss," said little Ben to the cat, "pray give me some of the fur from the tip of thy tail."

Though he addressed the black cat so civilly, yet Ben was determined to have the fur, whether she were willing or not. Puss, who had no great zeal for the fine arts, would have resisted if she could; but the boy was armed with his mother's scissors, and very dexterously clipped off fur enough to make a paint-brush. This was of so much use to him, that he applied to Madam Puss again and again, until her warm coat of fur had become so thin and ragged, that she could hardly keep comfortable through the winter. Poor thing! she was forced to creep close into the chimney-corner, and eyed Ben with a very rueful physiognomy. But Ben considered it more necessary that he should have paint-brushes, than that Puss should be warm.

About this period, Friend West received a visit from Mr. Pennington, a merchant of Philadelphia, who was likewise a member of the Society of Friends. The visitor, on entering the parlor, was surprised to see it ornamented with drawings of Indian chiefs, and of birds with beautiful plumage, and of the wild flowers of the forest. Nothing of the kind was ever seen before in the habitation of a Quaker farmer.

"Why, Friend West," exclaimed the Philadelphia merchant, "what has possessed thee to cover thy walls with all these pictures? Where on earth didst thou get them?"

Then Friend West explained that all these pictures were painted by little Ben, with no better materials than red and yellow ochre and a piece of indigo, and with brushes made of the black cat's fur.

"Verily," said Mr. Pennington, "the boy hath a wonderful faculty. Some of our friends might look upon these matters as vanity; but little Benjamin appears to have been born a painter; and Providence is wiser than we are."

The good merchant patted Benjamin on the head, and evidently considered him a wonderful boy. When his parents saw how much their son's performances were admired, they no doubt remembered the prophecy of the old Quaker preacher, respecting Ben's future eminence. Yet they could not understand how he was ever to become a very great and useful man, merely by making pictures.

One evening, shortly after Mr. Pennington's return to Philadelphia, a package arrived at Springfield, directed to our little friend Ben.

"What can it possibly be?" thought Ben, when it was put into his hands. "Who can have sent me such a great square package as this?"

On taking off the thick brown paper which enveloped it, behold! there was a paint-box, with a great many cakes of paint, and brushes of various sizes. It was the gift of good Mr. Pennington. There were likewise several squares of canvas, such as artists use for painting pictures upon, and, in addition to all these treasures, some beautiful engravings of landscapes. These were the first pictures that Ben had ever seen, except those of his own drawing.

What a joyful evening was this for the little artist! At bedtime, he put the paint-box under his pillow, and got hardly a wink of sleep; for, all night long, his fancy was painting pictures in the darkness. In the morning, he hurried to the garret, and was seen no more till the dinner-hour; nor did he give himself time to eat more than a mouthful or two of food, before he hurried back to the garret again. The next day, and the next, he was just as busy as ever; until at last his mother thought it time to ascertain what he was about. She accordingly followed him to the garret.

On opening the door, the first object that presented itself to her eyes was our friend Benjamin, giving the last touches to a beautiful picture. He had copied portions of two of the engravings, and made one picture out of both, with such admirable skill that it was far more beautiful than the originals. The grass, the trees, the water, the sky, and the houses, were all painted in their proper colors. There, too, was the sunshine and the shadow, looking as natural as life.

"My dear child, thou hast done wonders!" cried his mother.

The good lady was in an ecstasy of delight. And well might she be proud of her boy; for there were touches in this picture, which old artists, who had spent a lifetime in the business, need not have been ashamed of. Many a year afterwards, this wonderful production was exhibited at the Royal Academy in London.

When Benjamin was quite a large lad, he was sent to school at Philadelphia. Not long after his arrival, he had a slight attack of fever, which confined him to his bed. The light, which would otherwise have disturbed him, was excluded from his chamber by means of closed wooden shutters. At first it appeared so totally dark, that Ben could not distinguish any object in the room. By degrees, however, his eyes became accustomed to the scanty light.

He was lying on his back, looking up towards the ceiling, when suddenly he beheld the dim apparition of a white cow, moving slowly over his head! Ben started, and rubbed his eyes, in the greatest amazement.

"What can this mean?" thought he.

The white cow disappeared; and next came several pigs, who trotted along the ceiling, and vanished into the darkness of the chamber. So lifelike did these grunters look, that Ben almost seemed to hear them squeak.

"Well, this is very strange!" said Ben to himself.

When the people of the house came to see him, Benjamin told them of the marvellous circumstance which had occurred. But they would not believe him.

"Benjamin, thou art surely out of thy senses!" cried they. "How is it possible that a white cow and a litter of pigs should be visible on the ceiling of a dark chamber?"

Ben, however, had great confidence in his own eye-sight, and was determined to search the mystery to the bottom. For this purpose, when he was again left alone, he got out of bed, and examined the window-shutters. He soon perceived a small chink in one of them, through which a ray of light found its passage and rested upon the ceiling. Now the science of optics will inform us that the pictures of the white cow and the pigs, and of other objects out of doors, came into the dark chamber through this narrow chink, and were painted over Benjamin's head. It is greatly to his credit that he discovered the scientific principle of this phenomenon, and by means of it constructed a Camera Obscura, or Magic Lantern, out of a hollow box. This was of great advantage to him in drawing landscapes.

Well; time went on, and Benjamin continued to draw and paint pictures, until he had now reached the age when it was proper that he should choose a business for life. His father and mother were in considerable perplexity about him. According to the ideas of the Quakers, it is not right for people to spend their lives in occupations that are of no real and sensible advan-tage to the world. Now, what advantage could the world expect from Benjamin's pictures? This was a difficult question; and, in order to set their minds at rest, his parents determined to consult the preachers and wise men of their society. Accordingly, they all assembled in the meeting-house, and discussed the matter from beginning to end.

Finally, they came to a very wise decision. It seemed so evident that Providence had created Benjamin to be a painter, and had given him abilities which would be thrown away in any other business, that the Quakers resolved not to oppose his inclination. They even acknowledged that the sight of a beautiful picture might convey instruction to the mind, and might bene-fit the heart, as much as a good book or a wise discourse. They therefore committed the youth to the direction of God, being well assured that he best knew what was his proper sphere of usefulness. The old men laid their

hands upon Benjamin's head, and gave him their blessing, and the women kissed him affectionately.   All consented that he should go forth into the world, and learn
to be a painter, by studying the best pictures of ancient
and modern times.

So our friend Benjamin left the dwelling of his
parents, and his native woods and streams, and the
good Quakers of Springfield, and the Indians who had
given him his first colors, — he left all the places and
persons whom he had hitherto known, — and returned
to them no more.   He went first to Philadelphia, and
afterwards to Europe.   Here he was noticed by many
great people, but retained all the sobriety and simplicity
which he had learned among the Quakers.   It is related
of him, that, when he was presented at the court of the
Prince of Parma, he kept his hat upon his head, even
while kissing the Prince's hand.

When he was twenty-five years old, he went to London, and established himself there as an artist.   In due
course of time, he acquired great fame by his pictures,
and was made chief painter to King George the Third,
and President of the Royal Academy of Arts.   When
the Quakers of Pennsylvania heard of his success, they
felt that the prophecy of the old preacher, as to little
Ben's future eminence, was now accomplished.   It is
true, they shook their heads at his pictures of battle
and bloodshed, such as the Death of Wolfe, — thinking
that these terrible scenes should not be held up to the
admiration of the world.

But they approved of the great paintings in which he
represented the miracles and sufferings of the Redeemer
of Mankind.   King George employed him to adorn a
large and beautiful chapel at Windsor Castle, with pictures of these sacred subjects.   He likewise painted a
magnificent picture of Christ Healing the Sick, which
he gave to the Hospital at Philadelphia.   It was exhibited to the public, and produced so much profit that
the Hospital was enlarged, so as to accommodate thirty
more patients.   If Benjamin West had done no other
good deed than this, yet it would have been enough to

entitle him to an honorable remembrance forever. At this very day, there are thirty poor people in the Hospital, who owe all their comforts to that same picture.

We shall mention only a single incident more. The picture of Christ Healing the Sick was exhibited at the Royal Academy in London, where it covered a vast space, and displayed a multitude of figures as large as life. On the wall, close beside this admirable picture, hung a small and faded landscape. It was the same that little Ben had painted in his father's garret, after receiving the paint-box and engravings from good Mr. Pennington.

He lived many years in peace and honor, and died in 1820, at the age of eighty-two. The story of his life is almost as wonderful as a fairy tale; for there are few stranger transformations than that of a little unknown Quaker boy, in the wilds of America, into the most distinguished English painter of his day. Let us each make the best use of our natural abilities, as Benjamin West did; and, with the blessing of Providence, we shall arrive at some good end. As for fame, it is but little matter whether we acquire it or not.

"Thank you for the story, my dear father," said Edward, when it was finished. "Do you know, that it seems as if I could see things without the help of my eyes? While you were speaking, I have seen little Ben, and the baby in its cradle, and the Indians, and the white cow and the pigs, and kind Mr. Pennington, and all the good old Quakers, almost as plainly as if they were in this very room."

"It is because your attention was not disturbed by outward objects," replied Mr. Temple. "People, when deprived of sight, often have more vivid ideas than those who possess the perfect use of their eyes. I will venture to say that George has not attended to the story quite so closely."

"No, indeed," said George, "but it was a very pretty

story for all that.   How I should have laughed to see Ben making a paint-brush out of the black cat's tail! I intend to try the experiment with Emily's kitten."

" Oh, no, no, George ! " cried Emily, earnestly.   " My kitten cannot spare her tail."

Edward being an invalid, it was now time for him to retire to bed.   When the family bade him good-night, he turned his face towards them, looking very loth to part.

" I shall not know when morning comes," said he sorrowfully.   " And besides I want to hear your voices all the time ; for, when nobody is speaking, it seems as if I were alone in a dark world ! "

" You must have faith, my dear child," replied his mother.   " Faith is the soul's eyesight ; and when we possess it, the world is never dark nor lonely."

CHAPTER III

THE next day, Edward began to get accustomed to his new condition of life. Once, indeed, when his parents were out of the way, and only Emily was left to take care of him, he could not resist the temptation to thrust aside the bandage, and peep at the anxious face of his little nurse. But, in spite of the dimness of the chamber, the experiment caused him so much pain, that he felt no inclination to take another look. So, with a deep sigh, he resigned himself to his fate.

"Emily, pray talk to me!" said he, somewhat impatiently.

Now, Emily was a remarkably silent little girl, and did not possess that liveliness of disposition which renders some children such excellent companions. She seldom laughed, and had not the faculty of making many words about small matters. But the love and earnestness of her heart taught her how to amuse poor Edward, in his darkness. She put her knitting-work into his hands.

"You must learn how to knit," said she.

"What! without using my eyes?" cried Edward.

"I can knit with my eyes shut," replied Emily.

Then, with her own little hands, she guided Edward's fingers, while he set about this new occupation. So awkward were his first attempts, that any other little girl would have laughed heartily. But Emily preserved her gravity, and showed the utmost patience in taking up the innumerable stitches which he let down. In the course of an hour or two, his progress was quite encouraging.

When evening came, Edward acknowledged that the day had been far less wearisome than he anticipated. But he was glad, nevertheless, when his father and mother, and George and Emily, all took their seats around his chair. He put out his hand to grasp each of their hands, and smiled with a very bright expression upon his lips.

"Now I can see you all, with my mind's eye," said he; "and now, father, pray tell us another story."

So Mr. Temple began.

Sir Isaac Newton

Born. 1642.   Died 1727

On Christmas Day, in the year 1642, Isaac Newton was born, at the small village of Woolsthorpe, in England. Little did his mother think, when she beheld her new-born babe, that he was destined to explain many matters which had been a mystery ever since the creation of the world.

Isaac's father being dead, Mrs. Newton was married again to a clergyman, and went to reside at North Witham. Her son was left to the care of his good old grandmother, who was very kind to him, and sent him to school. In his early years, Isaac did not appear to be a very bright scholar, but was chiefly remarkable for his ingenuity in all mechanical occupations. He had a set of little tools, and saws of various sizes, manufactured by himself. With the aid of these, Isaac contrived to make many curious articles, at which he worked with so much skill, that he seemed to have been born with a saw or chisel in his hand.

The neighbors looked with vast admiration at the things which Isaac manufactured. And his old grandmother, I suppose, was never weary of talking about him. "He 'll make a capital workman, one of these days," she would probably say. "No fear but what Isaac will do well in the world, and be a rich man before he dies."

It is amusing to conjecture what were the anticipations of his grandmother and the neighbors, about Isaac's future life. Some of them, perhaps, fancied that he would make beautiful furniture of mahogany, rosewood, or polished oak, inlaid with ivory and ebony, and magnificently gilded. And then, doubtless, all the rich people would purchase these fine things, to adorn their drawing-rooms. Others probably thought that little Isaac was destined to be an architect, and would build splendid mansions for the nobility and gentry, and churches, too, with the tallest steeples that had ever been seen in England.

Some of his friends, no doubt, advised Isaac's grandmother to apprentice him to a clock-maker; for, besides his mechanical skill, the boy seemed to have a taste for mathematics, which would be very useful to him in that profession. And then, in due time, Isaac would set up for himself, and would manufacture curious clocks, like those that contain sets of dancing figures, which issue from the dial-plate when the hour is struck; or like those where a ship sails across the face of the clock, and is seen tossing up and down on the waves, as often as the pendulum vibrates.

Indeed, there was some ground for supposing that Isaac would devote himself to the manufacture of clocks; since he had already made one, of a kind which nobody had ever heard of before. It was set a-going, not by wheels and weights, like other clocks, but by the dropping of water. This was an object of great wonderment to all the people round about; and it must be confessed that there are few boys, or men either, who could contrive to tell what o'clock it is by means of a bowl of water.

Besides the water-clock, Isaac made a sun-dial. Thus his grandmother was never at a loss to know the hour; for the water-clock would tell it in the shade, and the dial in the sunshine. The sun-dial is said to be still in existence at Woolsthorpe, on the corner of the house where Isaac dwelt. If so, it must have marked the passage of every sunny hour that has elapsed, since Isaac Newton was a boy. It marked all the famous moments of his life; it marked the hour of his death; and still the sunshine creeps slowly over it, as regularly as when Isaac first set it up.

Yet we must not say that the sun-dial has lasted longer than its maker; for Isaac Newton will exist long after the dial — yea, and long after the sun itself — shall have crumbled to decay.

Isaac possessed a wonderful faculty of acquiring knowledge by the simplest means. For instance, what method do you suppose he took, to find out the strength of the wind? You will never guess how the boy could compel that unseen, inconstant, and ungovernable wanderer, the wind, to tell him the measure of its strength. Yet nothing can be more simple. He jumped against the wind, and by the length of his jump he could calculate the force of a gentle breeze, a brisk gale, or a tempest. Thus, even in his boyish sports, he was continually searching out the secrets of philosophy.

Not far from his grandmother's residence there was a windmill, which operated on a new plan. Isaac was in the habit of going thither frequently, and would spend whole hours in examining its various parts. While the mill was at rest, he pried into its internal machinery. When its broad sails were set in motion by the wind, he watched the process by which the mill-stones were made to revolve, and crush the grain that was put into the hopper. After gaining a thorough knowledge of its construction, he was observed to be unusually busy with his tools.

It was not long before his grandmother, and all the neighborhood, knew what Isaac had been about. He had constructed a model of the windmill. Though not so large, I suppose, as one of the box-traps which boys set to catch squirrels, yet every part of the mill and its machinery was complete. Its little sails were neatly made of linen, and whirled round very swiftly when the mill was placed in a draught of air. Even a puff of wind from Isaac's mouth, or from a pair of bellows, was sufficient to set the sails in motion. And, what was most curious, if a handful of grains of wheat were put into the little hopper, they would soon be converted into snow-white flour.

Isaac's playmates were enchanted with his new windmill. They thought that nothing so pretty, and so wonderful, had ever been seen in the whole world.

"But, Isaac," said one of them, "you have forgotten one thing that belongs to a mill."

"What is that?" asked Isaac; for he supposed that, from the roof of the mill to its foundation, he had forgotten nothing.

"Why, where is the miller?" said his friend.

"That is true! — I must look out for one," said Isaac; and he set himself to consider how the deficiency should be supplied.

He might easily have made the miniature figure of a man; but then it would not have been able to move about, and perform the duties of a miller. As Captain Lemuel Gulliver had not yet discovered the island of Lilliput, Isaac did not know that there were little men in the world, whose size was just suited to his windmill. It so happened, however, that a mouse had just been caught in the trap; and as no other miller could be found, Mr. Mouse was appointed to that important office. The new miller made a very respectable appearance in his dark gray coat. To be sure, he had not a very good character for honesty, and was suspected of sometimes stealing a portion of the grain which was given him to grind. But perhaps some two-legged millers are quite as dishonest as this small quadruped.

As Isaac grew older, it was found that he had far more important matters in his mind than the manufacture of toys, like the little windmill. All day long, if left to himself, he was either absorbed in thought, or engaged in some book of mathematics, or natural philosophy. At night, I think it probable, he looked up with reverential curiosity to the stars, and wondered whether they were worlds like our own, — and how great was their distance from the earth, — and what was the power that kept them in their courses. Perhaps, even so early in life, Isaac Newton felt a presentiment that he should be able, hereafter, to answer all these questions.

When Isaac was fourteen years old, his mother's

second husband being now dead, she wished her son to leave school, and assist her in managing the farm at Woolsthorpe. For a year or two, therefore, he tried to turn his attention to farming. But his mind was so bent on becoming a scholar, that his mother sent him back to school, and afterwards to the University of Cambridge.

I have now finished my anecdotes of Isaac Newton's boyhood. My story would be far too long, were I to mention all the splendid discoveries which he made after he came to be a man. He was the first that found out the nature of Light; for, before his day, nobody could tell what the sunshine was composed of. You remember, I suppose, the story of an apple's falling on his head, and thus leading him to discover the force of gravitation, which keeps the heavenly bodies in their courses. When he had once got hold of this idea, he never permitted his mind to rest, until he had searched out all the laws by which the planets are guided through the sky. This he did as thoroughly as if he had gone up among the stars and tracked them in their orbits. The boy had found out the mechanism of a windmill; the man explained to his fellow-men the mechanism of the universe.

While making these researches he was accustomed to spend night after night in a lofty tower, gazing at the heavenly bodies through a telescope. His mind was lifted far above the things of this world. He may be said, indeed, to have spent the greater part of his life in worlds that lie thousands and millions of miles away; for where the thoughts and the heart are, there is our true existence.

Did you never hear the story of Newton and his little dog Diamond? One day, when he was fifty years old, and had been hard at work more than twenty years, studying the theory of Light, he went out of his chamber, leaving his little dog asleep before the fire. On the table lay a heap of manuscript papers, containing all the discoveries which Newton had made during those twenty years. When his master was gone, up rose little

Diamond, jumped upon the table, and overthrew the lighted candle. The papers immediately caught fire.

Just as the destruction was completed, Newton opened the chamber-door, and perceived that the labors of twenty years were reduced to a heap of ashes. There stood little Diamond, the author of all the mischief. Almost any other man would have sentenced the dog to immediate death. But Newton patted him on the head with his usual kindness, although grief was at his heart.

"Oh, Diamond, Diamond," exclaimed he, "thou little knowest the mischief thou hast done."

This incident affected his health and spirits for some time afterwards; but, from his conduct towards the little dog, you may judge what was the sweetness of his temper.

Newton lived to be a very old man, and acquired great renown, and was made a Member of Parliament, and received the honor of knighthood from the king. But he cared little for earthly fame and honors, and felt no pride in the vastness of his knowledge. All that he had learned only made him feel how little he knew in comparison to what remained to be known.

"I seem to myself like a child," observed he, "playing on the sea-shore, and picking up here and there a curious shell or a pretty pebble, while the boundless ocean of Truth lies undiscovered before me."

At last, in 1727, when he was fourscore and five years old, Sir Isaac Newton died, — or rather he ceased to live on earth. We may be permitted to believe that he is still searching out the infinite wisdom and goodness of the Creator, as earnestly, and with even more success, than while his spirit animated a mortal body. He has left a fame behind him, which will be as endurable as if his name were written in letters of light, formed by the stars upon the midnight sky.

"I love to hear about mechanical contrivances — such as the water-clock and the little windmill," remarked

George. "I suppose if Sir Isaac Newton had only thought of it, he might have found out the steam-engine, and railroads, and all the other famous inventions that have come into use since his day."

"Very possibly he might," replied Mr. Temple; "and, no doubt, a great many people would think it more useful to manufacture steam-engines, than to search out the system of the universe. Other great astronomers, besides Newton, have been endowed with mechanical genius. There was David Rittenhouse, an American, — he made a perfect little water-mill, when he was only seven or eight years old. But this sort of ingenuity is but a mere trifle in comparison with the other talents of such men."

"It must have been beautiful," said Edward, "to spend whole nights in a high tower, as Newton did, gazing at the stars, and the comets, and the meteors. But what would Newton have done, had he been blind? or if his eyes had been no better than mine?"

"Why, even then, my dear child," observed Mrs. Temple, "he would have found out some way of enlightening his mind, and of elevating his soul. But, come! little Emily is waiting to bid you good-night. You must go to sleep, and dream of seeing all our faces."

"But how sad it will be, when I awake!" murmured Edward.

CHAPTER IV

IN the course of the next day, the harmony of our little family was disturbed by something like a quarrel between George and Edward.

The former, though he loved his brother dearly, had found it quite too great a sacrifice of his own enjoyments, to spend all his play-time in a darkened chamber. Edward, on the other hand, was inclined to be despotic. He felt as if his bandaged eyes entitled him to demand that everybody, who enjoyed the blessing of sight, should contribute to his comfort and amusement. He therefore insisted that George, instead of going out to play foot-ball, should join with himself and Emily in a game of questions and answers.

George resolutely refused, and ran out of the house. He did not revisit Edward's chamber till the evening, when he stole in, looking confused, yet somewhat sullen, and sat down beside his father's chair. It was evident, by a motion of Edward's head and a slight trembling of his lips, that he was aware of George's entrance, though his footsteps had been almost inaudible. Emily, with her serious and earnest little face, looked from one to the other, as if she longed to be a messenger of peace between them.

Mr. Temple, without seeming to notice any of these circumstances, began a story.

SAMUEL JOHNSON

Born 1709. Died 1784

"Sam," said Mr. Michael Johnson of Litchfield, one morning, "I am very feeble and ailing to-day. You must go to Uttoxeter in my stead, and tend the book-stall in the market-place there."

This was spoken, above a hundred years ago, by an

elderly man, who had once been a thriving bookseller at Litchfield, in England. Being now in reduced circumstances, he was forced to go, every market-day, and sell books at a stall, in the neighboring village of Uttoxeter.

His son, to whom Mr. Johnson spoke, was a great boy of very singular aspect. He had an intelligent face; but it was seamed and distorted by a scrofulous humor, which affected his eyes so badly, that sometimes he was almost blind. Owing to the same cause, his head would often shake with a tremulous motion, as if he were afflicted with the palsy. When Sam was an infant, the famous Queen Anne had tried to cure him of this disease, by laying her royal hands upon his head. But though the touch of a king or queen was supposed to be a certain remedy for scrofula, it produced no good effect upon Sam Johnson.

At the time which we speak of, the poor lad was not very well dressed, and wore shoes from which his toes peeped out; for his old father had barely the means of supporting his wife and children. But, poor as the family were, young Sam Johnson had as much pride as any nobleman's son in England. The fact was, he felt conscious of uncommon sense and ability, which, in his own opinion, entitled him to great respect from the world. Perhaps he would have been glad, if grown people had treated him as reverentially as his schoolfellows did. Three of them were accustomed to come for him, every morning; and while he sat upon the back of one, the two others supported him on each side, and thus he rode to school in triumph!

Being a personage of so much importance, Sam could not bear the idea of standing all day in Uttoxeter market, offering books to the rude and ignorant country people. Doubtless he felt the more reluctant on account of his shabby clothes, and the disorder of his eyes, and the tremulous motion of his head.

When Mr. Michael Johnson spoke, Sam pouted, and made an indistinct grumbling in his throat; then he looked his old father in the face, and answered him loudly and deliberately.

"Sir," said he, "I will not go to Uttoxeter market!"

Mr. Johnson had seen a great deal of the lad's obstinacy ever since his birth; and while Sam was younger, the old gentleman had probably used the rod, whenever occasion seemed to require. But he was now too feeble, and too much out of spirits, to contend with this stubborn and violent-tempered boy. He therefore gave up the point at once, and prepared to go to Uttoxeter himself.

"Well, Sam," said Mr. Johnson, as he took his hat and staff, "if for the sake of your foolish pride, you can suffer your poor sick father to stand all day in the noise and confusion of the market, when he ought to be in his bed, I have no more to say. But you will think of this, Sam, when I am dead and gone!"

So the poor old man (perhaps with a tear in his eye, but certainly with sorrow in his heart) set forth towards Uttoxeter. The gray-haired, feeble, melancholy Michael Johnson! How sad a thing it was, that he should be forced to go, in his sickness, and toil for the support of an ungrateful son, who was too proud to do anything for his father, or his mother, or himself! Sam looked after Mr. Johnson, with a sullen countenance, till he was out of sight.

But when the old man's figure, as he went stooping along the street, was no more to be seen, the boy's heart began to smite him. He had a vivid imagination, and it tormented him with the image of his father, standing in the market-place of Uttoxeter and offering his books to the noisy crowd around him. Sam seemed to behold him, arranging his literary merchandise upon the stall in such a way as was best calculated to attract notice. Here was Addison's Spectator, a long row of little volumes; here was Pope's translation of the Iliad and Odyssey; here were Dryden's poems, or those of Prior. Here, likewise, were Gulliver's Travels, and a variety of little gilt-covered children's books, such as Tom Thumb, Jack the Giant-queller, Mother Goose's Melodies, and others which our great-grandparents used to read in their childhood. And here were sermons for the pious, and pamphlets for the politicians, and ballads, some merry and some dismal ones, for the country people to sing.

Sam, in imagination, saw his father offer these books, pamphlets, and ballads, now to the rude yeomen, who perhaps could not read a word, — now to the country squires, who cared for nothing but to hunt hares and foxes, — now to the children, who chose to spend their coppers for sugar-plums or gingerbread, rather than for picture-books. And if Mr. Johnson should sell a book to man, woman, or child, it would cost him an hour's talk to get a profit of only sixpence.

"My poor father!" thought Sam to himself. "How his head will ache, and how heavy his heart will be! I am almost sorry that I did not do as he bade me!"

Then the boy went to his mother, who was busy about the house. She did not know of what had passed between Mr. Johnson and Sam.

"Mother," said he, "did you think father seemed very ill to-day?"

"Yes, Sam," answered his mother, turning with a flushed face from the fire, where she was cooking their scanty dinner. "Your father did look very ill, and it is a pity he did not send you to Uttoxeter in his stead. You are a great boy now, and would rejoice, I am sure, to do something for your poor father, who has done so much for you."

The lad made no reply. But again his imagination set to work, and conjured up another picture of poor Michael Johnson. He was standing in the hot sun-shine of the market-place, and looking so weary, sick, and disconsolate, that the eyes of all the crowd were drawn to him. "Had this old man no son," the people would say among themselves, "who might have taken his place at the bookstall, while the father kept his bed?" And perhaps — but this was a terrible thought for Sam! — perhaps his father would faint away, and fall down in the market-place, with his gray hair in the dust, and his venerable face as deathlike as that of a corpse. And there would be the bystanders gazing earnestly at Mr. Johnson, and whispering: "Is he dead? Is he dead?"

And Sam shuddered, as he repeated to himself, "Is he dead?"

"Oh, I have been a cruel son!" thought he, within his own heart. "God forgive me! God forgive me!"

But God could not yet forgive him; for he was not truly penitent. Had he been so, he would have hastened away that very moment to Uttoxeter, and have fallen at his father's feet, even in the midst of the crowded market-place. There he would have confessed his fault, and besought Mr. Johnson to go home, and leave the rest of the day's work to him. But such was Sam's pride and natural stubbornness, that he could not bring himself to this humiliation. Yet he ought to have done so, for his own sake, and for his father's sake, and for God's sake.

After sunset old Michael Johnson came slowly home, and sat down in his customary chair. He said nothing to Sam; nor do I know that a single word ever passed between them on the subject of the son's disobedience. In a few years, his father died, and left Sam to fight his way through the world by himself. It would make our story much too long, were I to tell you even a few of the remarkable events of Sam's life. Moreover, there is the less need of this, because many books have been written about that poor boy, and the fame that he acquired, and all that he did or talked of doing, after he came to be a man.

But one thing I must not neglect to say. From his boyhood upward, until the latest day of his life, he never forgot the story of Uttoxeter market. Often when he was a scholar of the University of Oxford, or master of an Academy at Edial, or a writer for the London booksellers, — in all his poverty and toil, and in all his success, — while he was walking the streets without a shilling to buy food, or when the greatest men of England were proud to feast him at their table, — still that heavy and remorseful thought came back to him : — "I was cruel to my poor father in his illness!"

Many and many a time, awake or in his dreams, he seemed to see old Michael Johnson, standing in the dust and confusion of the market-place, and pressing his withered hand to his forehead as if it ached.

Alas! my dear children, it is a sad thing to have such a thought as this to bear us company through life.

Though the story was but half finished, yet, as it was longer than usual, Mr. Temple here made a short pause. He perceived that Emily was in tears, and Edward turned his half-veiled face towards the speaker, with an air of great earnestness and interest. As for George, he had withdrawn into the dusky shadow behind his father's chair.

CHAPTER V

IN a few moments Mr. Temple resumed his story, as follows : —

SAMUEL JOHNSON

CONTINUED

Well, my children, fifty years had passed away since young Sam Johnson had shown himself so hard-hearted towards his father. It was now market-day in the village of Uttoxeter.

In the street of the village you might see cattle-dealers with cows and oxen for sale, and pig-drovers, with herds of squeaking swine, and farmers, with cart-loads of cabbages, turnips, onions, and all other produce of the soil. Now and then a farmer's red-faced wife trotted along on horseback, with butter and cheese in two large panniers. The people of the village, with country squires and other visitors from the neighborhood, walked hither and thither, trading, jesting, quarrelling, and making just such a bustle as their fathers and grandfathers had made half a century before.

In one part of the street, there was a puppet-show, with a ridiculous Merry-Andrew, who kept both grown people and children in a roar of laughter. On the opposite side was the old stone church of Uttoxeter, with ivy climbing up its walls, and partly obscuring its Gothic windows.

There was a clock in the gray tower of the ancient church ; and the hands on the dial-plate had now almost reached the hour of noon. At this busiest hour of the market, a strange old gentleman was seen making his way among the crowd. He was very tall and bulky, and wore a brown coat and small-clothes, with black worsted stockings and buckled shoes. On his head was a three-cornered hat, beneath which a bushy gray wig thrust itself out, all in disorder. The old gentleman elbowed the people aside, and forced his way through the midst of them with a singular kind of gait, rolling his body hither and thither, so that he needed twice as much room as any other person there.

"Make way, sir!" he would cry out, in a loud, harsh voice, when somebody happened to interrupt his progress. — "Sir, you intrude your person into the public thoroughfare!"

"What a queer fellow this is!" muttered the people among themselves, hardly knowing whether to laugh or to be angry.

But, when they looked into the venerable stranger's face, not the most thoughtless among them dared to offer him the least impertinence. Though his features were scarred and distorted with the scrofula, and though his eyes were dim and bleared, yet there was something of authority and wisdom in his look, which impressed them all with awe. So they stood aside to let him pass; and the old gentleman made his way across the market-place, and paused near the corner of the ivy-mantled church. Just as he reached it, the clock struck twelve.

On the very spot of ground where the stranger now stood, some aged people remembered that old Michael Johnson had formerly kept his bookstall. The little children, who had once bought picture-books of him, were grandfathers now.

"Yes; here is the very spot!" muttered the old gentleman to himself.

There this unknown personage took his stand, and removed the three-cornered hat from his head. It was the busiest hour of the day. What with the hum of human voices, the lowing of cattle, the squeaking of pigs, and the laughter caused by the Merry-Andrew, the market-place was in very great confusion. But the stranger seemed not to notice it, any more than if the silence of a desert were around him. He was wrapt in his own thoughts. Sometimes he raised his furrowed brow to Heaven, as if in prayer; sometimes he bent his head, as if an insupportable weight of sorrow were upon him. It increased the awfulness of his aspect, that there was a motion of his head, and an almost continual tremor throughout his frame, with singular twitchings and contortions of his features.

The hot sun blazed upon his unprotected head; but he seemed not to feel its fervor. A dark cloud swept across the sky, and rain-drops pattered into the market-place; but the stranger heeded not the shower. The people began to gaze at the mysterious old gentleman, with superstitious fear and wonder. Who could he be? Whence did he come? Wherefore was he standing bare-headed in the market-place? Even the school-boys left the Merry-Andrew, and came to gaze, with wide-open eyes, at this tall, strange-looking old man.

There was a cattle-drover in the village, who had recently made a journey to the Smithfield market, in London. No sooner had this man thrust his way through the throng, and taken a look at the unknown personage, than he whispered to one of his acquaintances: —

"I say, neighbor Hutchins, would ye like to know who this old gentleman is?"

"Ay, that I would," replied neighbor Hutchins; "for a queerer chap I never saw in my life! Somehow, it makes me feel small to look at him. He's more than a common man."

"You may well say so," answered the cattle-drover. "Why, that's the famous Doctor Samuel Johnson, who, they say, is the greatest and learnedest man in England. I saw him in London streets, walking with one Mr. Boswell."

Yes; the poor boy — the friendless Sam — with whom we began our story, had become the famous Doctor Samuel Johnson! He was universally acknowledged as the wisest man and greatest writer in all England. He had given shape and permanence to his native language, by his Dictionary. Thousands upon thousands of people had read his Idler, his Rambler, and his Rasselas. Noble and wealthy men, and beautiful ladies, deemed it their highest privilege to be his companions. Even the king of Great Britain had sought his acquaintance, and told him what an honor he considered it, that such a man had been born in his dominions. He was now at the summit of literary renown.

But all his fame could not extinguish the bitter remembrance which had tormented him through life. Never, never, had he forgotten his father's sorrowful and upbraiding look. Never — though the old man's troubles had been over so many years — had he forgiven himself for inflicting such a pang upon his heart. And now, in his old age, he had come hither to do penance, by standing at noon-day in the market-place of Uttoxeter, on the very spot where Michael Johnson had once kept his bookstall. The aged and illustrious man had done what the poor boy refused to do. By thus expressing his deep repentance and humiliation of heart, he hoped to gain peace of conscience and the forgiveness of God.

My dear children, if you have grieved — I will not say, your parents — but if you have grieved the heart of any human being who has a claim upon your love, then think of Samuel Johnson's penance! Will it not be better to redeem the error now, than to endure the agony of remorse for fifty years? Would you not rather say to a brother — "I have erred! Forgive me!" — than perhaps to go hereafter, and shed bitter tears upon his grave?

Hardly was the story concluded, when George hastily arose, and Edward likewise, stretching forth his hands into the darkness that surrounded him, to find his brother. Both accused themselves of unkindness; each besought the other's forgiveness; and having done so, the trouble of their hearts vanished away like a dream.

"I am glad! I am so glad!" said Emily, in a low, earnest voice. "Now I shall sleep quietly to-night."

"My sweet child," thought Mrs. Temple, as she kissed her, "mayest thou never know how much strife there is on earth! It would cost thee many a night's rest."

CHAPTER VI

A BOUT this period, Mr. Temple found it necessary to take a journey, which interrupted the series of Biographical Stories for several evenings. In the interval, Edward practised various methods of employing and amusing his mind.

Sometimes he meditated upon beautiful objects which he had formerly seen, until the intensity of his recollection seemed to restore him the gift of sight, and place everything anew before his eyes. Sometimes he repeated verses of poetry, which he did not know to be in his memory, until he found them there, just at the time of need. Sometimes he attempted to solve arithmetical questions, which had perplexed him while at school.

Then, with his mother's assistance, he learned the letters of the string-alphabet, which is used in some of the Institutions for the Blind, in Europe. When one of his friends gave him a leaf of Saint Mark's Gospel, printed in embossed characters, he endeavored to read it by passing his fingers over the letters as blind children do.

His brother George was now very kind, and spent so much time in the darkened chamber, that Edward often insisted upon his going out to play. George told him all about the affairs at school, and related many amusing incidents that happened among his comrades, and informed him what sports were now in fashion, and whose kite soared the highest, and whose little ship sailed fleetest on the Frog Pond. As for Emily, she repeated stories which she had learned from a new book, called THE FLOWER PEOPLE, in which the snow-drops, the violets, the columbines, the roses, and all that lovely tribe are represented as telling their secrets to a little girl. The flowers talked sweetly, as flowers should; and Edward almost fancied that he could behold their bloom and smell their fragrant breath.

Thus, in one way or another, the dark days of Edward's confinement passed not unhappily. In due time, his father returned; and the next evening, when the family were assembled, he began a story.

"I must first observe, children," said he, "that some writers deny the truth of the incident which I am about to relate to you. There certainly is but little evidence in favor of it. Other respectable writers, however, tell it for a fact; and, at all events, it is an interesting story, and has an excellent moral."

So Mr. Temple proceeded to talk about the early days of

Oliver Cromwell

Born 1599. Died 1658

Not long after King James the First took the place of Queen Elizabeth on the throne of England, there lived an English knight at a place called Hinchinbrooke. His name was Sir Oliver Cromwell. He spent his life, I suppose, pretty much like other English knights and squires in those days, hunting hares and foxes, and drinking large quantities of ale and wine. The old house in which he dwelt had been occupied by his ancestors before him for a good many years. In it there was a great hall, hung round with coats of arms, and helmets, cuirasses and swords which his forefathers had used in battle, and with horns of deer and tails of foxes, which they or Sir Oliver himself had killed in the chase.

This Sir Oliver Cromwell had a nephew, who had been called Oliver, after himself, but who was generally known in the family by the name of little Noll. His father was a younger brother of Sir Oliver. The child was often sent to visit his uncle, who probably found him a troublesome little fellow to take care of. He was forever in mischief, and always running into some danger or other, from which he seemed to escape only by miracle.

Even while he was an infant in the cradle a strange

accident had befallen him. A huge ape, which was kept in the family, snatched up little Noll in his forepaws and clambered with him to the roof of the house. There this ugly beast sat grinning at the affrighted spectators, as if he had done the most praiseworthy thing imaginable. Fortunately, however, he brought the child safe down again; and the event was afterwards considered an omen that Noll would reach a very elevated station in the world.

One morning, when Noll was five or six years old, a royal messenger arrived at Hinchinbrooke, with tidings that King James was coming to dine with Sir Oliver Cromwell. This was a high honor, to be sure, but a very great trouble; for all the lords and ladies, knights, squires, guards, and yeomen, who waited on the king, were to be feasted as well as himself; and more provisions would be eaten, and more wine drunk, in that one day, than generally in a month. However, Sir Oliver expressed much thankfulness for the king's intended visit, and ordered his butler and cook to make the best preparations in their power. So a great fire was kindled in the kitchen; and the neighbors knew by the smoke which poured out of the chimney, that boiling, baking, stewing, roasting, and frying were going on merrily.

By and by the sound of trumpets was heard, approaching nearer and nearer; and a heavy, old-fashioned coach, surrounded by guards on horseback, drove up to the house. Sir Oliver, with his hat in his hand, stood at the gate to receive the king. His Majesty was dressed in a suit of green, not very new; he had a feather in his hat, and a triple ruff round his neck; and over his shoulder was slung a hunting-horn, instead of a sword. Altogether, he had not the most dignified aspect in the world; but the spectators gazed at him as if there was something superhuman and divine in his person. They even shaded their eyes with their hands, as if they were dazzled by the glory of his countenance.

"How are ye, man?" cried King James, speaking in a Scotch accent; for Scotland was his native country. "By my crown, Sir Oliver, but I am glad to see ye!"

The good knight thanked the king, at the same time kneeling down, while his Majesty alighted. When King James stood on the ground, he directed Sir Oliver's attention to a little boy, who had come with him in the coach. He was six or seven years old, and wore a hat and feather, and was more richly dressed than the king himself. Though by no means an ill-looking child, he seemed shy, or even sulky; and his cheeks were rather pale, as if he had been kept moping within doors, instead of being sent out to play in the sun and wind.

"I have brought my son Charlie to see ye," said the king. "I hope, Sir Oliver, ye have a son of your own, to be his playmate."

Sir Oliver Cromwell made a reverential bow to the little prince, whom one of the attendants had now taken out of the coach. It was wonderful to see how all the spectators, even the aged men, with their gray beards, humbled themselves before this child. They bent their bodies till their beards almost swept the dust. They looked as if they were ready to kneel down and worship him.

The poor little prince! From his earliest infancy not a soul had dared to contradict him; everybody around him had acted as if he were a superior being; so that, of course, he had imbibed the same opinion of himself. He naturally supposed that the whole kingdom of Great Britain and all its inhabitants had been created solely for his benefit and amusement. This was a sad mistake; and it cost him dear enough after he had ascended his father's throne.

"What a noble little prince he is!" exclaimed Sir Oliver, lifting his hands in admiration. "No, please your Majesty, I have no son to be the playmate of his Royal Highness; but there is a nephew of mine, some-where about the house. He is near the prince's age, and will be but too happy to wait upon his Royal Highness."

"Send for him, man! send for him!" said the king.

But, as it happened, there was no need of sending for Master Noll. While King James was speaking, a rugged, bold-faced, sturdy little urchin thrust himself through the throng of courtiers and attendants, and greeted the prince with a broad stare. His doublet and hose (which had been put on new and clean in honor of the king's visit) were already soiled and torn with the rough play in which he had spent the morning. He looked no more abashed than if King James were his uncle and the prince one of his customary playfellows.

This was little Noll himself.

"Here, please your Majesty, is my nephew," said Sir Oliver, somewhat ashamed of Noll's appearance and demeanor. "Oliver, make your obeisance to the king's Majesty!"

The boy made a pretty respectful obeisance to the king; for, in those days, children were taught to pay reverence to their elders. King James, who prided himself greatly on his scholarship, asked Noll a few questions in the Latin Grammar, and then introduced him to his son. The little prince, in a very grave and dignified manner, extended his hand, not for Noll to shake, but that he might kneel down and kiss it.

"Nephew," said Sir Oliver, "pay your duty to the prince."

"I owe him no duty," cried Noll, thrusting aside the prince's hand, with a rude laugh. "Why should I kiss that boy's hand?"

All the courtiers were amazed and confounded, and Sir Oliver the most of all. But the king laughed heartily, saying that little Noll had a stubborn English spirit, and that it was well for his son to learn betimes what sort of people he was to rule over.

So King James and his train entered the house; and the prince, with Noll and some other children, was sent to play in a separate room while his Majesty was at dinner. The young people soon became acquainted; for boys, whether the sons of monarchs or of peasants, all like play, and are pleased with one another's society. What games they diverted themselves with, I cannot tell. Perhaps they played at ball — perhaps at blindman's buff — perhaps at leap-frog — perhaps at prison-bars. Such games have been in use for hundreds of years; and princes as well as poor children have spent some of their happiest hours in playing at them.

Meanwhile, King James and his nobles were feasting with Sir Oliver in the great hall. The king sat in a gilded chair, under a canopy, at the head of a long table. Whenever any of the company addressed him, it was with the deepest reverence. If the attendants offered him wine, or the various delicacies of the festival, it was upon their bended knees. You would have thought, by these tokens of worship, that the monarch was a supernatural being; only he seemed to have quite as much need of those vulgar matters, food and drink, as any other person at the table. But fate had ordained that good King James should not finish his dinner in peace.

All of a sudden, there arose a terrible uproar in the room where the children were at play. Angry shouts and shrill cries of alarm were mixed up together; while the voices of elder persons were likewise heard, trying to restore order among the children. The king, and everybody else at the table, looked aghast; for perhaps the tumult made them think that a general rebellion had broken out.

"Mercy on us!" muttered Sir Oliver; "that graceless nephew of mine is in some mischief or other. The naughty little whelp!"

Getting up from table, he ran to see what was the matter, followed by many of the guests, and the king among them. They all crowded to the door of the play-room.

On looking in, they beheld the little Prince Charles, with his rich dress all torn, and covered with the dust of the floor. His royal blood was streaming from his nose in great abundance. He gazed at Noll with a mixture of rage and affright, and at the same time a puzzled expression, as if he could not understand how any mortal boy should dare to give him a beating. As for Noll, there stood his sturdy little figure, bold as a lion, looking as if he were ready to fight not only the prince, but the king and kingdom too.

"You little villain!" cried his uncle. "What have you been about? Down on your knees, this instant, and ask the prince's pardon. How dare you lay hands on the king's Majesty's royal son?"

"He struck me first," grumbled the valiant little Noll; "and I 've only given him his due."

Sir Oliver and the guests lifted up their hands in astonishment and horror. No punishment seemed severe enough for this wicked little varlet, who had dared to resent a blow from the king's own son. Some of the courtiers were of opinion that Noll should be sent prisoner to the Tower of London, and brought to trial for high treason. Others, in their great zeal for the king's service, were about to lay hands on the boy, and chastise him in the royal presence.

But King James, who sometimes showed a good deal of sagacity, ordered them to desist.

"Thou art a bold boy," said he, looking fixedly at little Noll; "and, if thou live to be a man, my son Charlie would do wisely to be friends with thee."

"I never will!" cried the little prince, stamping his foot.

"Peace, Charlie, peace!" said the king; then addressing Sir Oliver and the attendants, "Harm not the urchin; for he has taught my son a good lesson, if Heaven do but give him grace to profit by it. Hereafter should he be tempted to tyrannize over the stubborn race of Englishmen, let him remember little Noll Cromwell, and his own bloody nose!"

So the king finished his dinner and departed; and, for many a long year, the childish quarrel between Prince Charles and Noll Cromwell was forgotten. The prince, indeed, might have lived a happier life and have met a more peaceful death had he remembered that quarrel, and the moral which his father drew from it. But, when old King James was dead, and Charles sat upon his throne, he seemed to forget that he was but a man, and that his meanest subjects were men as well as he. He wished to have the property and lives of the people of England entirely at his own disposal. But the Puritans, and all who loved liberty, rose against him, and beat him in many battles, and pulled him down from his throne.

Throughout this war between the king and nobles on one side, and the people of England on the other, there was a famous leader, who did more towards the ruin of royal authority, than all the rest. The contest seemed like a wrestling-match between King Charles and this strong man. And the king was overthrown.

When the discrowned monarch was brought to trial, that warlike leader sat in the judgment-hall. Many judges were present besides himself; but he alone had the power to save King Charles, or to doom him to the scaffold. After sentence was pronounced, this victorious general was entreated by his own children, on their knees, to rescue his Majesty from death.

"No!" said he sternly. "Better that one man should perish, than that the whole country should be ruined for his sake. It is resolved that he shall die!"

When Charles, no longer a king, was led to the scaffold, his great enemy stood at a window of the royal palace of Whitehall. He beheld the poor victim of pride, and an evil education, and misused power, as he laid his head upon the block. He looked on, with a steadfast gaze, while a black-veiled executioner lifted the fatal axe, and smote off that anointed head at a single blow.

"It is a righteous deed," perhaps he said to himself. "Now Englishmen may enjoy their rights."

At night, when the body of Charles was laid in the coffin, in a gloomy chamber, the general entered, lighting himself with a torch. Its gleam showed that he was now growing old; his visage was scarred with the many battles in which he had led the van; his brow was wrinkled with care, and with the continual exercise of stern authority. Probably there was not a single trait, either of aspect or manner, that belonged to the little Noll, who had battled so stoutly with Prince Charles. Yet this was he!

He lifted the coffin-lid, and caused the light of his torch to fall upon the dead monarch's face. Then, probably, his mind went back over all the marvellous events that had brought the hereditary king of England to this dishonored coffin, and had raised himself, an humble individual, to the possession of kingly power. He was a king, though without the empty title, or the glittering crown.

"Why was it," said Cromwell to himself — or might have said — as he gazed at the pale features in the coffin, — "Why was it, that this great king fell, and that poor Noll Cromwell has gained all the power of the realm?"

And, indeed, why was it?

King Charles had fallen, because, in his manhood the same as when a child, he disdained to feel that every human creature was his brother. He deemed himself a superior being, and fancied that his subjects were created only for a king to rule over. And Cromwell rose, because, in spite of his many faults, he mainly fought for the rights and freedom of his fellow-men; and therefore the poor and the oppressed all lent their strength to him.

"Dear father, how I should hate to be a king!" exclaimed Edward.

"And would you like to be a Cromwell?" inquired his father.

"I should like it well," replied George, "only I would not have put the poor old king to death. I would have sent him out of the kingdom, or perhaps have allowed him to live in a small house, near the gate of the royal palace. It was too severe, to cut off his head."

"Kings are in such an unfortunate position," said Mr. Temple, "that they must either be almost deified by their subjects, or else be dethroned and beheaded. In either case it is a pitiable lot."

"Oh, I had rather be blind than be a king!" said Edward.

"Well, my dear Edward," observed his mother, with a smile, "I am glad you are convinced that your own lot is not the hardest in the world."

CHAPTER VII

IT was a pleasant sight (for those who had eyes) to see how patiently the blinded little boy now submitted to what he had at first deemed an intolerable calamity. The beneficent Creator has not allowed our comfort to depend on the enjoyment of any single sense. Though he has made the world so very beautiful, yet it is possible to be happy without ever beholding the blue sky, or the green and flowery earth, or the kind faces of those whom we love. Thus it appears that all the external beauty of the universe is a free gift from God, over and above what is necessary to our comfort. How grateful, then, should we be to that Divine Benevolence, which showers even superfluous bounties upon us!

One truth, therefore, which Edward's blindness had taught him, was, that his mind and soul could dispense with the assistance of his eyes. Doubtless, however, he would have found this lesson far more difficult to learn, had it not been for the affection of those around him. His parents, and George and Emily, aided him to bear his misfortune; if possible, they would have lent him their own eyes. And this, too, was a good lesson for him. It taught him how dependent on one another God has ordained us to be; insomuch that all the necessities of mankind should incite them to mutual love.

So Edward loved his friends, and perhaps all the world, better than he ever did before. And he felt grateful towards his father for spending the evenings in telling him stories — more grateful, probably, than any of my little readers will feel towards me for so carefully writing those same stories down.

"Come, dear father," said he, the next evening, "now tell us all about some other little boy, who was destined to be a famous man."

"How would you like a story of a Boston boy?" asked his father.

"Oh, pray let us have it!" cried George, eagerly. "It will be all the better if he has been to our schools, and has coasted on the Common, and sailed boats in the Frog Pond. I shall feel acquainted with him then."

"Well, then," said Mr. Temple, "I will introduce you to a Boston boy, whom all the world became acquainted with, after he grew to be a man."

The story was as follows: —

BENJAMIN FRANKLIN

Born 1706.   Died 1790

In the year 1716, or about that period, a boy used to be seen in the streets of Boston, who was known among his school-fellows and playmates by the name of Ben Franklin. Ben was born in 1706; so that he was now about ten years old. His father, who had come over from England, was a soap-boiler and tallow-chandler, and resided in Milk Street, not far from the old South Church.

Ben was a bright boy at his book, and even a brighter one when at play with his comrades. He had some remarkable qualities which always seemed to give him the lead, whether at sport or in more serious matters. I might tell you a number of amusing anecdotes about him. You are acquainted, I suppose, with his famous story of the WHISTLE, and how he bought it with a whole pocketful of coppers, and afterwards repented of his bargain. But Ben had grown a great boy since those days, and had gained wisdom by experience; for it was one of his peculiarities, that no incident ever happened to him without teaching him some valuable lesson. Thus he generally profited more by his misfortunes, than many people do by the most favorable events that could befall them.

Ben's face was already pretty well known to the inhabitants of Boston. The selectmen, and other people of note, often used to visit his father, for the sake of talking about the affairs of the town or province.   Mr. Franklin was considered a person of great wisdom and integrity, and was respected by all who knew him, although he supported his family by the humble trade of boiling soap and making tallow-candles.

While his father and the visitors were holding deep consultations about public affairs, little Ben would sit on his stool in a corner, listening with the greatest interest, as if he understood every word.   Indeed, his features were so full of intelligence, that there could be but little doubt, not only that he understood what was said, but that he could have expressed some very sagacious opinions out of his own mind.   But, in those days, boys were expected to be silent in the presence of their elders.   However, Ben Franklin was looked upon as a very promising lad, who would talk and act wisely by and by.

" Neighbor Franklin," his father's friends would sometimes say, "you ought to send this boy to college and make a minister of him."

" I have often thought of it," his father would reply ; "and my brother Benjamin promises to give him a great many volumes of manuscript sermons, in case he should be educated for the church.   But I have a large family to support, and cannot afford the expense."

In fact, Mr. Franklin found it so difficult to provide bread for his family, that, when the boy was ten years old, it became necessary to take him from school.   Ben was then employed in cutting candle-wicks into equal lengths, and filling the moulds with tallow ; and many families in Boston spent their evenings by the light of the candles which he had helped to make.   Thus, you see, in his early days, as well as in his manhood, his labors contributed to throw light upon dark matters.

Busy as his life now was, Ben still found time to keep company with his former school-fellows.   He and the other boys were very fond of fishing, and spent many of their leisure hours on the margin of the mill-pond, catching flounders, perch, eels, and tom-cod, which came up thither with the tide.   The place where they fished is now, probably, covered with stone pavements and brick buildings, and thronged with people, and with vehicles of all kinds. But, at that period, it was a marshy spot on the outskirts of the town, where gulls flitted and screamed overhead, and salt meadow-grass grew under foot.

On the edge of the water there was a deep bed of clay, in which the boys were forced to stand, while they caught their fish. Here they dabbled in mud and mire like a flock of ducks.

"This is very uncomfortable," said Ben Franklin one day to his comrades, while they were standing mid-leg deep in the quagmire.

"So it is," said the other boys. "What a pity we have no better place to stand!"

If it had not been for Ben nothing more would have been done or said about the matter. But it was not in his nature to be sensible of an inconvenience, without using his best efforts to find a remedy. So, as he and his comrades were returning from the water-side, Ben suddenly threw down his string of fish with a very determined air: —

"Boys," cried he, "I have thought of a scheme, which will be greatly for our benefit, and for the public benefit!"

It was queer enough, to be sure, to hear this little chap — this rosy-cheeked, ten-year-old boy — talking about schemes for the public benefit! Nevertheless, his companions were ready to listen, being assured that Ben's scheme, whatever it was, would be well worth their attention. They remembered how sagaciously he had conducted all their enterprises, ever since he had been old enough to wear small-clothes.

They remembered, too, his wonderful contrivance of sailing across the mill-pond by lying flat on his back, in the water, and allowing himself to be drawn along by a paper-kite. If Ben could do that, he might certainly do anything.

"What is your scheme, Ben? — what is it?" cried they all.

It so happened that they had now come to a spot of ground where a new house was to be built. Scattered round about lay a great many large stones, which were to be used for the cellar and foundation. Ben mounted upon the highest of these stones, so that he might speak with the more authority.

"You know, lads," said he, "what a plague it is to be forced to stand in the quagmire yonder — over shoes and stockings (if we wear any) in mud and water. See! I am bedaubed to the knees of my small-clothes, and you are all in the same pickle. Unless we can find some remedy for this evil, our fishing business must be entirely given up. And, surely, this would be a terrible misfortune!"

"That it would! — that it would!" said his comrades, sorrowfully.

"Now I propose," continued Master Benjamin, "that we build a wharf, for the purpose of carrying on our fisheries. You see these stones. The workmen mean to use them for the underpinning of a house; but that would be for only one man's advantage. My plan is to take these same stones, and carry them to the edge of the water and build a wharf with them. This will not only enable us to carry on the fishing business with comfort, and to better advantage, but it will likewise be a great convenience to boats passing up and down the stream. Thus, instead of one man, fifty, or a hundred, or a thousand, besides ourselves, may be benefited by these stones. What say you, lads? — shall we build the wharf?"

Ben's proposal was received with one of those uproarious shouts, wherewith boys usually express their delight at whatever completely suits their views. Nobody thought of questioning the right and justice of building a wharf, with stones that belonged to another person.

"Hurrah, hurrah!" shouted they. "Let's set about it!"

It was agreed that they should all be on the spot, that evening, and commence their grand public enterprise by moonlight. Accordingly, at the appointed time, the whole gang of youthful laborers assembled, and eagerly began to remove the stones. They had not calculated how much toil would be requisite, in this important part of their undertaking. The very first stone which they laid hold of proved so heavy, that it almost seemed to be fastened to the ground. Nothing but Ben Franklin's cheerful and resolute spirit could have induced them to persevere.

Ben, as might be expected, was the soul of the enterprise. By his mechanical genius, he contrived methods to lighten the labor of transporting the stones; so that one boy, under his directions, would perform as much as half a dozen, if left to themselves. Whenever their spirits flagged, he had some joke ready, which seemed to renew their strength by setting them all into a roar of laughter. And when, after an hour or two of hard work, the stones were transported to the water-side, Ben Franklin was the engineer to superintend the construction of the wharf.

The boys, like a colony of ants, performed a great deal of labor by their multitude, though the individual strength of each could have accomplished but little. Finally, just as the moon sank below the horizon, the great work was finished.

"Now, boys," cried Ben, "let's give three cheers, and go home to bed. To-morrow, we may catch fish at our ease!" "Hurrah! hurrah! hurrah!" shouted his comrades.

Then they all went home, in such an ecstasy of delight that they could hardly get a wink of sleep.

The story was not yet finished; but George's impatience caused him to interrupt it.

"How I wish that I could have helped to build that wharf!" exclaimed he. "It must have been glorious fun. Ben Franklin forever, say I!"

"It was a very pretty piece of work," said Mr. Temple. "But wait till you hear the end of the story."

"Father," inquired Edward, "whereabouts in Boston was the mill-pond, on which Ben built his wharf?"

"I do not exactly know," answered Mr. Temple; "but I suppose it to have been on the northern verge of the town, in the vicinity of what are now called Merrimack and Charlestown streets. That thronged portion of the city was once a marsh. Some of it, in fact, was covered with water."

CHAPTER VIII

A S the children had no more questions to ask, Mr. Temple proceeded to relate what consequences ensued from the building of Ben Franklin's wharf.

BENJAMIN FRANKLIN

CONTINUED

In the morning, when the early sunbeams were gleaming on the steeples and roofs of the town, and gilding the water that surrounded it, the masons came, rubbing their eyes, to begin their work at the foundation of the new house. But, on reaching the spot, they rubbed their eyes so much the harder. What had become of their heap of stones?

"Why, Sam," said one to another, in great perplexity, "here 's been some witchcraft at work, while we were asleep. The stones must have flown away through the air!"

"More likely they have been stolen!" answered Sam.

"But who on earth would think of stealing a heap of stones?" cried a third. "Could a man carry them away in his pocket?"

The master-mason, who was a gruff kind of man, stood scratching his head, and said nothing, at first. But, looking carefully on the ground, he discerned innumerable tracks of little feet, some with shoes, and some barefoot. Following these tracks with his eye, he saw that they formed a beaten path towards the waterside.

"Ah, I see what the mischief is," said he, nodding his head. "Those little rascals, the boys! they have stolen our stones to build a wharf with!"

The masons immediately went to examine the new

structure. And, to say the truth, it was well worth looking at, so neatly, and with such admirable skill, had it been planned and finished. The stones were put together so securely, that there was no danger of their being loosened by the tide, however swiftly it might sweep along. There was a broad and safe platform to stand upon, whence the little fishermen might cast their lines into deep water, and draw up fish in abundance. Indeed, it almost seemed as if Ben and his comrades might be forgiven for taking the stones, because they had done their job in such a workmanlike manner.

"The chaps that built this wharf understood their business pretty well," said one of the masons. "I should not be ashamed of such a piece of work myself."

But the master-mason did not seem to enjoy the joke. He was one of those unreasonable people, who care a great deal more for their own rights and privileges, than for the convenience of all the rest of the world.

"Sam," said he, more gruffly than usual, "go call a constable."

So Sam called a constable, and inquiries were set on foot to discover the perpetrators of the theft. In the course of the day, warrants were issued, with the signature of a Justice of the Peace, to take the bodies of Benjamin Franklin and other evil-disposed persons, who had stolen a heap of stones. If the owner of the stolen property had not been more merciful than the master-mason, it might have gone hard with our friend Benjamin and his fellow-laborers. But, luckily for them, the gentleman had a respect for Ben's father, and, moreover, was amused with the spirit of the whole affair. He therefore let the culprits off pretty easily.

But, when the constables were dismissed, the poor boys had to go through another trial, and receive sentence, and suffer execution too, from their own fathers. Many a rod, I grieve to say, was worn to the stump, on that unlucky night.

As for Ben, he was less afraid of a whipping than of his father's disapprobation. Mr. Franklin, as I have mentioned before, was a sagacious man, and also an inflexibly upright one. He had read much, for a person in his rank of life, and had pondered upon the ways of the world, until he had gained more wisdom than a whole library of books could have taught him. Ben had a greater reverence for his father, than for any other person in the world, as well on account of his spotless integrity, as of his practical sense and deep views of things.

Consequently, after being released from the clutches of the law, Ben came into his father's presence, with no small perturbation of mind.

"Benjamin, come hither," began Mr. Franklin, in his customary solemn and weighty tone.

The boy approached, and stood before his father's chair, waiting reverently to hear what judgment this good man would pass upon his late offence. He felt that now the right and wrong of the whole matter would be made to appear.

"Benjamin," said his father, "what could induce you to take property which did not belong to you?"

"Why, father," replied Ben, hanging his head, at first, but then lifting his eyes to Mr. Franklin's face, "if it had been merely for my own benefit, I never should have dreamed of it. But I knew that the wharf would be a public convenience. If the owner of the stones should build a house with them, nobody will enjoy any advantage except himself. Now, I made use of them in a way that was for the advantage of many persons. I thought it right to aim at doing good to the greatest number."

"My son," said Mr. Franklin, solemnly, "so far as it was in your power, you have done a greater harm to the public, than to the owner of the stones."

"How can that be, father?" asked Ben.

"Because," answered his father, "in building your wharf with stolen materials, you have committed a moral wrong. There is no more terrible mistake, than to violate what is eternally right, for the sake of a seeming expediency. Those who act upon such a principle do the utmost in their power to destroy all that is good in the world."

"Heaven forbid!" said Benjamin.

"No act," continued Mr. Franklin, "can possibly be for the benefit of the public generally, which involves injustice to any individual. It would be easy to prove this by examples. But, indeed, can we suppose that our all-wise and just Creator would have so ordered the affairs of the world, that a wrong act should be the true method of attaining a right end? It is impious to think so! And I do verily believe, Benjamin, that almost all the public and private misery of mankind arises from a neglect of this great truth — that evil can produce only evil — that good ends must be wrought out by good means."

"I will never forget it again," said Benjamin, bowing his head.

"Remember," concluded his father, "that, whenever we vary from the highest rule of right, just so far we do an injury to the world. It may seem otherwise for the moment; but, both in Time and in Eternity, it will be found so."

To the close of his life, Ben Franklin never forgot this conversation with his father; and we have reason to suppose that, in most of his public and private career, he endeavored to act upon the principles which that good and wise man had then taught him.

After the great event of building the wharf, Ben continued to cut wick-yarn and fill candle-moulds for about two years. But, as he had no love for that occupation, his father often took him to see various artisans at their work, in order to discover what trade he would prefer. Thus Ben learned the use of a great many tools, the knowledge of which afterwards proved very useful to him. But he seemed much inclined to go to sea. In order to keep him at home, and likewise to gratify his taste for letters, the lad was bound apprentice to his elder brother, who had lately set up a printing-office in Boston.

Here he had many opportunities of reading new books, and of hearing instructive conversation. He exercised himself so successfully in writing composition, that, when no more than thirteen or fourteen years old, he became a contributor to his brother's newspaper. Ben was also a versifier, if not a poet. He made two doleful ballads, — one about the shipwreck of Captain Worthilake, and the other about the pirate Black Beard, who, not long before, infested the American seas.

When Ben's verses were printed, his brother sent him to sell them to the town's-people, wet from the press. "Buy my ballads!" shouted Benjamin, as he trudged through the streets, with a basketful on his arm. "Who 'll buy a ballad about Black Beard? A penny apiece! a penny apiece! who 'll buy my ballads?"

If one of those roughly composed and rudely printed ballads could be discovered now, it would be worth more than its weight in gold.

In this way our friend Benjamin spent his boyhood and youth, until, on account of some disagreement with his brother, he left his native town and went to Philadelphia. He landed in the latter city, a homeless and hungry young man, and bought three-pence worth of bread to satisfy his appetite. Not knowing where else to go, he entered a Quaker meeting-house, sat down, and fell fast asleep. He has not told us whether his slumbers were visited by any dreams. But it would have been a strange dream, indeed, and an incredible one, that should have foretold how great a man he was destined to become, and how much he would be honored in that very city, where he was now friendless and unknown.

So here we finish our story of the childhood of Benjamin Franklin. One of these days, if you would know what he was in his manhood, you must read his own works, and the history of American Independence.

"Do let us hear a little more of him!" said Edward; "not that I admire him so much as many other characters; but he interests me, because he was a Yankee boy."

"My dear son," replied Mr. Temple, "it would require

a whole volume of talk, to tell you all that is worth knowing about Benjamin Franklin. There is a very pretty anecdote of his flying a kite in the midst of a thunder-storm, and thus drawing down the lightning from the clouds, and proving that it was the same thing as electricity. His whole life would be an interesting story, if we had time to tell it."

"But, pray, dear father, tell us what made him so famous," said George. "I have seen his portrait a great many times. There is a wooden bust of him in one of our streets, and marble ones, I suppose, in some other places. And towns, and ships of war, and steamboats, and banks, and academies, and children, are often named after Franklin. Why should he have grown so very famous?"

"Your question is a reasonable one, George," answered his father. "I doubt whether Franklin's philosophical discoveries, important as they were, or even his vast political services, would have given him all the fame which he acquired. It appears to me that Poor Richard's Almanac did more than anything else towards making him familiarly known to the public. As the writer of those proverbs, which Poor Richard was supposed to utter, Franklin became the counsellor and household friend of almost every family in America. Thus, it was the humblest of all his labors that has done the most for his fame."

"I have read some of those proverbs," remarked Edward; "but I do not like them. They are all about getting money, or saving it."

"Well," said his father, "they were suited to the condition of the country; and their effect, upon the whole, has doubtless been good, — although they teach men but a very small portion of their duties."

CHAPTER IX

HITHERTO, Mr. Temple's narratives had all been about boys and men. But, the next evening, he bethought himself that the quiet little Emily would perhaps be glad to hear the story of a child of her own sex. He therefore resolved to narrate the youthful adventures of Christina of Sweden, who began to be a Queen at the age of no more than six years. If we have any little girls among our readers, they must not suppose that Christina is set before them as a pattern of what they ought to be. On the contrary, the tale of her life is chiefly profitable as showing the evil effects of a wrong education, which caused this daughter of a king to be both useless and unhappy.

Here follows the story.

QUEEN CHRISTINA
Born 1626.   Died 1689

In the royal palace at Stockholm, the capital city of Sweden, there was born, in 1626, a little princess. The king, her father, gave her the name of Christina, in memory of a Swedish girl with whom he had been in love. His own name was Gustavus Adolphus; and he was also called the Lion of the North, because he had gained greater fame in war than any other prince or general then alive. With this valiant king for their commander, the Swedes had made themselves terrible to the Emperor of Germany and to the King of France, and were looked upon as the chief defence of the Protestant religion.

The little Christina was by no means a beautiful child. To confess the truth, she was remarkably plain. The queen, her mother, did not love her so much as she ought; partly, perhaps, on account of Christina's want of beauty, and, also, because both the king and queen had wished for a son, who might have gained as great renown in battle as his father had.

The king, however, soon became exceedingly fond of the infant princess. When Christina was very young, she was taken violently sick. Gustavus Adolphus, who was several hundred miles from Stockholm, travelled night and day, and never rested until he held the poor child in his arms. On her recovery, he made a solemn festival, in order to show his joy to the people of Sweden, and express his gratitude to Heaven. After this event, he took his daughter with him in all the journeys which he made throughout his kingdom.

Christina soon proved herself a bold and sturdy little girl. When she was two years old, the king and herself, in the course of a journey, came to the strong fortress of Colmar. On the battlements were soldiers clad in steel armor, which glittered in the sunshine. There were likewise great cannons, pointing their black mouths at Gustavus and little Christina, and ready to belch out their smoke and thunder; for whenever a king enters a fortress, it is customary to receive him with a royal salute of artillery.

But the captain of the fortress met Gustavus and his daughter, as they were about to enter the gateway.

"May it please your Majesty," said he, taking off his steel cap, and bowing profoundly, "I fear that if we receive you with a salute of cannon, the little princess will be frightened almost to death."

Gustavus looked earnestly at his daughter, and was indeed apprehensive that the thunder of so many cannon might perhaps throw her into convulsions. He had almost a mind to tell the captain to let them enter the fortress quietly, as common people might have done, without all this head-splitting racket. But no; this would not do.

"Let them fire," said he, waving his hand. "Christina is a soldier's daughter, and must learn to bear the noise of cannon."

So the captain uttered the word of command, and immediately there was a terrible peal of thunder from the cannon, and such a gush of smoke, that it enveloped the whole fortress in its volumes. But, amid all the din and confusion, Christina was seen clapping her little hands, and laughing in an ecstasy of delight. Probably nothing ever pleased her father so much as to see that his daughter promised to be fearless as himself. He determined to educate her exactly as if she had been a boy, and to teach her all the knowledge needful to the ruler of a kingdom and the commander of an army.

But Gustavus should have remembered that Providence had created her to be a woman, and that it was not for him to make a man of her.

However, the king derived great happiness from his beloved Christina. It must have been a pleasant sight to see the powerful monarch of Sweden playing in some magnificent hall of the palace, with his merry little girl. Then he forgot that the weight of a kingdom rested upon his shoulders. He forgot that the wise Chancellor Oxenstiern was waiting to consult with him how to render Sweden the greatest nation of Europe. He forgot that the Emperor of Germany and the King of France were plotting together how they might pull him down from his throne.

Yes; Gustavus forgot all the perils and cares and pompous irksomeness of a royal life, and was as happy, while playing with his child, as the humblest peasant in the realm of Sweden. How gayly did they dance along the marble floor of the palace, this valiant king, with his upright, martial figure, his war-worn visage, and commanding aspect, and the small, round form of Christina, with her rosy face of childish merriment! Her little fingers were clasped in her father's hand, which had held the leading-staff in many famous victories. His crown and sceptre were her playthings. She could disarm Gustavus of his sword, which was so terrible to the princes of Europe.

But alas! the king was not long permitted to enjoy Christina's society. When she was four years old, Gus-

tavus was summoned to take command of the allied
armies of Germany, which were fighting against the
Emperor. His greatest affliction was the necessity of
parting with his child; but people in such high stations
have but little opportunity for domestic happiness. He
called an assembly of the Senators of Sweden, and confided Christina to their care, saying that each one of
them must be a father to her, if he himself should fall
in battle.

At the moment of his departure, Christina ran towards
him and began to address him with a speech which somebody had taught her for the occasion. Gustavus was
busied with thoughts about the affairs of the kingdom,
so that he did not immediately attend to the childish
voice of his little girl. Christina, who did not love to
be unnoticed, immediately stopped short, and pulled him
by the coat.

"Father," said she, "why do not you listen to my
speech?"

In a moment, the king forgot everything, except that
he was parting with what he loved best in all the world.
He caught the child in his arms, pressed her to his bosom,
and burst into tears. Yes; though he was a brave man,
and though he wore a steel corselet on his breast, and
though armies were waiting for him to lead them to battle,
— still, his heart melted within him and he wept. Christina, too, was so afflicted that her attendants began to
fear that she would actually die of grief. But probably
she was soon comforted; for children seldom remember
their parents quite so faithfully as their parents remember them.

For two years more, Christina remained in the palace
at Stockholm. The queen, her mother, had accompanied Gustavus to the wars. The child, therefore, was
left to the guardianship of five of the wisest men in the
kingdom. But these wise men knew better how to manage the affairs of state, than how to govern and educate
a little girl, so as to render her a good and happy
woman.

When two years had passed away, tidings were

brought to Stockholm, which filled everybody with triumph and sorrow at the same time. The Swedes had won a glorious victory at Lutzen. But alas! the war-like king of Sweden, the Lion of the North, the father of our little Christina, — had been slain at the foot of a great stone, which still marks the spot of that hero's death.

Soon after this sad event, a General Assembly, or Congress, consisting of deputations from the nobles, the clergy, the burghers, and the peasants of Sweden was summoned to meet at Stockholm. It was for the purpose of declaring little Christina to be queen of Sweden, and giving her the crown and sceptre of her deceased father. Silence being proclaimed, the Chancellor Oxenstiern arose.

"We desire to know," said he, "whether the people of Sweden will take the daughter of our dead king, Gustavus Adolphus, to be their Queen."

When the Chancellor had spoken, an old man with white hair and in coarse apparel stood up in the midst of the assembly. He was a peasant, Lars Larrson by name, and had spent most of his life in laboring on a farm.

"Who is this daughter of Gustavus?" asked the old man. "We do not know her. Let her be shown to us."

Then Christina was brought into the hall and placed before the old peasant. It was strange, no doubt, to see a child — a little girl of six years old — offered to the Swedes as their ruler, instead of the brave king, her father, who had led them to victory so many times. Could her baby fingers wield a sword in war? Could her childish mind govern the nation wisely in peace?

But the Swedes do not appear to have asked themselves these questions. Old Lars Larrson took Christina up in his arms, and gazed earnestly into her face. He had known the great Gustavus well; and his heart was touched, when he saw the likeness which the little girl bore to that heroic monarch.

"Yes," cried he, with the tears gushing down his furrowed cheeks, "this is truly the daughter of our Gus-

tavus! Here is her father's brow!—here is his piercing
eye! She is his very picture. This child shall be our
queen!"

Then all the proud nobles of Sweden, and the reverend clergy, and the burghers, and the peasants, knelt
down at the child's feet, and kissed her hand.

"Long live Christina, queen of Sweden!" shouted they.

Even after she was a woman grown, Christina remembered the pleasure which she felt in seeing all these men
at her feet, and hearing them acknowledge her as their
supreme ruler. Poor child! she was yet to learn that
power does not insure happiness. As yet, however, she
had not any real power. All the public business, it is
true, was transacted in her name; but the kingdom was
governed by a number of the most experienced statesmen, who were called a Regency.

But it was considered necessary that the little queen
should be present at the public ceremonies, and should
behave just as if she were in reality the ruler of the
nation. When she was seven years of age, some ambassadors from the Czar of Muscovy came to the Swedish court. They wore long beards, and were clad in a
strange fashion, with furs, and other outlandish ornaments; and as they were inhabitants of a half-civilized
country, they did not behave like other people. The
Chancellor Oxenstiern was afraid that the young queen
would burst out a-laughing, at the first sight of these
queer ambassadors; or else that she would be frightened by their unusual aspect.

"Why should I be frightened?" said the little queen;
—"and do you suppose that I have no better manners
than to laugh? Only tell me how I must behave; and
I will do it."

Accordingly, the Muscovite ambassadors were introduced; and Christina received them, and answered their
speeches, with as much dignity and propriety as if she
had been a grown woman.

All this time, though Christina was now a queen, you
must not suppose that she was left to act as she pleased.
She had a preceptor, named John Mathias, who was a

very learned man, and capable of instructing her in all
the branches of science. But there was nobody to teach
her the delicate graces and gentle virtues of a woman.
She was surrounded almost entirely by men, and had
learned to despise the society of her own sex. At the
age of nine years, she was separated from her mother,
whom the Swedes did not consider a proper person to
be entrusted with the charge of her. No little girl, who
sits by a New England fireside, has cause to envy Christina, in the royal palace at Stockholm.

Yet she made great progress in her studies. She
learned to read the classical authors of Greece and
Rome, and became a great admirer of the heroes and
poets of old times. Then, as for active exercises, she
could ride on horseback as well as any man in her kingdom. She was fond of hunting, and could shoot at a
mark with wonderful skill. But dancing was the only
feminine accomplishment with which she had any
acquaintance.

She was so restless in her disposition, that none of
her attendants were sure of a moment's quiet, neither
day nor night. She grew up, I am sorry to say, a very
unamiable person, ill-tempered, proud, stubborn, and, in
short, unfit to make those around her happy, or to be
happy herself. Let every little girl, who has been
taught self-control, and a due regard for the rights of
others, thank Heaven that she has had better instruction than this poor little queen of Sweden.

At the age of eighteen, Christina was declared free to
govern the kingdom by herself, without the aid of a
regency. At this period of her life, she was a young
woman of striking aspect, a good figure and intelligent
face, but very strangely dressed. She wore a short
habit of gray cloth, with a man's vest over it, and a
black scarf around her neck, but no jewels, nor ornaments of any kind.

Yet, though Christina was so negligent of her appearance, there was something in her air and manner that
proclaimed her as the ruler of a kingdom. Her eyes, it
is said, had a very fierce and haughty look. Old Gen-

eral Wrangel, who had often caused the enemies of Sweden to tremble in battle, actually trembled himself, when he encountered the eyes of the queen. But it would have been better for Christina if she could have made people love her, by means of soft and gentle looks, instead of affrighting them by such terrible glances.

And now I have told you almost all that is amusing or instructive, in the childhood of Christina. Only a few more words need be said about her; for it is neither pleasant nor profitable to think of many things that she did, after she grew to be a woman.

When she had worn the crown a few years, she began to consider it beneath her dignity to be called a queen, because the name implied that she belonged to the weaker sex. She therefore caused herself to be proclaimed KING, thus declaring to the world that she despis. 1 her own sex, and was desirous of being ranked among men. But in the twenty-eighth year of her age, Christina grew tired of royalty, and resolved to be neither a king nor a queen any longer. She took the crown from her head, with her own hands, and ceased to be the ruler of Sweden. The people did not greatly regret her abdication; for she had governed them ill, and had taken much of their property to supply her extravagance.

Having thus given up her hereditary crown, Christina left Sweden and travelled over many of the countries of Europe. Everywhere she was received with great ceremony, because she was the daughter of the renowned Gustavus, and had herself been a powerful queen. Perhaps you would like to know something about her personal appearance, in the latter part of her life. She is described as wearing a man's vest, a short gray petticoat, embroidered with gold and silver, and a black wig, which was thrust awry upon her head. She wore no gloves, and so seldom washed her hands that nobody could tell what had been their original color. In this strange dress, and, I suppose, without washing her hands or face, she visited the magnificent court of Louis the Fourteenth.

She died in 1689. None loved her while she lived, nor regretted her death, nor planted a single flower upon her grave. Happy are the little girls of America, who are brought up quietly and tenderly, at the domestic hearth, and thus become gentle and delicate women! May none of them ever lose the loveliness of their sex, by receiving such an education as that of Queen Christina!

Emily, timid, quiet, and sensitive, was the very reverse of little Christina. She seemed shocked at the idea of such a bold and masculine character as has been described in the foregoing story.

"I never could have loved her," whispered she to Mrs. Temple; and then she added, with that love of personal neatness, which generally accompanies purity of heart, — "It troubles me to think of her unclean hands!"

"Christina was a sad specimen of womankind indeed," said Mrs. Temple. "But it is very possible for a woman to have a strong mind, and to be fitted for the active business of life, without losing any of her natural delicacy. Perhaps some time or other, Mr. Temple will tell you a story of such a woman."

It was now time for Edward to be left to repose. His brother George shook him heartily by the hand, and hoped, as he had hoped twenty times before, that to-morrow or the next day Ned's eyes would be strong enough to look the sun right in the face.

"Thank you, George," replied Edward, smiling; "but I am not half so impatient as at first. If my bodily eyesight were as good as yours, perhaps I could not see things so distinctly with my mind's eye. But now there is a light within which shows me the little Quaker artist, Ben West, and Isaac Newton with his windmill, and stubborn Sam Johnson, and stout Noll Cromwell, and shrewd Ben Franklin, and little Queen Christina, with the Swedes kneeling at her feet. It seems as if I really saw these personages face to face. So I can bear the darkness outside of me pretty well."

When Edward ceased speaking, Emily put up her mouth and kissed him as her farewell for the night.

"Ah, I forgot!" said Edward, with a sigh. "I cannot see any of your faces. What would it signify to see all the famous people in the world, if I must be blind to the faces that I love?"

"You must try to see us with your heart, my dear child," said his mother.

Edward went to bed, somewhat dispirited, but quickly falling asleep was visited with such a pleasant dream of the sunshine and of his dearest friends, that he felt the happier for it all the next day. And we hope to find him still happy when we meet again.